STUDENT COMPANION

to accompany

Human Geography

Culture, Society, and Space

Sixth Edition

H. J. de Blij
Marshall University

Alexander B. Murphy
University of Oregon

includes

Study Guide

A. Steele Becker
University of Nebraska at Kearney

Jacqueline V. Becker

Take Note!

Art Notebook

Virtual Field Guide

Margaret M. Gripshover
Marshall University

Glenn R. Miller
Bridgewater State College

Website access card

John Wiley & Sons, Inc.

New York • Chichester • Weinheim • Brisbane • Singapore • Toronto

COVER PHOTO: Gary John Norman/Tony Stone Images

ISBN 0-471-32024-2

Printed in the United States of America

10 9 8 7 6 5 4 3 2 1

Printed and bound by Courier Kendallville, Inc.

TABLE OF CONTENTS

STUDY GUIDE

HOW TO USE THIS STUDY GUIDE

This study guide has been written to help you in using *Human Geography*, Sixth Edition in a college-level course to guide you to a better understanding of the important discipline of geography. It is written in a clear and logical manner with the full appreciation of the pressures, scholastic and otherwise, that you will face in an academic environment as we approach the twenty-first century.

Most, if not all, of the material in *Human Geography*, Sixth Edition, will be new to you. This is not a course of simple memorization. Geography is based upon the understanding of *concepts* and *relationships*. A college-level text covers more material in greater depth than anything a student is familiar with from high school. Using this guide will help you overcome many of the problems you will encounter in this course.

The Sixth Edition of *Human Geography* has undergone extensive reorganization as well as updating of information to make it a text that is relevant and applicable to a rapidly changing world approaching the twenty-first century. Issues of gender, political devolution, and environment receive particular attention and have been woven into all parts of the text. Statistical information is the most recent that is available and is supported by a wide variety of maps, pictures, and illustrations. In short, the book is a complete cultural geography text for a college course of the late 1990s.

The format for each chapter of the guide is the same. Each chapter begins with a **chapter introduction** that presents expanded discussion on the "Key Points" in the box at the beginning of the chapter. In some cases you will be referred to text material, maps, or illustrations in previous chapters to use in helping you better understand the material currently being covered. This is followed by a **chapter quiz** consisting of **multiple-choice** and **true/false** questions on material from the **entire** chapter, not just the introduction. Answers to the **multiple-choice** and **true/false** questions may be found at the end of the study guide. The last portion of the guide contains a series of **study questions** that are designed to make you think conceptually about the entire chapter.

To gain maximum benefit from the study guide it is important that you read the introduction in the guide **and** the entire chapter ***before*** it is covered in lecture. The multiple-choice and true/false questions should be used to test your retention of information from these three sources. You should reread the chapter before attempting the study questions at the end of each chapter in the guide, since these are designed as comprehensive questions to help you tie together facts and concepts. Students are cautioned to remember the guide **is not** a substitute for the text. It **must** be used in combination with the text.

ADDITIONAL HELPFUL HINTS

1. Lectures *must* be attended regularly because your instructor may cover material not in the text. Take good notes and ask questions for clarification.

2. Review lecture notes as soon as possible. Rewrite sections you have trouble reading while the material is still fresh in your mind.

3. Begin reviewing for quizzes and exams well before their scheduled date.

4. Having access to a *current* atlas will be an enormous asset for you in this course.

PART ONE: GEOGRAPHY, CULTURE, AND THE ENVIRONMENT

CHAPTER 1. INTRODUCTION: GEOGRAPHY AND HUMAN GEOGRAPHY

CHAPTER INTRODUCTION

Humans are geographers by nature. They can think territorially or spatially and have an awareness of, and curiosity about the distinctive nature of places. Even children possess qualities of geographers, creating carefully mapped realms in tiny places. Places possess an emotional quality and we all must belong *somewhere*. Humans' insatiable curiosity and the place-centered element within us gave birth to geography as an academic discipline. Conquest and commerce generated a need to know about the world and *pragmatism* was added long ago by traders and explorers. *Geography* literally means "to describe the Earth," and the practical aspects of geography first arose among the Greeks, Romans, Mesopotamians, and Phoenicians.

Divisions

Physical and human geography are two great branches of the discipline and their origins can be traced to the Greeks and later the Romans. Greek scholars were curious about the world, particularly the physical aspects, and collected information from traders and travelers. The Romans, unlike the Greeks, were empire builders and brought many different cultures under their control. They added to the Greek knowledge of the physical Earth and added information about different cultures they encountered or conquered. By the end of the Roman era, theories about a spherical Earth, latitudinal climatic zones, environmental influences on humans, and humans' role in modifying the Earth were established. The latter two are quite significant because today environmental geography is emerging as a link between human and physical geography.

Traditions

During the twentieth century, geography has been marked by four durable traditions; *earth-science* (physical geography), *cultural-environmental* (encompasses a wide range of topics and has a difficult, even controversial history), *locational theory* (the heart of geography since it is the spatial focus of the discipline) has become a modern element of human geography, and *area-analysis* (primarily involves the description of areas and regions), giving rise to what is today called *regional science*. These "Four Traditions of Geography" were first "identified" in an article by University of Chicago geographer W.D. Pattison in 1964. He argued that these were four areas where geographic teaching, research, and other activity were concentrated.

New Themes

In the 1980s, rising concerns about geographic illiteracy in America prompted the National Geography Society, and several other organizations, to begin campaigns to reintroduce geography into school curricula. In a 1986 publication, the NGS proposed a useful five-theme framework for geography as developed by the Geography Education National Implementation Project (GENIP). Three of the themes correspond to traditions identified earlier: location, interaction between humans and environments, and regions.

As the fourth tradition, the NGS proposed a single word, *place*, because all places on the surface of the Earth have distinguishing human and physical characteristics. The fifth theme, *movement*, refers to the mobility of goods, ideas, and people, an appropriate theme in light of the mobile world that we live in today.

Maps

Maps— graphic representations of all or part of the Earth's surface drawn to scale—are the most important tool of geographers. Maps and geography are practically synonymous, and mapmaking (cartography) is as old as geography itself. The spatial perspective is geography's unifying bond and there is no better way to demonstrate the insights gained through spatial analysis than through the use of maps. Maps are our "window on the world."

Maps are used to portray the distinctive character of places; their relationship to environmental issues; the movements of people, goods, and ideas; and regions of various types. Maps are used to wage war, make political propaganda, solve medical problems, locate shopping centers, bring relief to refugees, warn of natural hazards—in short, for countless purposes.

Maps are not *always* printed. Everyone has a *mental map*—a map in their mind—that has developed over years of looking at wall maps, atlas maps, maps in books, magazines, and newspapers. A person's perception of places and regions is influenced by their individual mental maps as well as printed maps. Since people's perception of different places is a combination of general information, personal experiences, and what is called "hear-say" in the legal profession, that perception is not always accurate. Look carefully at Figure 1-9 in your text and you will begin to get some idea of the influence that mental maps and perception of places have on people.

CHAPTER QUIZ

MULTIPLE-CHOICE QUESTIONS

1. This text focuses on human geography. What is the other half of geography called.
   a. environmental
   b. spatial
   c. physical
   d. regional

2. When geographers look at the way places and things are laid out on the cultural landscape, they are taking a:
   a. pattern analysis
   b. distribution measurement
   c. spatial perspective
   d. map measurement

3. Which of Pattison's four traditions of geography, listed below, deals with physical changes on the Earth's surface some of which may impact human cultures.
   a. earth-science
   b. culture-environment
   c. locational
   d. area-analysis

4. When the National Geographic Society developed what they called the "five themes" of geography. they added two new ones. They are:
   a. time and space
   b. region and state
   c. urban and rural
   d. place and movement

5. Of the following, which can **not** be shown on a map.
   a. housing styles
   b. river flow direction
   c. diffusion of disease
   d. relative location

6. What event markedly changed Chicago's relative location (which already had good centrality).
   a. new interstate highway
   b. more railroads
   c. opening of the St. Lawrence Seaway
   d. new airport

7. Symbols on maps represent many different things. Arrows can show:
   a. direction of migration
   b. numbers of people
   c. intensity of traffic on routes
   d. all of the above

8. The spread of various aspects of culture, such as language, knowledge, skills, religion, etc., from one place to another is called:
   a. distribution
   b. relocation
   c. diffusion
   d. infection

9. Geographers define and delimit a region by:
   a. establishing criteria
   b. walking the region
   c. asking others how they define the region
   d. using climate changes

10. A city is an example of a __?__ region.
    a. formal
    b. functional
    c. perceptual
    d. physical

TRUE/FALSE QUESTIONS

1. Human geography encompasses several subfields and has an environmental component. (TF)
2. Medical geography is not a part of human geography. It belongs to physical geography. (TF)
3. The four traditions of geography are not as important as they once were. (TF)
4. The National Geographic Society left out physical geography in its five themes. (TF)
5. The only thing maps can tell us is the absolute location of places. (TF)
6. The relative location of a place can change constantly but only for the better. (TF)
7. A map of worldwide precipitation can show us areas prone to droughts and floods. (TF)
8. The Pacific Ocean affects precipitation on more continental landmasses than any other ocean. (TF)
9. All regions have clear and concise boundaries. (TF)
10. A country is divided into separate regions. No region overlaps another and each is equal in importance. (TF)

STUDY QUESTIONS

1. Why is the spatial perspective so important to geographers? How do patterns and distribution fit into this concept?
2. Discuss the four traditions of geography. Which one do you think is the most important? Why? What is the relationship between the four?
3. Make a list of some of the many ways maps are used. Do you understand the importance of relative location as shown in Figure 1-3? Can you find a map of another place that shows good relative location as described in the text?
4. We all live in a region as well as a country or state. What region do you live in? How is it defined? Is it a formal, functional or perceptual region as defined in your text? Do you have different perceptions about your region?
5. How is your mental map of the city and/or region you live in? After reading the part about mental maps in this chapter, do you think you need to improve yours? Close your eyes. How many Western European nations can you visualize? Go to a map of Europe and see how well you did. Can you accurately visualize the major city locations in your country?

CHAPTER 2. CULTURE, ENVIRONMENTS, AND REGIONS

CHAPTER INTRODUCTION

Culture is an all-encompassing term that defines the tangible lifestyle of a people and their prevailing values and beliefs. The concept of culture is closely identified with anthropology. Over more than a century ago most anthropologists believed that culture was learned. However, recent advances in sociobiology and related fields suggest that certain behaviors may be genetically determined, so that culture has an "instinctive" component as well as a "learned" one. This chapter discusses the development of culture, the human imprint on the landscape, culture and environment, and cultural perceptions and processes. The key points covered in this chapter are outlined below.

Culture and Human Geography
The concept of culture lies at the heart of human geography. Locational decisions, patterns, and landscapes are fundamentally influenced by cultural attitudes and practices. The concept of culture, like the regional concept discussed in the previous chapter, appears to be deceptively simple, but in fact is complex and challenging. The definitions of culture vary widely, as does our use of the word itself, but all refer in one way or another to humans, their development, ideas, and adaptation to the world in which they live.

Components
Culture is made up of four major components. The first of these is a *cultural trait*—a single attribute of a culture—such as eating with certain utensils. The second component is a *cultural complex*—a discrete combination of traits exhibited by a particular culture—such as keeping cattle for different purposes. The third component is a *culture system*—culture complexes with traits in common that can be grouped together —such as ethnicity, language, religion, and other cultural elements. The final component, the *cultural region*—the area within which a particular culture system prevails—is marked by all the attributes of a culture. Culture regions may be expressed on a map, but many geographers prefer to describe these as *geographic regions* since their definition is based on a combination of cultural properties plus locational and environmental circumstances.

Topics
Key topics in cultural geography include *cultural landscapes*—the human imprint on the Earth's surface. These create a distinct and characteristic landscape which reveals much about the culture presently occupying the area, as well as those that came before. A second key topic focuses upon *cultural hearths*—the sources of civilizations from which radiate ideas, innovations, and ideologies. Cultural geographers identify both ancient and modern cultural hearths (see Figure 2-4 in your text).

Cultural diffusion—the process by which innovations and ideas spread to other areas—involves several types of diffusion. *Expansion diffusion* may take the form of contagious diffusion where some item of culture is spread through a local population by contact from person to person. In the case of *hierarchial diffusion*, another form of expansion diffusion, an idea or innovation spreads by trickling down from larger to smaller adoption units. Innovations often leapfrog over wide areas, with geographic distance a less important influence. The early spread of the FAX machine is a good example of this type of diffusion. A third type of expansion diffusion is *stimulus diffusion*, a process where an idea or innovation is not readily adopted by a population but results in local experimentation and eventual changes in the way of doing things. The Industrial Revolution, for example, did not immediately spread to pre- or non-industrial societies, but did stimulate attempts to mechanize local handicraft production.

The different forms of expansion diffusion take place through populations that are stable. It is the innovation or idea that does the moving. *Relocation diffusion*—the spreading of innovations by a migrating population—involves the actual movement of individuals who have already adopted the idea or innovation, and who carry it to a new, perhaps distant locale, where they disseminate it (see Focus on: Acculturation and Transculturation). The spread of European emigrants around the world during the period of Europeanization is a classic example.

The topic of *cultural perception*—the way that members of a culture view themselves as well as how they view other cultures—is a combination of tangible and intangible elements that help to define the personality of a region. We all have impressions and images of various regions and cultures, even though they may not always be accurate. *Perceptual regions* are intellectual constructs designed to help us understand the nature and distribution of phenomena in human geography. These perceptions are based on our accumulated knowledge about such regions and cultures. Perceptual regions can differ considerably, depending on the individual's mental maps of various communities and cultures.

The final considered topic, *cultural environment*—the relationships between human societies and the natural environment—, is complex. On the one hand environment affects societies in countless ways from the types of crops grown to the houses they build, but societies also modify their natural environments in ways that range from slight to severe. One thing is certain, however. While human behavior is not controlled by the environment, (as the now defunct concept of environmental determinism suggested), no culture, no matter how sophisticated, can completely escape the forces of nature.

CHAPTER QUIZ

MULTIPLE-CHOICE QUESTIONS

1. When a discrete number of culture traits is combined it is referred to as a culture:
   a. region
   b. complex
   c. realm
   d. system

2. Features placed on the land change its natural look. Geographers call this the cultural:
   a. realm
   b. system
   c. landscape
   d. land change

3. The birth place of a civilization is called a/an:
   a. culture hearth
   b. origin region
   c. agricultural home base
   d. source region

4. When an idea or invention spreads outward from its source area and also remains strong in its source area, it is said to have spread by:
   a. stimulus diffusion
   b. migrant diffusion

c. expansion diffusion
d. transculturation

5. When the Spanish overthrew the Aztecs in Mexico, they adopted some of the Aztec ways and ideas. At the same time the Aztecs adopted some of the Spanish ways and ideas. This process is called:
   a. migrant diffusion
   b. relocation diffusion
   c. transculturation
   d. acculturation

6. The cultural landscape is dominated everywhere by:
   a. farming
   b. architecture
   c. the pace of life
   d. urbanization

7. Perceptual culture regions are:
   a. known to have sharply defined boundaries
   b. different in definition from person to person
   c. defined by using at least three criteria
   d. found only on islands

8. The idea that human cultural behavior is controlled by the environment in which they live is called:
   a. possibilism
   b. environmental ecology
   c. environmental determinism
   d. environmental regional identity

9. The influence of the natural environment on humanity declines:
   a. toward higher latitudes
   b. with increasing technology
   c. in agrarian societies
   d. in urban societies

10. Broad generalizations about the impact of the environment on humans are:
    a. more accurate today than in the past
    b. almost always sustained
    c. rarely sustained
    d. more accurate for traditional agrarian societies

TRUE/FALSE QUESTIONS

1. Culture does <u>not</u> include the behavior of people. (TF)

2. A cultural trait can only be found in one particular culture. (TF)

3. Cultural systems are only found in the developed countries of the world. (TF)

4. Cultural landscapes are about the same in most developed countries. (TF)

5. Nomadic people leave a large imprint on their cultural landscape because they keep traveling the same routes over and over. (TF)

6. Culture hearths first appeared in the Western Hemisphere. (TF)

7. Most information spread from culture hearths by hierarchical diffusion. (TF)

8. The wheel, after being introduced into Mesopotamia, quickly diffused to Egypt. (TF)

9. Culture regions can become political battlegrounds and even physical battlegrounds because of people's emotional attachments to the land and traditions. (TF)

10. People must learn to live with their physical environment because changing or trying to control it causes problems. (TF)

STUDY QUESTIONS

1. Define the six components of culture. In your own geographical region, can you think of any culture traits that seem to stand out from the normal traits with which you are familiar?

2. After reading about cultural landscapes, can you see the signs of how your culture region's landscape has changed over time? Study things such as building styles, rivers, outgrowth of cities, etc. If you area attending a college or university away from home, look for material changes in the landscape. Talk to a long-time resident who can tell you about changes that have taken place.

3. Why do you think it is important to study about culture hearths? When you look at Figure 2-4, in your text can you understand how expansion and relocation diffusion worked in carrying ideas and inventions to distant lands?

4. If you live in a large city, can you see signs of acculturation in ethnic neighborhoods? If you come from a rural environment, is everyone alike or are there ethnic differences that might be evident in the way people layout farm buildings or house-building styles dating from an earlier time?

5. Look at Figure 2-8 in your text. In which perceptual region is your home state? Does this map fit with your perception of what region you live in? If it doesn't, how do you perceive where you live? What do you base your reasoning on? Do you identify strongly with your home region?

CHAPTER 3. THE EARTH AS HUMANITY'S HOME

CHAPTER INTRODUCTION

This chapter introduces you to the physical and environmental aspects of the Earth, both past and present, and the impact of human occupancy. It also focuses on the development of humanity during one of the most fascinating geologic epochs, the Holocene. During this epoch, humanity developed socially, politically, and economically. In addition, the number of humans occupying the Earth soared. There is much to learn from this chapter, both to lay the foundation for the remainder of the text and to broaden your knowledge of human and Earth history that led to the world we live in today.

Environment
Despite what you may think, the Earth's environment is not stable and environmental change is humankind's constant companion. To understand the geography of culture, it is necessary to understand the complexity of the environment within which humanity lives. Many changes in the environment have occurred since early hunter-gatherers began to exploit the Earth's resources and deal with their environment. The survival of humanity may well depend on an understanding and appreciation of environmental conditions.

Earth's environment frequently changes, and warming and cooling of the planet are natural. Far more of the Earth's surface is water than land, as a glance at any world map will reveal, and only a small percentage of the total surface is suitable for human occupancy. Humanity is quite old, but compared to the age of the earth, we are recent occupiers. The Earth is currently in the grip of a long series of glacial advances (cooling periods) and retreats (warming periods); modern human civilization emerged during a warm spell between glaciations.

Technological progress notwithstanding, terrain and climate continue to influence the distribution and nature of human life and activity. Compare, for example, Figure 3-6 (Global Terrain), Figure 3-7 (World Climates), and Figure 4-1 (World Population Distribution). Ask yourself why people are where they are **and** why they are **not** in other places. In essence, humans are "where they have always been," relative to terrain and climate. What has changed is the number.

Human Development and Innovation
The various stages in Earth history have been divided into periods of geologic time (see Table 3-1). The most recent geologic time period, the Holocene epoch, refers to the most recent 10,000 plus years of Earth's history. Because of the cultural-geographical characteristics of this period of great environmental variation, it is sometimes referred to as "Holocene humanity." Within this short time humanity did what it had not done in previous interglaciations.

Perhaps the single most significant event of the early Holocene was the domestication by humans of plants and animals, which may have occurred nearly simultaneously in areas as far removed as the Middle East and Southeast Asia. Agriculture developed and surpluses were stored for future use. Villages grew larger, towns and cities emerged, and political organization became increasingly complex; inventions multiplied, and tools became more efficient. Certain communities thrived, sometimes at the expense of others. The earliest states appear to have emerged about 5500 years ago in the middle East and southeastern Turkey. The spiral leading toward empires, colonial realms, and global power struggles had begun.

Human Population
Humans have always used *resources* (sometimes defined as anything that humans value), but that use is dependant on, among other things, the number of humans and the technology available to them. The hu-

man population growth spiral began during the Holocene epoch. Numbers at the beginning of this epoch have been estimated at between 4 and 8 million, but the numbers grew and declined during the previous Pleistocene epoch. Population growth during the Holocene began slowly at first, then ever faster. Modern humanity is indeed the product of the Holocene epoch.

During the Holocene the Earth changed as never before, not because of geologic forces but because of the imprint of humanity. That imprint has become stronger over time, especially over the last 200 years when human population growth and pressure on resources have reached unprecedented levels. This began with the Industrial Revolution in Europe and spread globally during the period of Europeanization and colonialization. During the twentieth century, the Earth has especially felt the strains created by the human population. Raw materials are used up at an ever faster rate while the air, water, and land become polluted or damaged. Together, these events have rendered environmental change one of the key issues of the twenty-first century.

CHAPTER QUIZ

MULTIPLE-CHOICE QUESTIONS

1. Today humanity lives in the geologic era called the:
   a. Paleozoic
   b. Cretaceous
   c. Cenozoic
   d. Pleistocene

2. The last ice age reached its climax during the __?__ epoch.
   a. Holocene
   b. Pliocene
   c. Pleistocene
   d. Miocene

3. A glacial period was in progress as recently as __?__ years ago.
   a. 6,000
   b. 8,000
   c. 10,000
   d. 12,000

4. Human population growth began during which of the following geologic epochs.
   a. Miocene
   b. Holocene
   c. Paleocene
   d. Pleistocene

5. Cultural geographer Carl Sauer suggested that plant domestication may have begun more than 14,000 years ago in:
   a. Mesopotamia
   b. Mesoamerica

c. southeastern Asia
d. eastern China

6. The development of sedentary and irrigated agriculture and the rise of villages and towns initially occurred in:
   a. Southwest Asia
   b. East Africa
   c. South America
   d. Southeast Asia

7. Ancient Babylon was located on the Euphrates River in present-day:
   a. Iran
   b. Turkey
   c. Iraq
   d. Greece

8. Which of the following human activities transforms more of the Earth's surface than any other.
   a. manufacturing
   b. urbanization
   c. farming
   d. transportation

9. The Inca Empire was a mountain-based state in which of the following mountain systems.
   a. Alps
   b. Rockies
   c. Himalayas
   d. Andes

10. The continent which consists mainly of plateaus, and therefore supports fewer people than the single country of India is:
    a. Australia
    b. Africa
    c. South America
    d. Asia

TRUE/FALSE QUESTIONS

1. The Mesozoic era ended about 65 million years ago with the extinction of many plants and animals. (TF)

2. Today Earth is going through the end of an ice age caused by global warming. (TF)

3. The Holocene epoch has been humankind's time of the greatest cultural development. (TF)

4. The Paleolithic period is the latest stage of the Stone Age. (TF)

5. It is believed by most geographers that wheat and barley were among the first domesticated crops in Southwestern Asia. (TF)

6. Domestication of plants and animals kept people nomadic because animals ate all the nearby grass and land was worn out from farming. (TF)

7. The first cities arose in the Fertile Crescent. (TF)

8. The El Niño Southern/Oscillation is created by a temperature rise in the southern Atlantic Ocean. (TF)

9. In general, mountainous regions do **not** support any population clusters, and never have. (TF)

10. Because of global warming, the Earth will never experience another ice age. (TF)

STUDY QUESTIONS

1. When you read about the Pleistocene epoch can you understand the environmental problems our human ancestors faced? Can you understand why some branches of the early human family tree died out?

2. Why is the Holocene epoch different from previous epochs? List the accomplishments of humankind during this period and contrast it to previous periods. What do you think might happen when Earth goes into another ice age? How might people survive? Relate this to Figure 3-1.

3. What negative impact are humans having on Earth's environment? How does a natural event like El Niño Southern/Oscillation affect our environment? Does human change in the environment make El Niño's effects worse?

4. Why do geographers consider Köppen's climate classifications so important? Compare Figure 3-7 of World Climates with Figure 16-1 of World Agriculture Regions, pages 216-217 in your text. What correlations can you find between climate and crops grown? How can you tell from the climate map where people are most likely to live?

PART TWO: POPULATION PATTERNS AND PROCESSES

CHAPTER 4. FUNDAMENTALS OF POPULATION GEOGRAPHY

CHAPTER INTRODUCTION

No event in human history has equaled the rapid increase in population over the last 10,000 years. This is in sharp contrast to the 200,000 years following the emergence of *Homo sapiens* in Africa, during which the earth's human population grew very slowly, its numbers rising and falling in response to the "traditional" controllers of population: environmental change, disease, and availability of food. As the last glaciation retreated and the Holocene epoch began, the amount of habitable space increased and unprecedented events began to occur in Earth's history.

The study of population is termed *demography,* derived from ancient Greek words roughly meaning to "describe and write about people." The focus of *population geography* is on the spatial aspects of demography. The key questions in geography are *where* and *why there?* These lead to some penetrating insights into population issues.

Population Growth
The dominant issue concerning population in the late 1990s is *growth.* The world's population is currently growing by about 90 million per year, (that is more than ten times the *total* estimated world population at the beginning of the Holocene) and the bulk of this growth is occurring in the world's poorer countries. The Earth's environments and natural resources are strained by the needs of a mushrooming human population, a population that has increased *fourfold* from its level just a hundred years earlier. Problems resulting from unprecedented population growth have become especially acute in the twentieth century. A continued high rate of population growth in the twenty-first century could have a calamitous impact, causing irreversible damage to the natural systems on which we depend for our existence and survival.

Population Distribution
From the beginning, humanity has been unevenly distributed over the land and this pattern has only been intensified during the twentieth century. Whether urban or rural, populations tend to cluster in certain areas (see Figure 4-1) because, as you will recall from earlier discussions, much of the Earth is unsuitable for human occupancy (refer back to Figures 3-6 and 3-7). To handle contrasts of this type on maps, geographers use measures of population *distribution*—the locations on the Earth's surface where individuals or groups (depending on the scale of the map) are concentrated—and the *density* of the population figured as the number of people per unit area of land.

Figure 4-1 shows patterns of population distribution for the world using the dot method. It shows that the world's three largest population concentrations all lie on the Eurasian landmass —*East Asia*, *South Asia*, and *Europe*—each associated with a major civilization. It also reminds us that the overwhelming majority of the world's population inhabits the Northern Hemisphere.

East Asia, centered on China but extending to Korea and Japan, contains about one-quarter of the world's population—nearly 1.3 billion in China alone. The map shows that the population is concentrated toward the coast with ribbon-like extensions found on the basins and lowlands of China's major rivers.

The great majority of people in East Asia are farmers.

India lies at the center of the South Asian concentration with extensions to Pakistan, Bangladesh, and the island of Sri Lanka. This is one of the greatest concentrations of people on Earth with about 1.5 billion people. It is a confined region (the Himalaya Mountains on the north and the desert west of the Indus River in Pakistan) with a rapidly growing population. By almost any estimate, the capacity of the region to support this population has been exceeded. As in East Asia, the majority are farmers.

Europe, the third-ranking population cluster, also lies in Eurasia but at the opposite end from China. This cluster contains about 700 million people, which puts it in a class with the South Asian concentration, but the similarity ends there. In Europe, unlike East and South Asia, terrain and environment are not as closely related to population distribution. Another contrast lies in the fact that the majority of the European population live in cities and towns, leaving the rural countryside more open and sparsely populated. These contrasts with the East and South Asian clusters reflect the impact of the Industrial Revolution on Europe over the last 200 years.

Population Density

Population density can be measured on the basis of several different criteria, revealing contrasting aspects of a country's demography. Figure 4-2 illustrates density via the isopleth method. The data in Resource C at the end of this book provide the area, total population, and density per square mile for every country (one must examine such data with caution, however, since the high cost and organizational challenges of census taking often produce unreliable data [see Focus on: Reliability of Population Data]). *Arithmetic* and *physiologic* population densities are the two most common approaches. These two methods become more meaningful and useful when compared with each other (see Table 4-1).

CHAPTER QUIZ

MULTIPLE-CHOICE QUESTIONS

1. Demography is the study of:
   a. physical geography
   b. people
   c. animals
   d. climate

2. Which country has the highest arithmetic density of people.
   a. Japan
   b. Bangladesh
   c. India
   d. Netherlands

3. Physiologic density of a country relates the total population of a country to the:
   a. number of people living on farmlands
   b. population divided into total acres of farmland
   c. acres of farmland available
   d. population living in villages and city

4. About __?__ of the world's population lives in East Asia.
   a. one-half
   b. one-third
   c. one-fifth
   d. one-fourth

5. One of the greatest concentrations of population, according to your text, is:
   a. in Argentina
   b. on the Ganges River plain in northern India
   c. in Bangladesh
   d. on the Nile River

6. In Germany __?__ percent of the people live in cities.
   a. 85
   b. 90
   c. 50
   d. 75

7. In the United States, the largest urban complex, called a megalopolis, lies:
   a. in Florida and north to South Carolina
   b. along the Pacific coast in Southern California
   c. in Chicago and its surrounding area
   d. from Boston to Baltimore

8. South East Asia has __?__ clusters of population.
   a. contiguous
   b. few
   c. discrete
   d. large

9. The population of Sub-Saharan Africa is nearly:
   a. 200 million
   b. 350 million
   c. 400 million
   d. 600 million

10. Geographically, the spatial distribution of population in Australia and South America is:
    a. very scattered
    b. concentrated in the interior regions
    c. peripheral
    d. concentrated on plateaus

TRUE/FALSE QUESTIONS

1. In the less developed countries, people tend to cluster in the urban areas because there is little farmland. (TF)

2. Population distribution dot-maps are used primarily to show where people live. (TF)

3. Physiologic density maps more accurately show populations densities because they are based on urban land clusters. (TF)

4. In China, farmers far out-number people living in cities. (TF)

5. The country of Bangladesh has a population of nearly 125 million people living in an area about the size of Iowa. (TF)

6. In contrast to East and South Asia, Europe's population centers are not closely related to terrain and environment. Instead they are related exclusively to the coal-fields. (TF)

7. In the United States the largest urban agglomeration is located along the eastern seaboard. (TF)

8. Southeast Asia does not have large contiguous urban areas because it is made up of islands. (TF)

9. In Africa, there are no agglomerations comparable to those in Asia. (TF)

10. With land reforms it would be possible for South America to support a much larger population. (TF)

STUDY QUESTIONS

1. List and explain the problems high population growth rates are causing in the world today.

2. Define and discuss the difference between arithmetic and physiologic densities. What is lacking in each? Why aren't either of these completely accurate?

3. How does the spatial distribution of population of North America and Europe differ from that of East Asia and South Asia? How are populations spatially distributed in South America and Australia?

4. How does Japan support its large population? What special problems does this country have that are not faced by the other developed nations?

CHAPTER 5. PROCESSES AND CYCLES OF POPULATION CHANGE

CHAPTER INTRODUCTION

Population does not increase in an even manner from country to country. The differences include age, gender, life expectancy, and geographic distribution, and may be identified between countries but are more significant internally. A country that has a large percentage of its population at 15 years of age or below will have enormous needs for education, jobs, and housing in the years ahead. A country where the population is "aging" such as the United States or France can face shortages of younger workers and problems with their retirement systems. The list goes on but you get the point: that a population is far more than mere numbers. This is an extremely important chapter, and when you have studied it, you will have a much better understanding of the complex issues of world population.

Population Trends
Never before in human history have so many people filled the Earth's living space, and never has world population grown as rapidly as it has during the past 100 years. The population explosion of the past 200 years has increased the world's population from under 1 billion to approximately 6 billion. It took from the dawn of history to the year 1820 for the Earth's population to reach 1 billion. It now is taking only a decade to add each new billion. It is still possible that there will be 10 billion human inhabitants on the planet by the middle of the twenty-first century.

Population Growth Rates
Rapid population growth varies over time and space. Europe's rapid growth occurred during the nineteenth century, the result of the Second Agricultural Revolution. At this time better farming methods and improved organization resulted in increased food supplies, especially to cities and towns. This was immediately followed by the Industrial Revolution, during which sanitation facilities made the towns and cities safer from epidemics, and modern medical practices became widespread. Disease prevention through vaccination introduced a new era in public health. Death rates declined markedly—by 50 percent between 1750 and 1850—while birth rates remained high. The change is especially spectacular when viewed in the context of doubling time—the number of years it takes a population to double—which was 150 years in 1750 but only 35 years in 1850.

One effect of this increase in the rate of natural population growth was increased migration. Millions of people left Europe to emigrate to other parts of the world—North and South America, Australia, South Africa, and elsewhere. When European colonization began in earnest during the nineteenth century, the Europeans brought with them their newfound methods of sanitation and medical techniques and death rates in Africa, India, and South America began to decline. Indigenous populations began to grow, and at ever increasing rates. Today, South America's growth rates have declined, but Africa's have increased. As mentioned previously, the fastest growing populations today are invariably taking place in those poorer countries that have the greatest difficulties providing the basic amenities of life for their citizens.

Disease and famine were the major controllers of population for the world as a whole until the last 100 years. Diseases still kill millions of people each year, especially infants and children, but the overall-effects have been reduced, at least in many countries. The impact of famine has likewise been reduced, as a result of the Second and Third (Green) Agricultural Revolutions. Although hundreds of millions of people remain inadequately nourished, the threat of global hunger has receded—perhaps temporarily.

Reduction Of Growth Rates

Reducing population growth rates is a complicated and sensitive issue. In the richer, more developed countries, general modernization and education has resulted in lower growth rates. Therefore, these countries total populations do not approach those of the poorer countries. The benefits enjoyed by the wealthier, developed nations that have led to their slower rates of population have not been shared by much of the world. A key issue to the reduction of population growth rates is to improve the status of women and to secure their rights in society. In the Muslim countries of Southwest Asia and Sub-Saharan Africa, two of the regions with the highest rates of population growth, women often live in near-Medieval conditions or, at best, as second class citizens. Tradition plays a powerful role, but the barrier to better education for women is the real key. In places where women's education levels have risen, there has been an accompanying decline in population growth rates; not to mention a general improvement in the well-being of the population.

The demographic transition model, which compares birth and death rates in a population over time (see text page 77), suggests that the world's population will stabilize in the twenty-first century (see Focus on: A Stabilizing Population?), but the model may not be universally applicable. The sequence of stages of the demographic transition has been observed in a several European countries, but what transpired economically and socially in Europe may not apply for the rest of the world. It may be unwise, therefore, to assume that the demographic cycles that occurred in already industrialized countries will spread, eventually, to the rest of the world.

CHAPTER QUIZ

MULTIPLE-CHOICE QUESTIONS

1. At the present time, about __?__ million people are added to the world's population each year.
   a. 150
   b. 100
   c. 90
   d. 80

2. Today, Russia is experiencing a __?__ population growth rate.
   a. rising
   b. declining
   c. negative
   d. stable

3. When we talk about maps showing regional distribution and density of populations, what two aspects of population are these maps unable to show us.
   a. number and rate of growth
   b. ethnic differences and where the people came from
   c. what the people do for a living and how much they make
   d. numbers of men and women and their ages

4. The region with the lowest birth rates is:
   a. Europe
   b. North America

c. Southeast Asia
d. Antarctica

5. The total fertility rate of a country measures the total number of:
   a. women able to have children
   b. children between one year old and age ten
   c. women between 13 and 45
   d. children born to women of childbearing age

6. Crude death rates are highest in:
   a. tropical Africa
   b. China
   c. South Africa
   d. South America

7. Which of the following did <u>not</u> have an effect on keeping population growth rates down before 1820.
   a. the Little Ice Age
   b. wars
   c. plagues
   d. advances in medicine

8. The actual demographic transition is represented by which two of the four stages of the demographic transition model.
   a. 1 and 4
   b. 2 and 3
   c. 3 and 4
   d. 2 and 4

9. It is thought by some that perhaps today's developing countries will __?__ of the demographic transition model.
   a. not go through all four stages
   b. have to go through all four stages
   c. not follow any stages
   d. only go through stages two and three

10. As a tool for development, the demographic transition model is most useful in one place.
    a. United States
    b. Europe
    c. Japan
    d. Canada

TRUE/FALSE QUESTIONS

1. Because of the world's falling population growth rate, there is no longer fear of a population explosion. (TF)

2. Growth rates are rising in all Muslim countries. (TF)

3. Not all of the countries with low birth rates are wealthy. (TF)

4. Thomas Malthus thought the world's population growth would be slowed by disease. (TF)

5. Studying a country's age-sex pyramid can quickly tell you whether a country has a high growth rate or is stabilizing. (TF)

6. Population geography is the spatial component of demography. (TF)

7. Natural increase of a population is the number of births minus the number of immigrants. (TF)

8. Crude death rates decline more rapidly than birth rates. (TF)

9. European colonization reduced natural periodic checks on population growth. (TF)

10. Most countries in the world are at the same stage of the demographic transition model. (TF)

STUDY QUESTIONS

1. Look at Figure 5-1. Note where the high population growth rate countries are. Do you see a pattern?

2. Even though the world's overall population growth rate has slowed, why is there still concern about another population explosion? Explain exponential growth and why the base population is so important worldwide and by country. Use text Figure 5-3 to help you. What kinds of problems can you foresee for those countries that have a high rate of growth today?

3. Study Figures 5-4 and 5-5. Explain what you can learn by looking at these age-sex pyramids.

4. Study the section under the heading Demographic Cycles. Write down all the terms and their definitions in this section.

5. After studying the demographic cycle do you understand why the four stages might not apply to today's developing countries? How did European colonization affect these countries?

CHAPTER 6. MIGRATION AND ITS CAUSES

CHAPTER INTRODUCTION

Humans have always been mobile. Throughout history humans have sought new frontiers and the search still continues today. For more than 90 percent of human history there were hunter-gatherers, a practice that required frequent relocation. Such movement is called *migration* and while the reasons for such movement are different today, human mobility has actually increased in modern times.

Human mobility is of central interest in human geography because it is an inherently spatial process. Human movement speeds the diffusion of ideas and innovations. It intensifies spatial interaction and transforms whole regions. And as you will see in this chapter, it is often closely linked to environmental conditions.

Why People Move

Many factors stimulate the migration process. They include armed conflict, economic conditions (real or perceived), political strife, cultural circumstances (such as linguistic or religious differences), environmental change (growing more common today), and technological advances (which makes information about destinations more easily obtainable and movement easier). Migration today occurs for various reasons but those listed are the principle ones.

Migrants move on the basis of their perceptions of particular destinations, taking into consideration both direction and distance. Direction, like location, can be viewed in two ways: *absolute* and *relative*. Absolute direction refers to astronomically determined direction and thus is what we think of as *compass* direction. Relative direction is more perceptual and often imprecise, as in the case of the Sunbelt. The residents of North Dakota, for example, would agree that it lies to the south and that Florida is part of the Sunbelt, but not everyone would agree that Utah is also. Different people have different perceptions.

Distance, like direction, can be measured in both absolute and relative terms. *Absolute distance* is the physical distance between two points usually using kilometers or miles; it can be read on maps using the scale of the map. Absolute distance does not change. *Relative distance*—measured not in linear terms such as miles or kilometers, but in terms such as cost or time—has different meanings for different people and cultures. It can change due to, say, a new method of transportation or the discovery of a shorter route. Research has shown that people's perception of both distance and direction can be greatly distorted and that distance particularly affects the accuracy of migrants perception of their destinations.

Patterns Of Migration

Rarely does migration take place in a single step, rather it usually takes place in stages. Rural-to-urban movement occurs in steps, often to a small community and then to a larger one and perhaps eventually to an even larger one in a region of more favorable environmental conditions. Migrants also tend to relocate repeatedly after reaching the land of their destination. Early immigrants to America, for example, often first settled in regions where relatives or friends were located, moving "West" after a time seeking land of their own or better opportunity, often moving several times before settling permanently. Some, of course, found the new surroundings not to their liking and returned east or perhaps to their original source region in a counter or return migration. Almost all migration flows have this aspect.

Factors Of Migration

The decision to migrate usually results from a combination of conditions and perceptions that tend to induce people to leave their abodes. Geographers who study human migration call the negative conditions and perceptions *push factors*. The positive conditions and perceptions that effectively attract people to new locale from other areas are called *pull factors* (see Focus on: Theories About Migration). Push factors are likely to be perceived more accurately than pull factors, since people are more likely to be familiar with their place of residence (source) than the locale to which they are moving. Push factors include individual considerations ranging from work or retirement conditions to weather and climate. Pull factors tend to be more vague and many migrants move on the basis of excessively positive images and expectations regarding their destinations.

Our final look at the reasons people move focuses on the luxury of choice and the fear of compulsion. These may be classed as *voluntary* and *forced migrations*. There are different cases within each of these categories and it is not always easy to make a clear determination. In the case of the millions of Europeans who came to the Americas, most were seeking opportunity and better living conditions. These same motives carried others far from Europe to the African and Asian colonies. The prevailing force was the "pull" of opportunity and thus for the most part, emigrants from Europe left by choice.

Several of the world's largest migration streams have been forced migrations, which result from the imposition of power by stronger peoples over weaker ones. By far the most important of these was the Transatlantic *slave trade*, which carried tens of millions of Africans from their homes to the Americas, with enormous loss of life. From 12 million to over 30 million Africans were sold into slavery (see Figure 6-3) and nothing in human history compares to the Atlantic slave trade. Both source and destination regions were affected, with the African sources being socially and demographically devastated for generations. Forced counter migration continues today when governments send back migrants caught entering their countries illegally.

CHAPTER QUIZ

MULTIPLE-CHOICE QUESTIONS

1. Which country has the most mobile population.
   a. England
   b. United States
   c. France
   d. Ireland

2. Emigration occurs when a person:
   a. moves from their home country
   b. relocates to another part of their own country
   c. enters a new country as a migrant
   d. moves to another location in the same town

3. Which of the following is the best answer for why people migrate.
   a. armed conflict and civil war
   b. a combination of factors
   c. political circumstances
   e. economic conditions

4. In the last few centuries, which of the following source areas has had the most voluntary emigrants.
   a. Africa
   b. South Asia

c. Europe
d. the Caribbean

5. One of the world's largest forced migrations and most devastating was the slave trading. Which of the following was **not** a consequence of that event.
   a. children were orphaned
   b. communities were disrupted
   c. equal numbers of men and women were taken
   d. mostly young men were taken

6. In 1997 it was officially reported there were about __?__ million refugees in the world.
   a. 18
   b. 22
   c. 25
   d. 28

7. Which group of people suffered the worst as refugees after the Gulf War in 1991?
   a. Iranians
   b. Kurdish
   c. Palestinians
   d. Kuwait people

8. What former European country has had the largest number of refugees since World War II?
   a. Bulgaria
   b. Czechoslovakia
   c. Albania
   d. Yugoslavia

9. In the Western Hemisphere which country had a serious refugee problem that was drug related?
   a. Mexico
   b. Columbia
   c. Cuba
   d. Haiti

10. Today the number of refugees in the United States is:
    a. increasing
    b. negligible
    c. non-existent
    d. unknown

TRUE/FALSE QUESTIONS

1. Absolute direction is compass direction. (TF)

2. Relative direction and relative distance are both perceptual. (TF)

3. The term internal migration is how geographers describe the migration of black families that moved from the South to the North in the United States. (TF)

4. Economic conditions have not been a major reason for emigration. (TF)

5. When major floods or famines occur, people do not migrate, they stay and wait out the disaster. (TF)

6. Because of distance decay, many migrants move in what is called step migration. (TF)

7. In today's world the refugee population is growing faster than the total population. (TF)

8. There are many more international refugees than intranational refugees. (TF)

9. During Afghanistan's war with the former Soviet Union, there were no international refugees because the Soviets surrounded the country. (TF)

10. In forecasting the future, experts believe the refugee problem will lessen and probably disappear. (TF)

STUDY QUESTIONS

1. Describe external and internal migration. What is the difference? How has internal migration affected the United States' great urban areas?

2. List and define the factors that make people migrate. How do push/pull factors come into play? Read the Focus on: Theories About Migration. Relate the five "laws" and apply them to migrations given as examples in this chapter.

3. List the differences between voluntary and forced migration.

4. When we speak of refugees we use the terms intranational and international. Define each. Why is it a problem to determine exactly how many refugees are in the world today? How does the United Nations' definition of a refugee fit into this problem?

5. List the three characteristics that distinguish refugees from migrants. Can you describe situations that might create intranational refugees? Describe the situations that have created refugee crises in Africa during the 1990s.

6. Why do you think the Western Hemisphere has many fewer refugees at this time?

CHAPTER 7. ROUTES OF HUMAN MOBILITY

CHAPTER INTRODUCTION

This chapter examines *where* people move. Each day in our modern world, people are on the move and American society today is the world's most mobile. Movement may be long or short, internal or external (within a political unit or across its borders), temporary or permanent. By the time that you have finished this chapter your understanding of human movement will give you new insights into the world of the late 1990s.

Forms of Human Mobility

Mobility of all kinds is one of the defining characteristics of a culture. The great majority of people have a daily routine that takes them through a regular sequence of short moves that geographers call *activity* (or *action*) *space*. The magnitude of activity space varies in different societies, and American society is the world's most mobile. Technology has greatly expanded activity spaces, particularly in the wealthier, more developed countries.

There are three general types of movement recognized by geographers and others who study human mobility. *Cyclic movement*—movement that has a closed route—defines your activity space. When you go to daily classes or a job you are participating in cyclic movement. If your trip involves a lengthy period of residency after your arrival—such as temporary relocation for college attendance or service in the armed services—you engaged in *periodic movement*. Both cyclic and periodic movements occur in many forms. Finally, *migratory movement* describes human movement from a source to a destination without a return journey, and is the most significant form of movement discussed in this chapter. A society's mobility is measured as the sum of cyclic, periodic, and migratory movement by its population.

Permanent Relocation

The past five centuries have witnessed human migration on an unprecedented scale, much of it generated by events in Europe. Major modern migration flows are shown in Figure 7-1. The voluntary migration of Europeans to the New World, the migration of Europeans to their overseas colonial empires (these two migrations may have totaled 75 million between 1835 and 1935), and the forced migration of Africans to the Americas, are among migration streams that have transformed the world. The immense impact of the forced migration of Africans during the slave trade on both sides of the Atlantic sets it apart from all the other migrations.

When early humans began migrating from Africa to Eurasia, Australia, and the Americas, they faced only natural boundaries. Rivers and mountain ranges may have presented barriers, but they did not stop the inexorable march of human migration. For today's migrants, political boundaries, not natural ones, form the most difficult obstacles. Agencies that monitor the annual stream of human migration use the world's political framework to keep track of migrants. Those who cross international borders are *external migrants* and those who relocate within their national boundaries are *internal migrants*. In any given year, internal migrants greatly outnumber external migrants. However, it is the external migrants who change countries' vital statistics, affect their economies, and often influence their politics.

External migrations took Europeans to America and other parts of the world; the arrival of the Europeans, in turn, caused other people to move (see text Figure 7-1). External migrations (authorized movements and organized resettlements, as well as refugee movements) usually occur after wars. Following World War II, Germans migrated westward from their homes in Eastern Europe and millions of migrants left Europe altogether to go to the United States.

Internal migration involves relocation within a country. Such movements can also produce significant population shifts, even though the migrants do not cross any international borders. Internal migrations, involving major population shifts, have occurred in the former Soviet Union, the United States, China, and other large countries. Such movements are *usually* easier to accomplish because no international borders are crossed. For the same reason, the numbers of people moving is more difficult to determine, at least in most countries.

We noted earlier that Americans are the world's most mobile people. Etched on the U.S. population map are the effects of two historic internal migrations; the westward movement of the population as a whole, and the northward migration of black Americans from the rural South to the urban North. The West is still a major migration destination as can be seen in Figure 7-5. In the United States, the Northeast and the Midwest have been losing population for decades, while the South and West have been gaining.

Controlling Migration

Migration control and its attendant problems have become hot issues around the world. Efforts to restrict migrations are nothing new; media coverage, democratic debate, and political wrangling only make it seem so. China's Great Wall was built in part as a barrier to emigration, as was the Berlin Wall and the fences along the Rio Grande—all evidence of the desire of governments to control the movement of people across their borders. Physical as well as legal barriers are placed in the way of migrants, but few countries have succeeded in controlling immigration effectively.

CHAPTER QUIZ

MULTIPLE-CHOICE QUESTIONS

1. Between 1835 and 1935 perhaps as many as __?__ million people left Europe for the New World and other overseas's territories..
   a. 35
   b. 50
   c. 75
   d. 90

2. In the sixteenth century, African slaves were first brought to which of the following destinations in the New World.
   a. the United States
   b. Brazil
   c. the Caribbean
   d. Panama

3. The most difficult obstacles faced by people migrating today are __?__ barriers.
   a. physical
   b. economic
   c. transportation
   d. political

4. In the post-World War II period, millions of foreign workers migrated from North Africa to which of the following European countries.
   a. Spain
   b. France
   c. Germany
   d. Hungary

5. Before the formation of the European Union, which of the following countries provided a natural stepping stone for migrants from North Africa into Europe.
   a. Italy
   b. Yugoslavia
   c. Turkey
   d. Spain

6. In 1892, during the tsarist period in Russia, the eastward movement of peasants into Siberia was strengthened by:
   a. improving climatic conditions
   b. more freedom of movement granted by the government
   c. the construction of the Trans-Siberian Railroad
   d. the discovery of gold in the region

7. In 1990, the center of the U.S. population, as shown in Figure 7-5, was located in the state of:
   a. Iowa
   b. Indiana
   c. Kentucky
   d. Missouri

8. In the late 1990s, about 80 percent of African Americans living in rural areas remain in which of the following regions:
   a. the South
   b. the Midwest
   c. the West
   d. the Northeast

9. The first immigration laws passed by the United States Congress in 1882 were designed to specifically restrict the immigration of which of the following groups of people.
   a. Mexicans
   b. Chinese
   c. Japanese
   d. Indians

10. In the United States, restrictive legislation affecting European immigrants was passed in:
    a. 1991
    b. 1941
    c. 1921
    d. 1891

TRUE/FALSE QUESTIONS

1. Vacations are a type of nomadism. (TF)

2. In the past five centuries migration has slowly increased. (TF)

3. Today, having to cross country borders helps to record of the number of migrants or refugees. (TF)

4. Israel became a Jewish state in 1949. (TF)

5. Today in the United States, Asian immigrants outnumber those from Mexico. (TF)

6. Today, the internal migration flow in the United States is one-way to the South and Southwest. (TF)

7. The Midwest region of the United States is gaining population because people are tired of living in crowded eastern urban areas. (TF)

8. The Great wall of China was built primarily to keep people from emigrating. (TF)

9. Australia's immigration law of 1901 was passed to keep out all nonwhite immigrants. (TF)

10. Many countries have never passed immigration laws restricting persons of different ethnic backgrounds. (TF)

STUDY QUESTIONS

1. Define the three different kinds of migration movement and give examples of each.

2. After looking at text Figure 7-1, discuss European migration and some of its consequences, include post World War II migrations internal and external.

3. Look at text figure 7-5. Explain how internal and counter migration have caused this pattern.

4. Over the years, what measures have countries taken to restrict immigration? What ethnic groups were these measures aimed towards?

PART THREE: THE GLOBAL LINGUISTIC MOSAIC

CHAPTER 8. A GEOGRAPHY OF LANGUAGES

CHAPTER INTRODUCTION

Language is one of the cornerstones of national identity, cultural unity, and community cohesion. It is the most important *cultural glue*—an aspect that binds a culture together—because without language, there would be no culture. People have very strong feelings about their language and identify with it (people may be persuaded to change their religion, but not their language). When a people's language is threatened, the response is often passionate and protective.

Thousands of languages are spoken in the world today (linguists estimate between 5000 and 6000) and they serve as both unifiers and dividers of humanity. Ironically, all languages may have a common origin. Consider the following points carefully as you read this chapter.

Standard Language

Human languages, even those spoken in preliterate societies—peoples who speak their languages but do not write it—are fundamentally different from those of nonhuman primates. Human languages are not static but change constantly because a vital culture requires a flexible language and the potential vocabulary of any language is infinite.

Mature and complex cultures—technologically advanced societies—attempt to maintain a *standard language* sustained by national institutions and official state examinations. In the modern world, where innovations diffuse rapidly, such standards are difficult to uphold. One problem that arises is: who decides what the standard language will be? Not surprisingly, the answer has to do with influence and power—circumstances that often produce problems in a world where cultural identity and national self-interest are increasingly significant.

Classification and Distribution of Languages

The problem of language classification relates to the definition of language. At issue is what is a language (according to the dictionary:"human communication by voice") and what is a dialect ("language of a particular area or class")? The issue is a complex one and it is clear that the distinction is not based on an objective measure of mutual intelligibility. Instead, it must be recognized that what we consider a language is a function of society's view of what constitutes a cultural community—a matter that in turn is influenced by historical development in the political arena.

Language classification uses terms that are also employed in biology, and for the same reasons: some languages are related and some are not. *Language families* are thought to have a shared, but fairly distant, origin; in a *language subfamily*, the commonality is more definite. Subfamilies are divided into *language groups*, which consist of sets of individual languages.

Figure 8-2 shows the distribution of 20 major language families. On this map, only the Indo-European language family is broken down into subfamilies (greater detail is shown in Figure 8-3). Spatially, the Indo-European languages are the most widely dispersed. More people speak languages belonging to the Indo-European language family than those in any other family. There are good reasons for this pattern. When the European migration of emigrants and colonists spread over the world in the last 500 years, one of the cultural components that spread with them was their language. Add to this the fact that indigenous populations were virtually wiped out in the Americas and Australia (and their languages with them) and the European desire to spread the Christian faith, usually in the language of the European culture invading the area, and the patterns on the map become easier to understand.

Major World Languages

Chinese is spoken by more people than any other language (Table 8-1), with English ranking second. The numbers in Table 8-1, however, should be viewed as approximations only. English is the primary language of 350 million people in 6 major countries and numerous smaller countries with millions of inhabitants; it is also used as a second language of hundreds of millions in India, Africa, and elsewhere. English has also become the principal language of cross-culture communications, economics, and science. In a world where rapid communication and travel is becoming more the norm than the exception, this has some benefits, since there is no such thing as a "global language," at least not officially. Consider, for example, the possible problems on an international airline trip if the cockpit crew spoke one language and the airport control tower personnel another. Fortunately, there is supposed to be an English-speaking per-son in each location. English is also spreading with the World Wide Web, at least to countries where there is access.

The present distribution of languages, as revealed on maps, is useful in understanding cultural development and change. Figure 8-4, for example, indicates the four Dravidian languages are all spoken in a compact region in the south of the Indian Peninsula. The map thus suggests that these languages (which are older) and the cultures they represent were "pushed" southward by the advancing Indo-European speakers. Similar interesting patterns can be observed in Figure 8-3 by looking at the spatial pattern of the Germanic and Romance language subfamilies.

CHAPTER QUIZ

MULTIPLE-CHOICE QUESTIONS

1. A group of people who speak a language but have no written form of it, are said to be:
   a. illiterate
   b. prehistoric
   c. preliterate
   d. symbolic

2. All languages have at least one thing in common, they:
   a. change over time
   b. remain static
   c. do not borrow from other languages
   d. do not use symbols

3. Africa has more than __?__ spoken languages.
   a. 500
   b. 1000
   c. 1200
   d. 1500

4. Spatially the __?__ language family is the most widely dispersed.
   a. Afro-Asiatic
   b. Ural-Altaic
   c. Indo-European
   d. Khoisan

5. Latin was spread over Europe by the:
   a. Muslims
   b. Greeks
   c. Romans
   d. English

6. The language family in Sub-Saharan Africa with the most speakers is:
   a. Afro-Asiatic
   b. Niger-Congo
   c. Khoisan
   d. Indo-European

7. In India which Dravidian language has the most speakers.
   a. Telugu
   b. Tamil
   c. Kanarese
   d. Malayalam

8. The oldest language family in Sub-Saharan Africa is the __?__.
   a. Sudanic
   b. Afro-Asiatic
   c. Indo-European
   d. Khoisan

9. The language spoken by more Chinese than any other is:
   a. Mandarin
   b. Wu
   c. Cantonese
   d. Gung Ho

10. In British Hong Kong the language most often spoken was:
    a. Mandarin
    b. Cantonese
    c. English
    d. Japanese

TRUE/FALSE QUESTIONS

1. Today all of the world's languages are being preserved and will continue to be spoken. (TF)

2. Linguists estimate between 2000 and 3000 languages are being spoken in the world today. (TF)

3. In today's world, because of migration, most developed countries do **not** have a standard language. (TF)

4. Thanks to the English colonial masters, India has only about 100 different languages. (TF)

5. Native American languages remain strong in the United States. (TF)

6. In Europe, the Basque language is spoken in a very small area. (TF)

7. India has hundreds of languages, most of which are spoken by few people. (TF)

8. Close to 1000 languages in Africa are unwritten. (TF)

9. Languages that may seem to have the same roots but are very different, probably have words in common because of interaction between different cultures. (TF)

10. Speakers of the three major dialects of the Chinese language can easily understand each other. (TF)

STUDY QUESTIONS

1. What are the major components that make up the definition of language as spoken by humans? What is a standard language? How does the text explain a dialect and isoglosses?

2. Look at Figure 8-3. What does this tell you about the spread of the Indo-European languages? How do you think colonialism and migration (ancient and recent) helped in spreading these languages?

3. In Figure 8-5 we can see the location of Africa's language families. How does the text explain their location? How are different subfamilies related? Why is the Khoisan family considered the oldest?

4. Why is there debate over whether Chinese is one or several languages?

CHAPTER 9. DIFFUSION OF LANGUAGES

CHAPTER OUTLINE

Understanding the origin and diffusion of languages is essential to understanding the diffusion of humanity. By understanding where and how languages developed, we learn about the people who spoke them. Although there is disagreement on when language arose, there is no question that it was vital to the development of humanity. By studying the development and changes in languages we learn much about the development of humans and their cultures.

Language Origins

The search for the origins of language goes back tens of thousands of years. It has yielded information not only about how language changes but also about the environments where early languages were spoken. Linguistic reconstruction methods are still controversial, but with the help of computers, remarkable progress is being made in the reconstruction of ancient languages and their paths of diffusion.

The diversification of languages has long been charted through the analysis of *sound shifts*—finding similar words with the same meaning in different languages and determining their common language of origin. If it is possible to deduce a large part of the vocabulary of an extinct language, it may be possible to recreate the language that preceded it. This technique, called *deep reconstruction,* has yielded some important results. It takes humanity's linguistic family tree back thousands of years.

Scientists do not yet agree on how long ago language emerged. Some believe that the use of language began with the rise of *Homo sapiens* 200,000 or more years ago; others argue that simple vocal communication began much earlier.

The first major linguistic hypothesis proposed the existence of an ancestral *Proto-Indo-European* language (or closely related languages) as the predecessor of Latin, Greek, and Sanskrit, among other ancient languages. The proposed ancestral language(s) would link not only the romance language but also a number of other languages spoken from Britain to North Africa and South Asia.

The Language Tree

In the mid-nineteenth century August Schleicher, a German linguist, compared the world's language families to the branches of a tree. He suggested that the basic process of language formation is *language divergence*—differentiation over time and space. Languages would branch into dialects; isolation then increased the differences between dialects. Over time, dialects would become discrete languages. Schleicher's idea has stood the test of time and criticism, and the language-tree model remains central to language research (Figure 9-1).

A complicating factor is that with human mobility, languages did not merely diffuse through static populations; they also spread by relocation diffusion (see Chapter 2). If this caused long-isolated languages to make contact, *language convergence* occurred. Researchers then face special problems because the rules of reconstruction may or may not apply.

Modern cultural events add a further complication. We know that the languages of traditional, numerically smaller, and technologically less advanced people have been replaced, or greatly modified, by the languages of invaders. This process of *language replacement* goes on today, and there is every reason to believe that it has happened ever since humans began to use language. Thus languages change through divergence, convergence, and replacement, making the spatial search for origins problematic.

Recent Language Diffusion

The final stages of the dispersal of the older languages—before the global diffusion of English and other Indo-European languages—occurred in the Pacific realm and in the Americas. One would thus assume that the historical geography of these events would be easier to reconstruct than the complex situation in western Eurasia, but this is not the case. While the relatively recent spread of languages to these two realms does provide useful information for the reconstruction of language diffusion routes and processes, an examination of the debates over Pacific and American native languages reveals that the problems are not simple at all.

Much remains to be learned about the reasons behind the complexity of the Pacific language map, to say nothing about the debate over human migration to, and language development and diffusion in, the Americas. One theory holds that there were three "waves" of early human migration to the Americas from Asia producing three families of indigenous American languages. A majority of linguists still doubt the three-wave hypothesis and the three-family map of American languages. Genetic research and archeological studies will ultimately solve the issue. In the meantime, we are reminded of the gaps still remaining in our knowledge.

Influences On Individual Languages

Each of the languages in the world's language families has its own story of origin and dispersal. It is clear, however, that there are certain critical influences on the diffusion of individual tongues. First, speakers of non-written languages will not retain the same language very long if they lose contact with one another. Second, the diffusion of a single tongue over a large area occurs only when people remain in contact with one another and continue to rely on a common linguistic frame of reference. Three critical components therefore have influenced the world's linguistic mosaic: writing, technology, and political organization.

CHAPTER QUIZ

MULTIPLE-CHOICE QUESTIONS

1. The use of sound shifts helps trace languages back toward their origins. This technique is called:
   a. backward reconstruction
   b. root tracing
   c. deep reconstruction
   d. language foundation tracing

2. When the most wide-spread language family was studied backward, it is believed this family came from a language we now call:
   a. the mother tongue
   b. the ancestral language
   c. Proto-Indo-European
   d. Proto-Anatolian

3. In tracing languages backward many factors must be taken into consideration, such as:
   a. language convergence
   b. the replacement of language by invading forces
   c. linguistic islands
   d. all of the above

4. A pre-Proto-Indo-European language called Nostratic, and researched independently by two Russian researchers was based on words:
   a. for body parts and elements of the natural environment
   b. landforms and climate
   c. tools and utensils
   d. domesticated plants

5. In which of the following world regions did the last diffusion of the older languages take place.
   a. the Indian Ocean
   b. the Pacific and Americas
   c. the South Atlantic
   d. Central Asia

6. The diffusion of peoples and their languages into the Pacific north of Indonesia traces its roots to which of the following.
   a. coastal New Guinea
   b. coastal India
   c. coastal China
   d. coastal Australia

7. The current language map of the Americas is dominated by:
   a. Native American languages
   b. Austronesian languages
   c. Malayo-Polynesian languages
   d. Indo-European languages

8. As many as 40 language families have been recognized in the Old World, but linguists have identified as many as __?__ Native American language families in the Americas.
   a. 100
   b. 200
   c. 300
   d. 400

9. The world's linguistic mosaic has been influenced by three critical components. Which of the following is **not** one of these.
   a. transportation
   b. writing
   c. technology
   d. political organization

10. The development of the printing press in the late Middle Ages had an enormous influence on the development of the standard form of basic languages through the availability of printed texts. What was the subject of many of these early texts.
   a. commerce
   b. literature
   c. religion
   d. science

TRUE/FALSE QUESTIONS

1. The languages of Greek, Latin, and Sanskrit are related. (TF)

2. Occurring only in the past, language replacement occurred when invaders took over a small weaker group. (TF)

3. Those that believe the agriculture theory of language diffusion think the first language diffused from the Fertile Crescent. (TF)

4. The diffusion of people and their languages into the Pacific north of Indonesia and New Guinea began in China. (TF)

5. In the Western Hemisphere, as many as 200 Native American languages families have been identified. (TF)

6. The theory that North America's first immigrants arrived about 12,000 years ago has not been challenged. (TF)

7. Having a written language allows it to become stabilized. (TF)

8. Because many early printed texts were religious they changed the way people spoke. (TF)

9. When early large political systems collapsed language divergence took place. (TF)

10. Language can either bring people together or cause conflict. (TF)

STUDY QUESTIONS

1. Describe the process of deep reconstruction and the role of sound shifts. What factors create problems for people trying to reconstruct old languages?

2. Discuss the theories of language diffusion. How does Colin Renfrew carry one of these farther?

3. By looking at Figure 9-6, and reading the text, follow the diffusion of language in the Pacific. Discuss the problems encountered in interpreting the time frame and number of migrations.

4. Discuss the controversies surrounding the diffusion of languages in the Americas.

CHAPTER 10. MODERN LANGUAGE MOSAIC

CHAPTER INTRODUCTION

Language is an expression of culture, serving to both unite and divide people. The question of which language to use in a multilingual country is an important one since intercultural communication is essential for political stability. Sometimes an existing language will spread worldwide to serve as a means of communications between people, but in regions where several languages, and their cultures, meet and merge a whole new language may develop. The study of place names, both historical and contemporary, can also reveal much about a culture and its people. In the world of the late 1990s, when the cultural composition of many countries is changing, questions about language are of particular significance.

Choosing A Language

The United States has no *official language*—the language selected in multilingual countries, often by the educated and politically powerful elite, to promote internal cohesion; usually the language of the courts and government—even though we are a nation of emigrants and enormous ethnic mix. The reason for this is simply that if there were an "official" language selected for this country—no matter which language it might be— it would carry with it the implied preference for the particular culture of which it was the native tongue. It would also imply, rightly or wrongly, that other languages/cultures were not as important.

Historically, languages spread primarily by three means; commerce, religion, and conquest, within the parameters of expansion and/or relocation diffusion. The Indo-European languages spread globally in this manner and one in particular, English, diffused throughout the world during the era of colonialism. Largely because of the political and economic power of Britain and the United States, English today has become the global language of elites, commerce, and business.

Command of English undoubtedly is an advantage throughout the world and the position of some governments is that the advantages of being able to use English outweigh cultural considerations. Some countries have made English (or another foreign language) their official language, giving indigenous languages secondary status. This provokes charges of neocolonialism or favoring the interest of educated elites. The emotional attachment to language is not just a matter of protecting threatened tongues. It is also a practical issue.

Multilingualism

There is no truly monolingual—where only one language is spoken—country in the world today. Several, such as Japan, Uruguay, Iceland, and Poland, claim monolingualism but even in these countries there are small numbers of people who speak other languages. For example, more than a half-million Koreans live in Japan, and English-speaking Australia has more than 180,000 speakers of aboriginal languages.

Countries in which more than one language is in use are called *multilingual states*. In some of these countries linguistic fragmentation reflect strong cultural pluralism as well as divisive forces (see Figure 10-5). This is true in former colonial areas where peoples speaking different languages were thrown together, as happened in Africa and Asia. This also occurred in the Americas as Figure 10-2 shows. Multilingualism takes several forms and can be reflected in regional divisions (Canada, India, Peru, and Belgium), but in some countries (far fewer) there is less regional separation of speakers of different languages (for example South Africa).

Multilingual countries sometimes solve the problem of intercultural communication by making a foreign tongue their official ("umbrella") language, as shown in Table 10-1. For former colonies, this has often been the language of the colonists, even though they may have gained their independence in a violent revolution against those colonists. Such a policy is not without risks, however, and the long-term results of the use of a foreign language may not always be positive.

Lingua Franca

Traders have often succeeded in overcoming regional linguistic communication problems where language planners failed. Centuries ago people speaking different languages were forced to find ways to communicate for trade. This need resulted in the emergence of a *lingua franca*—any common language spoken by peoples with different native tongues, the result of linguistic convergence. The term comes from the Mediterranean region and its numerous trading posts during the period following the Crusades. In several areas of the world today, linguistic convergence has produced languages of mixed origin. Some of these have developed into major regional languages (see Figure 10-1).

Toponymy

The study of place names (toponymy) can reveal a great deal about the contents and historical geography of a cultural region..Even when time has erased other evidence, place names can reveal much about a cultural area. Welsh place names in Pennsylvania, French place names in Louisiana, or Dutch place names in Michigan reveal national origin as well as insight into language and dialect, routes of diffusion, and ways of life.

Toponyms—place names—make reading a map a fruitful and sometimes revealing experience. A careful eye will spot Roman names on the map of Britain, German names on the map of France, and Dutch names in Australia.

CHAPTER QUIZ

MULTIPLE-CHOICE QUESTIONS

1. The growing Hispanic population has begun to redefine the __?__ states of the United States.
   a. Southern
   b. Northern
   c. Western
   d. Central

2. Which of the following languages has become the one most often used as the primary medium of international communication in business.
   a. French
   b. English
   c. German
   d. Spanish

3. What language was created, and failed, in an effort to allow worldwide communication.
   a. Esperanto
   b. Frankish
   c. Spanenglish
   d. Frenenglish

4. The lingua franca of East Africa is:
   a. Bantu
   b. Swahili
   c. Hausa
   d. Arabic

5. Of the following countries, which has a division between the English and French speakers that may someday lead to a permanent division.
   a. Belgium
   b. France
   c. Canada
   d. Netherlands

6. Which European country has four regions where the people each speak a different language.
   a. Germany
   b. Netherlands
   c. Greece
   d. Switzerland

7. Which West African country has so many languages and lesser tongues that the government adopted English as its "official" language.
   a. Liberia
   b. Mali
   c. Ghana
   d. Nigeria

8. Place names can reveal much about a culture area even after that culture has gone. The study of place names is called:
   a. toponymy
   b. topography
   c. topo-anthropology
   d. topogeogology

9. When African colonies became independent countries, one of the first things they did was:
   a. redraw their boundaries
   b. kick out the government set up by departing colonial masters
   c. change place names
   d. declare an official language

10. In the Stewart system of classification of place names, *Rocky Mountains* is an example of a __?__ name.
   a. manufactured
   b. possessive
   c. descriptive
   d. commendatory

TRUE/FALSE QUESTIONS

1. In countries where people speak many languages, creating an official language can lead to many problems. (TF)

2. A lingua franca is a combination of French and another language. (TF)

3. During the colonial period, pidgin English developed in the Caribbean region when English was mixed with African languages, and was only spoken by the common people. (TF)

4. Pidgin and creole languages are important unifiers in a linguistically divided region or country. (TF)

5. There are no true monolingual states left in the world today. (TF)

6. In South Africa's past history, language differences led to wars. (TF)

7. It is likely Belgium will follow Czechoslovakia's lead and divide along linguistic lines in the near future. (TF)

8. India has two official languages. (TF)

9. Britain has place names that go back to the time of the Romans. (TF)

10. Place names have different classifications. One is mistake names, caused when people make historical errors in identification or translation. (TF)

STUDY QUESTIONS

1. How did English spread so far? Why are so many countries using it as a second language?

2. Discuss the process of creolization. How is it important in the formation and use of new languages?

3. Study Figures 10-3, 10-4, 10-5, and 10-6. Relate these figures to information about them in the text. Why do you think some of these countries have had so many problems? Why do you think Switzerland does not have any problem?

4. Why do some countries choose to declare official languages? What are the risks a country faces when it makes such a decision?

5. What does the study of toponymy reveal about past and current cultures of a place? What can we learn from two-part place names?

6. List and define the ten categories of place names. Try to think of an example of each.

7. List the reasons countries have changed place names. Pay special attention to the former Soviet Union.

PART FOUR: THE GEOGRAPHY OF RELIGION

CHAPTER 11. THE ORIGINS AND DISTRIBUTION OF RELIGIONS

CHAPTER INTRODUCTION

Religion is one of the key components of culture and, like language, can both unify or divide humans. Like language, but in a different way, religion confers identity. Religion dominates the lives and behavior of billions of people worldwide. In the world of the late 1990s, modernization, urbanization, secularism, and resurgent fundamentalism appear to be on a collision course. The question facing the world of the twenty-first century will be whether the modern-secular fundamentalist religious countries can coexist. The study of religion has many geographic dimensions today.

Like languages, religions are constantly changing. In the process, the great religions of the world have diffused across cultural barriers and language boundaries. Persuasion will not lead people to change the language they speak, but it can induce them to convert to a new faith—conversion still goes on today. Just as the map of languages continues to change, so do patterns of religious affiliation.

The cultural landscape is marked by religion—churches and mosques, cemeteries and shrines, statues and symbols, modes of dress, and personal habits. In industrialized societies, such overt religious displays have declined, but they are still common in more traditional societies.

The Geography of Religion

In many parts of the world, especially in non-Western areas, religion is such a vital part of culture that it practically constitutes the culture. Thus it becomes difficult to define exactly what a religion is, because religion manifests itself in so many different ways. In some societies, religion—at least in organized form—has become less significant in the lives of many people. In many societies in Africa and Asia, religious doctrine exerts tight control over much of the behavior of the people, through ritual and practice and even the orientation of the sleeping body at night. Even where religion is less dominant, its expression is still evident in many practices and beliefs.

Organized religion has powerful effects on human societies. It has been a major force in combating social ills, sustaining the poor, educating the deprived, and advancing medical knowledge. However, religion has also blocked scientific study, supported colonialism and exploitation, and condemned women to an inferior status in many societies. Like other bureaucracies, large-scale organized religion has all too often been unable to adjust to the times.

Major Religions

The distribution of the major religions among various world regions is depicted in Figure 11-1. The information on this map should be viewed as a generalization of a much more intricate set of distributions. Nevertheless, the map does reveal the dominance of the Christian religions, the several faiths of Christianity having been diffused through European colonialism and aggressive proselytism. Thus Christianity is today the world's most widely dispersed religion (see also Table 11-1). There are more than 1.6 billion Christians in the world today, divided between Roman Catholics (the largest segment), the Protestant churches, and Eastern Orthodox. Together, Christians account for nearly 40 percent of the members of the world's major religions.

The second true *global religion* (also called "universal faiths") is Islam. Despite the fact that it is the "newest" of the global religions—it arose in the western Arabia area in the sixth century—it is today the fastest growing of the world's major religions, and like the other major faiths has more than one branch. Like Christianity, Islam has diffused widely, but mainly in Africa and Asia. It dominates in Southwest Asia and North Africa and extends eastward into the former Soviet Union and China, with clusters in Indonesia, Bangladesh, and the Philippines. It even has adherents in the United States (see: Focus on: America's Black Muslims). Islam has more than 1 billion adherents, of whom more than half are outside the cultural realm often called the Islamic World. Southwest Asia and North Africa, however, remain the Islamic heartland, with about 400 million adherents. A comparison between Figures 11-1 and 7-1 shows that the largest Muslim country is Indonesia, with about 165 million believers.

Christianity and Islam together hold the allegiance of nearly half the world's population (see Table 11-1); no other faith even comes close. The third global religion, Buddhism, claims slightly less than 350 adherents. The third largest faith numerically, Hinduism, is not a global but a cultural faith concentrated in a single geographic realm, and is regarded as the world's oldest organized religion. The vast majority of the 750 million Hindus live in India, although Hinduism extends into Bangladesh, Myanmar, Sri Lanka, and Nepal.

In this chapter we have viewed the spatial distribution of the world's major religions and assessed their strengths in terms of number of adherents. In the next chapter we will examine the three geographic characteristics of religions: their locational origins, routes of diffusion, and their imprints on the cultural landscape.

CHAPTER QUIZ

MULTIPLE-CHOICE QUESTIONS

1. Which South American country, according to Figure 11-1, has the largest area of Traditional and Shamanist religions.
   a. Argentina
   b. Brazil
   c. Chile
   d. Uruguay

2. Which part of India is not a major area of the Hindu faith.
   a. northeast
   b. south
   c. northwest
   d. southwest

3. The largest division of Christianity in terms of number of adherents is:
   a. Orthodox
   b. Protestant
   c. Sikhism
   d. Roman Catholic

4. The largest number of adherents to the Christian faith are found in:
   a. Europe
   b. Sub-Saharan Africa

c. North America
d, South America

5. The most populous Muslim country is:
   a. Iran
   b. Saudi Arabia
   c. Indonesia
   d. Pakistan

6. Which of the following is the third largest of the global religions.
   a. Judaism
   b. Buddhism
   c. Islam
   d. Christianity

7. Judaism and Christianity both arose in which of the following present-day countries.
   a. Israel and Jordan
   b. Turkey and Greece
   c. Iraq and Iran
   d. Egypt and Israel

8. The rise of secularism can be traced to the rise of:
   a. Roman Catholicism
   b. Greek Orthodoxy
   c. Islam
   d. Protestantism

9. For centuries, Shintoism was the state religion of which of the following countries.
   a. China
   b. Korea
   c. Japan
   d. the Philippines

10. Islam has diffused widely and is considered a world religion, but is mainly found in:
    a. Europe and Asia
    b. Africa and Asia
    c. Africa and Europe
    d. North America and Asia

TRUE/FALSE QUESTIONS

1. In some cultures, religion is a dominating factor. (TF)

2. Religions have never been clearly evident in the cultural landscape. (TF)

3. Religion has condemned women to an inferior status in many societies. (TF)

4. In today's world, the Christian religions are the most widely dispersed. (TF)

5. The main division in Islam is between Sunni and Shiite. (TF)

6. The Hindu religion has a bureaucracy similar to that of Christianity and Islam. (TF)

7. Buddhism and Shintoism arose in Japan. (TF)

8. Hinduism is considered a cultural religion in India. (TF)

9. Animistic religions are centered on the belief that animals possess spirits. (TF)

10. Traditional religions still prevail where people resist outside influence. (TF)

STUDY QUESTIONS

1. List the different ways religion manifests itself. Although it can not be define exactly, list the different rituals that are commonly found in various religions. Also list the positive and negative effects religion has had on people and cultures.

2. Using information from previous chapters explain how Christianity spread across the globe?

3. Where is the heartland of Islam? Where in this region are the two divisions located?

4. List the ways Hinduism is different from Christianity and Islam.

5. Describe the distribution of Judaism.

6. Where are the source areas for the major religions?

7. List the factors that have led to the rise of secularism. Can you think of other factors in your culture that might play a role (hint: materialism)? List them.

8. What are the true global religions? What are regional religions? Name them and their locations. Where are most traditional religions located?

CHAPTER 12. RELIGION: LOCATION, DIFFUSION, AND CULTURAL LANDSCAPE

CHAPTER INTRODUCTION

Religion is the most recent major component of culture to develop. As a result, we know more about the development and dispersal of the major religions than we do of languages. In a world where cultural isolation is a thing of the past and religion is such an important part of culture, it is important to understand the different religions and their effect on the cultures of which they are a part. This chapter traces the spread of the belief systems that have contributed to the formation of modern cultural regions. It is remarkable that, after tens of thousands of years of human development and migration, the great faiths all arose within a few thousand kilometers of each other in South and Southwest Asia (Figure 12-1).

Hinduism

Hinduism is the oldest of the world's major religions and one of the oldest extant religions in the world. It is a cultural religion, having emerged without a prophet or a book of scriptures and without evolving a bureaucratic structure comparable to that of the Christian religions. Hinduism appears to have originated in the region of the Indus Valley in what is today Pakistan (see Figure 12-1), perhaps as much as 4000 years ago. Hinduism reached its fullest development in India, and spread into Southeast Asia before the advent of Christianity. It has not been widely disseminated.

Hinduism has remained essentially a cultural religion of South Asia and is more than a faith; it is a way of life. The cultural landscape of Hinduism is the cultural landscape of India. Temples and shrines, holy animals by the tens of millions, and the sights and sounds of endless processions and rituals all contribute to a unique atmosphere. The faith is a visual as well as an emotional experience.

Buddhism

Buddhism, with fewer than half as many adherents as Hinduism, arose in the sixth century B.C. in India. It was a reaction to the less desirable features of Hinduism such as its strict social hierarchy that protected the privileged and kept millions mired in poverty. Buddhism was founded by Prince Siddhartha, known to his followers as Gautama. The Buddha (enlightened one) was perhaps the first prominent Indian religious leader to speak out against Hinduism's caste system.

The faith grew rather slowly following the Buddha's death until the middle of the third century B.C. when the Emperor Asoka became a convert. During Asoka's rule there may have been more Buddhists than Hindu adherents in India, but after that period the strength of Hinduism began to reassert itself. Today Buddhism is practically extinct in India, although it still thrives in Sri Lanka, Southeast Asia, Nepal, Tibet, Korea, and Japan.

The Buddha received enlightenment as he sat under the Bodhi (enlightenment) tree and because of its association with the Buddha, the tree is revered and protected; it has diffused as far as China and Japan and marks the cultural landscape of many villages and towns. Buddhism's architecture includes some magnificent achievements, with the pagoda as perhaps the most familiar structure. Buddhism is experiencing a revival that started two centuries ago and has recently intensified. It has become a global religion and diffused to many areas of the world.

China

Confucianism was founded on the teachings of Confucius in the sixth century B.C. *Taoism* is believed to have been founded by an older contemporary of Confucius Lao-Tsu, who had great and lasting impacts on

Chinese life. In his teachings, Lao-Tsu focused on the proper form of political rule and the oneness of humanity and nature. According to Lao-Tsu, people should learn to live in harmony with nature (see Focus on: "Feng Shui"). Taoism became a cult of the masses.

Following his death, the teachings of Confucius diffused widely throughout East and Southeast Asia. From his writings and sayings emerged the *Confucian Classics*, a set of 13 texts that became the focus of Chinese education for 200 years and the Guide for Chinese civilization. In the more liberal atmosphere in Communist China today, both the Chinese religions of old **and** the Christian and Islamic faiths are reviving, and Confucianism and Taoism continue to shape Chinese society.

Judaism

Judaism grew out of the belief system of the Jews, one of several nomadic Semitic tribes living in Southwest Asia about 2000 B.C. It is the oldest religion to arise west of the Indus River and the history of the Jews is filled with upheavals. In the face of constant threats, the Jews have sustained their faith, the roots of which lie in the teachings of Abraham, who united his people.

Table 11-1 shows the Jewish faith has about 18 million adherents, but the distribution of Jews proves that Judaism is indeed a world religion and has a global importance far greater than its numbers would indicate.

Christianity and Islam

Christianity's three major branches (Roman Catholicism, Protestantism, and Orthodoxy) have diffused throughout the world by expansion combined with relocation diffusion. The cultural landscapes of Christianity's branches reflect the changes the faith has undergone over the centuries. Certain denominations have more durable cultural landscapes in which the authority and influence of the church remain visible.

Islam, the youngest of the world religions, has two major sects, the majority *Sunni* and the minority *Shiah* (see Figure 11-1). This division occurred almost immediately after the prophet Muhammad's death and took on regional overtones when Shiism became the state religion of Persia (now Iran). Like Christianity, Islam has diffused globally, but is a classic example of expansion diffusion from its Arabian source, followed by relocation diffusion (Figure 12-4). Islam achieved its greatest artistic expression, its most distinctive visible element, in architecture.

CHAPTER QUIZ

MULTIPLE-CHOICE QUESTIONS

1. Which of the following is the world's oldest major religion.
   a. Judaism
   b. Christianity
   c. Islam
   d. Hinduism

2. Hinduism evolved in what is today the country of:
   a. Pakistan
   b. Nepal
   c. Sri Lanka
   d. India

3. During the sixteenth century which of the following became a refuge for Hindus with the arrival of Islam and today remains predominately Hindu.
   a. Java
   b. Borneo
   c. Bali
   d. New Guinea

4. Taoism was probably founded by which of the following.
   a. Confucius
   b. Lao-Tsu
   c. Chang-Lee
   d. Mao Tse-tung

5. The oldest global religion to arise west of the Indus River was:
   a. Islam
   b. Christianity
   c. Buddhism
   d. Judaism

6. The continent with the largest population of adherents of the Jewish faith is:
   a. Europe
   b. North America
   c. Asia
   d. South America

7. The worldwide spread of Christianity was accomplished during the era of European colonialism, primarily in which century.
   a. sixteenth
   b. seventeenth
   c. eighteenth
   d. nineteenth

8. The rise of secularism is associated with which of the following events.
   a. the Industrial Revolution
   b. the Third Agricultural Revolution
   c. the Reformation
   d. the rise of the Eastern Orthodox faith

9. In the United States, the South's leading religious denomination is:
   a. Lutheran
   b. Catholic
   c. Presbyterian
   d. Baptist

10. Islam arose in which of the following present-day countries.
   a. Saudi Arabia
   b. Iran

c. Jordan
d. Egypt

TRUE/FALSE QUESTIONS

1. The world's great faiths arose in East Asia. (TF)

2. The caste system is part of the Hindu religion. (TF)

3. Hinduism is a very low key religion, and leaves very little visual evidence on the cultural landscape. (TF)

4. Asoka, emperor of an early Indian state, is credited with the diffusion of Buddhism to distant lands. (TF)

5. Because of the take-over of China by the communists, Confucianism no longer has much influence on the people. (TF)

6. Today, Judaism is divided into many branches. (TF)

7. When the Roman Empire became a Christian state and later divided, Emperor Constantine established the Eastern Orthodox Church in Constantinople. (TF)

8. Even today, cathedrals built in Medieval European towns are still a dominating feature on the landscape in some cities. (TF)

9. Christianity marks the cultural landscape with its use of large plots of land for cemeteries. (TF)

10. Islam diffusion is a classic example of expansion diffusion. (TF)

STUDY QUESTIONS

1. Using Figure 12-1, list the major world religions and their source areas. List their differences and similarities. How have some of these changed over the centuries?

2. Which religions are cultural or regional? Define the difference between cultural and secular. What are some of the traits that make a religion cultural?

3. Which of the major religions was spread by migrant diffusion? What religion replaced it in its source region?

4. Using Figure 12-4, trace the diffusion of Islam. How does Islam impact its cultural landscape? Discuss Islamic architecture.

CHAPTER 13. RELIGION, CULTURE, AND CONFLICT

CHAPTER INTRODUCTION

Of the forces shaping the geography of culture, language and religion are two of the most powerful, but as a divisive force religion plays a more prominent role. People may speak the same language but have quite different beliefs either as members of different major religions or different branches of the same faith. As you read this chapter you will gain insight into the perpetuating of cultural strife by religion, a problem that adds to the difficulties of peaceful human coexistence.

It is important for you to realize that religious conflicts usually involve more than differences in spiritual practices and beliefs. Religion functions as a symbol of a much wider set of cultural and political differences. The key points of this chapter are discussed below.

Interfaith Boundaries

Compare Figure 11-1 with a political map and you will see that some countries lie entirely within the realms of individual world religions, while other countries straddle *interfaith boundaries*, the boundaries between the world's major faiths. Boundaries between major religions that cross countries can be powerful sources of conflict, with serious implications for political cohesion and stability. Examine Figure 13-1 and you will see that several countries in Africa are in this situation, including Nigeria, Africa's most populous state.

Nigeria is a multilingual country of 110 million inhabitants. Superimposed on its linguistic diversity is religious regionalism: the north is a Muslim zone, whereas Christianity prevails in the south along with local traditional religions. Ethnic groups in the north and south see religion as the focal point of differences that go much deeper than that.

Will Nigeria's location astride an interfaith boundary ultimately destroy the country? The potential for a fracture along religious lines is growing, and any such development would have enormous social and political consequences. Nigeria is a crucible of West African culture and has served as a model for other countries with two or more religious groups within their borders. The breakup of Nigeria would indeed have far-reaching consequences.

Intrafaith Boundaries

Boundaries between branches of a major religion are generally less divisive than boundaries between different religions. A number of Western European countries have Catholic as well as Protestant communities, and often these are reflected in the regional distribution of the population, as in the case of Switzerland (Figure 13-4). In the late 1990s the great majority of these countries were not experiencing religious or ethnic conflict.

But intrafaith boundaries are still are capable of producing cultural conflict that can threaten the stability of entire countries. Consider the situation in Northern Ireland, where a Protestant majority and a Catholic minority are in conflict over coexistence and their future. This issue is not strictly religious, but stems from a time when all of Ireland was a British dependency and British Protestants migrated to Ireland. Most settled in the northeastern corner of the island (see Figure 13-5) where, following partitioning, they constituted the majority of the population and held all the economic and political advantages. The conflict today is over access to opportunities, civil rights, and political influence. But religion and religious history are the banners beneath which the opposing sides march.

Religious Fundamentalism

In the world of the late 1990s, religious leaders and millions of their followers are seeking to return to the basics of their faith. This drive toward *religious fundamentalism* is often born of frustration at the perceived breakdown of society's mores and values, loss of religious authority, failure to achieve economic goals, corruption of political systems, and loss of a sense of local control in the face of the globalization of culture and economy.

People of one society often fear fundamentalism in other societies without recognizing it in their own. In the United States, fundamentalism is often associated with Islam. However, religious fundamentalism is a world-wide phenomenon that affects virtually all religions, including Islam, Christianity, and Hinduism. Fundamentalism and extremism are closely related, and their appeal is global.

Today religions are affected by modernization. Education, radio, television, and travel have diffused notions of individual liberties, sexual equality, and freedom of choice; questions about religions as well as secular authority; and other ideas that may clash with religious dogma.

The drive toward fundamentalism in Christianity and Islam alike is creating a climate of mistrust that could lead to strife. The cultural cores of Christianity and Islam lie in close proximity in Europe and Southwest Asia/North Africa; the prospect of disharmony and conflict between them is growing.

CHAPTER QUIZ

MULTIPLE-CHOICE QUESTIONS

1. When we look at a map of Africa displaying religion locations there is an obvious division where __?__ dominate the north.
   a. Christian religions
   b. Animistic faiths
   c. Muslims
   d. traditional religions

2. In the late 1990s, Ethiopia lost territory with the succession of a predominately Muslim region. That new state is called:
   a. Amharic
   b. Oman
   c. Niger
   d. Eritrea

3. Before the devolution of the former Soviet Union, it was divided into how many Soviet Republics.
   a. 10
   b. 15
   c. 20
   d. 25

4. When the USSR collapsed, the Soviet Republics became independent states. In which of the following is there an interfaith boundary dividing Muslims and Christians that presents a serious problem for the future of the state.
   a. Azerbaijan
   b. Ukraine

c. Kazakhstan
d. Belarus

5. In Sri Lanka, the minority Hindu population is in conflict for political recognition by the majority religious group which is:
   a. Buddhism
   b. Muslims
   c. Christians
   d. Jews

6. Which Western European country listed below has both Catholic and Protestant adherents living together with little or no religious or ethnic conflict.
   a. Germany
   b. Switzerland
   c. Poland
   d. Ireland

7. The most destructive war of its kind in modern times was a conflict between two Muslim countries following different branches of the Islamic faith. These two countries were:
   a. Syria and Jordan
   b. Iran and Kuwait
   c. Turkey and Greece
   d. Iraq and Iran

8. This North African country suffers from the desire of some groups to create an Islamic Republic.
   a. Tunisia
   b. Morocco
   c. Algeria
   d. Mali

9. This West African nation is the fourth largest oil producer in OPEC (Organization of Petroleum Exporting Countries).
   a. Nigeria
   b. Guinea
   c. Gambia
   d. Mali

10. The new name given to the old city of Leningrad in the former Soviet Union is:
    a. Kiev
    b. St. Petersburg
    c. Petrograd
    d. Volgograd

TRUE/FALSE QUESTIONS

1. Interfaith boundaries keep religious conflicts from occurring. (TF)

2. In Nigeria, religious divisions may end up splitting the country into two republics. (TF)

3. The creation of Pakistan created an almost exclusive Hindu state. (TF)

4. The former Soviet Union created 15 republics and laid them out along religious and linguistic lines. They did such a good job that today, these now independent republics are getting along well. (TF)

5. In Ireland, the majority of the people are protestant. (TF)

6. Fundamentalism and extremism are **not** closely related. (TF)

7. Some Islamic countries are more liberal than others in applying the laws of the Koran. (TF)

8. In Iran, after the Shah was deposed, women suffered a set-back in freedoms they had gained. (TF)

9. Fundamentalism is always a unifying force. (TF)

10. Recent Muslim attacks in Egypt have hurt the economy. (TF)

STUDY QUESTIONS

1. Going region by region and country by country, as presented in the text, describe the problems of interfaith boundaries. Be sure to study the appropriate maps.

2. Why do many intrafaith boundaries cause less trouble? Hint: what commonalities do people have?

3. Where is the most contested religious site in the world located? Why are there so many conflicts over this particular site?

4. Discuss the rise of religious fundamentalism. Is it confined to one religion or many? What are some of the reasons given for this resurgence?

PART FIVE: LAND AND LAND USE IN THE RURAL SECTOR

CHAPTER 14. LIVELIHOODS OF RURAL PEOPLES

CHAPTER INTRODUCTION

All humans engage in some form of activity to provide food, clothing, shelter and the other amenities of life, but the varied activities of today owe their success to decisions of the past. The development of agriculture may well be the single most important development in human history. Its success supported both rural and urban populations. With the combination of agriculture and technology lies the ability to provide food and security for all humanity. How, and if, this challenge is met will determine the future of our species.

Economic Activity
Economic activities range from simple to complex, from ancient to modern. One way to classify these activities is to distinguish among different *types* of activities. For many years three basic types of economic activities were recognized: primary, the *extractive sector*, secondary, the *production sector*, and tertiary, the *service sector*. Rural life has long been dominated by primary economic activities, hunting and gathering (ancient means of survival), farming of all kinds, livestock herding, fishing, forestry and lumbering. Here workers and the natural environment come into direct contact and the environment sometimes suffers.

Agriculture
The deliberate tending of crops and livestock in order to produce food and fiber is properly called *agriculture*, an activity that may be less than 12,000 years old and emerged sequentially in several regions of the world. When humans embraced agriculture they changed the world and human culture forever. Food supplies became more dependable and quantities increased. This in turn led to population increases and, eventually, permanent settlements. Agriculture changes more of the Earth's surface than any other human activity and thus a *cultural landscape* that is reflective of the numbers, cultivation practices, settlement patterns, and other cultural characteristics of the population. It is the reason why huge numbers of humans can successfully occupy Earth today.

Revolutions
Agriculture actually developed in several stages, referred to as *revolutions* because of the changes in the way it was practiced. The First Agricultural Revolution achieved plant domestication, a gradual process that was global, often including duplicate domestication of certain plants in different parts of the world, and extending over a period of several thousand years. Humans learned about such things as plant selection, primitive methods of cultivation, and irrigation. Early agriculture was undoubtedly combined with gathering and some hunting as well as animal domestication.

The Second Agricultural Revolution, beginning in the latter part of the so-called Middle Ages, involved improved methods of cultivation, production, and storage. Exact points of origin are unknown but it seems certain that the process was gradual and centered in Europe. The hallmark of this revolution was improved production and organization. Without these changes, the Industrial Revolution would not have been possible and it in turn sustained the changes that were taking place in agriculture.

The Third Agriculture Revolution (still in progress and sometimes called the Green Revolution) is based on research and technology in plant genetics. It occurred at a time when the population explosion seemed to threaten the global food supply in the manner that Malthus had predicted two centuries earlier. The laboratory-developed new, higher yielding strains of grains and other crops seemed to suggest that the threat of global famine was a thing of the past. However, the race between population growth and food production is not over, and it remains to be seen whether or not the Third Agricultural Revolution can continue to overcome the challenge.

Survival

Subsistence agriculture, which produces little or no surplus and involves hundreds of millions of people in a struggle for survival, still prevails in large regions of tropical Africa, Asia, and the Americas. Here farmers grow food only to survive. Very likely they do not even own the soil that they till. Some subsistence farmers may, in fact, practice *shifting cultivation*, a method of tillage where plots are farmed until the soil is depleted and then the farmers move on and clear a new field. As many as 200 million people still subsist in this manner in tropical regions of Africa, Middle America, and South America, using methods that have not changed in thousands of years.

Sedentary or shifting, subsistence farming is not only a way of life but a state of mind for those who practice it. Experience has taught these farmers and their families that times of comparative plenty will be followed by times of scarcity. It should also serve to remind us that the security of plentiful food supplies in the technically advanced, wealthier countries is not shared by many of the Earth's population.

CHAPTER QUIZ

MULTIPLE CHOICE QUESTIONS

1. In which of the following economic sectors do we find the activity of farming:
   a. production
   b. marketing
   c. extractive
   d. service

2. Farming started about __?__ years ago.
   a. 8,000
   b. 10,000
   c. 12,000
   d. 14,000

3. The first tools used by humans in hunting were:
   a. made of stone
   b. simple clubs
   c. beaten into shape using copper
   d. more complex than we first realized

4. Fishing probably started:
   a. before hunting
   b. 200,000 years ago

c. during the last ice age when men could fish through the ice
d. when the water warmed and covered the continental shelves at the end of the last ice age

5. The first agricultural methods probably involved the:
   a. the sowing of seeds
   b. planting of roots and cuttings
   c. transplanting whole plants
   d. importing of food plants from other regions

6. Wild cattle may have first been domesticated for:
   a. use as draft animals
   b. their milk
   c. religious purposes
   d. their hides to build shelters

7. The earliest animals to be domesticated in Africa were:
   a. guinea fowl
   b. cattle
   c. chickens
   d. goats

8. Which of the following plays a big part in shifting cultivation.
   a. nomadic existence
   b. very fertile soil
   c. high population density
   d. control of fire

9. The colonial powers introduce forced farming in their colonies to:
   a. improved the lifestyle and wealth of the farmers
   b. make profits for themselves
   c. help farmers diversify their crops
   d. help farmers hold their communities together

10. Which of the following statements is **not** true about the Second Agricultural Revolution.
    a. it allowed people to live in larger urban clusters
    b. it started quickly and spread rapidly
    c. tools and equipment were modified and improved
    d. more efficient food storage and distribution was created

TRUE/FALSE QUESTIONS

1. The United States has more farmers than most countries. (TF)

2. Worldwide, people tend to eat more meat than vegetable products. (TF)

3. Drought is the worst enemy of present-day hunting and gathering societies. (TF)

4. Agriculture allowed people to have permanent settlements for the first time. (TF)

5. The development of stone tools never became very important in helping early humankind progress. (TF)

6. By using just fishing, hunting, and some gathering, various groups were able to establish some permanence in settlement. (TF)

7. Agriculture first started in the Americas. (TF)

8. It is now believed the Chinese may have been among the world's first farmers. (TF)

9. It is not possible to identify in which region any animal was first domesticated. (TF)

10. In the strictest use of the word, subsistence farming means farmers who only grow enough food to supply themselves and their family. (TF)

STUDY QUESTIONS

1. Discuss how hunting and gathering societies existed before agriculture. How did they live? What kind of tools did they devise and use? Why was the use of fire so important?

2. How did fishing change the lives of our early ancestors? Was their live any better? What means did they use to catch fish?

3. Using Figure 14-2 and Table 14-1, identify the sources of the many domesticated plants. Does the source of food plants you recognize surprise you? How many can you recognize as being something you have seen in your local grocery store?

4. Read the section on animal domestication and diffusion. Why was this such an important development in human history? Why do you think chickens are kept by so many societies worldwide? Why do you think Africa is trying to domesticate more animals today?

5. Discuss the ways colonial powers permanently changed farming practices when they colonized the different areas of the world.

CHAPTER 15. RURAL SETTLEMENT FORMS

CHAPTER INTRODUCTION

The basic human needs are food, clothing, and shelter. Of these, buildings reveal the most about a culture and those who build them, as a visible expression of the culture. When large permanent settlements evolved buildings became more substantial, specialized, and permanent. As culture became more complex the simple practicality of adaptation to, and protection from, the elements was expanded to include functional differentiation, reflecting the changing needs of people and culture.

Where People Live

Early humans all lived in "rural" areas. They were few in numbers and generally mobile. It was not until the development of agriculture that "permanent" settlements became the norm. As recently as several hundred years ago the vast majority of humans still resided in rural areas, generally in agricultural villages raising crops or livestock to support themselves. Towns and cities were few and the exception rather than the norm. It was a very different world than residents of modern, technically advanced cultures experience today.

In the late 1990s, about half the world's population still resides in rural areas. This is because the vast majority of humanity still farms the land, often in ways that have not changed significantly. In portions of East and South Asia as many as three out of four residents may live in a rural area. By contrast, in the United States, Canada, Western European countries, Japan, and Australia there are far more urban than rural dwellers, reflecting changes in industrialization, transportation, and urbanization over the last 100 years.

Rural Dwellings

The *cultural landscape* is the human imprint on the Earth's surface, and no human activity produces a more visible cultural landscape than agriculture. Much can be learned about a culture by observing rural settlement patterns. The forms, functions, building materials, and the spacing of rural dwellings reveal much about a region and its culture. The compact, crowded agricultural villages of India, for example, designed to conserve land for actual farming, stand in sharp contrast to the widely scattered individual farmsteads of the American Great Plains where more land may be actually occupied by buildings on each farm than the Indian farmer has for cultivation.

Social and economic opportunities and needs, natural environments, and traditions are also cultural characteristics that are revealed in the rural settlement scene. Large, elaborate dwellings reflect prosperity or social standing while a church, temple or other place of worship reveals something about the priorities of the culture. Dwellings may be concentrated along and near a road or waterway, suggesting available transportation, on high ground suggesting concern about frequent flooding, or on, say, southern slopes reflecting concerns about the winter months (this could also indicate a location in the Northern Hemisphere).

Building Materials

Except in the wealthier societies, most humans construct their dwellings of whatever local material is available commensurate with their experience and the natural environment. Wattle, wood, brick, and stone are among the building materials used in domestic architecture. The selection of the building material is also an indication of the climate of the region. Traditional rural societies are not wealthy and therefore cannot afford, for example, to import wood from great distances if it is not immediately available locally.

Log houses require considerable labor, to say nothing of available timber and transportation needs. They usually indicate a period of severe winter. Cut wood (lumber) is not immediately available in many areas and is expensive. The appearance of elaborate wood or brick dwellings in a region such as the North American Great Plains indicates wealth and an elaborate transportation system. Stone is a common building material if available locally and has great durability. Like wood, its appearance in the dwellings of a region considerably removed from local supplies indicates something about the affluence and social standing of the culture and its inhabitants.

Settlement Patterns

The form or layout of rural villages reflect historical circumstances, the nature of the land, and economic conditions. They range from linear and clustered to circular and grid pattern. Each has something to say about the culture that built them.

Early villages had to be near a reliable water supply, be defensible, and have sufficient land near-by for cultivation to name but a few concerns. They also had to adapt to local physical and environmental conditions, conditions which can be identified with a practiced eye. In Nepal in the Himalayan Mountains, villages cling to the slopes above the river bottoms, indicating awareness of spring floods with the melting of winter snows. Villages in the Netherlands are linear, crowded on the dikes surrounding land reclaimed from the sea. Grid-patterned villages in much of Latin America reflect the influence of their Spanish founders while circular villages in parts of Africa indicate a need for a safe haven for livestock at night. A careful examination of the rural settlement of a region reveals much about the culture, its history and traditions.

CHAPTER QUIZ

MULTIPLE-CHOICE QUESTIONS

1. In hamlets or villages where houses and other buildings are grouped in clusters, they are said to have a:
   a. nucleated settlement pattern
   b. dispersed settlement pattern
   c. linear settlement pattern
   d. elongated settlement pattern

2. Which of the following probably did **not** affect how our ancestors of 100.000 years ago built their shelters.
   a. flood prone areas
   b. hot weather
   c. ideas from neighboring villages
   d. available building materials

3. In which direction did the New England house style diffuse the farthest.
   a. north
   b. south
   c. southwest
   d. west

4. Which of the following was **not** a characteristic of the early Southern style house in the United States.
   a. a characteristic porch
   b. often built on a raised platform
   c. often built on a stone foundation
   d. usually had two stories

5. In China today, why are the farm and village houses being built of baked-mud walls and thatch roofs, when in past times they were made of brick and had tile roofs.
   a. scarcity of building materials
   b. people don't plan on living in the same place so long
   c. styles have changed
   d. the government will not provide the materials

6. The modern house type is most common in:
   a. Western Europe
   b. Japan
   c. the United States
   d. Canada

7. The log house probably originated in:
   a. Eastern Asia
   b. northern Europe
   c. Central Africa
   d. Mexico

8. Wood is generally the preferred building material for houses. If it is not available, the next most likely material is:
   a. wattle
   b. stone
   c. brick
   d. grass and brush

9. Which of the following house types, now found virtually everywhere in the United States, is considered a good example of maladaptive diffusion.
   a. Ranch
   b. New England
   c. Folk
   d. Lower Chesapeake

10. The smallest cluster of houses and nonresidential buildings, is known as a:
   a. village
   b. hamlet
   c. town
   d. rundling

TRUE/FALSE QUESTIONS

1. In the United States Midwest, rural houses tend to be laid out in a nucleated settlement pattern. (TF)

2. Our distant ancestors made their first homes in caves. (TF)

3. Communal living developed as human society developed and became more specialized. (TF)

4. Environment was a large determining factor in how early humans built their first shelters. (TF)

5. Some societies still build houses on stilts even though they no longer live in areas prone to floods. (TF)

6. In Africa today, even though they may have the same floor plan, many houses have corrugated metal instead of thatch roofs. This is an example of a modified traditional house. (TF)

7. Today, modernized traditional dwellings are the most common type found in the United States. (TF)

8. Oven baked bricks have replaced sun-dried brick as a building material throughout the world. (TF)

9. The definition of a village varies from country to country depending on the number of inhabitants. (TF)

10. The round village developed in East Africa and had a central cattle corral. (TF)

11. A majority of the world's people still live in villages. (TF)

12. All villages display social stratification. (TF)

STUDY QUESTIONS

1. List the five things a house can reveal about a region and its culture. What can be learned from the layout and function of houses?

2. Discuss the reasons for different settlement patterns. List in chronological order changes that probably occurred in housing structure since humans built their first shelters, and the probable reasons for these changes. Why is it so difficult to trace diffused building patterns?

3. Discuss the different types of building materials, where they might be found, and how they are used in relation to the environment. In today's world why are some building materials found far from their source areas? Why are they used so far from their sources?

4. How does the function of village and farm buildings differ between the prosperous Western countries and those poorer countries where subsistence farming is widely practiced?

CHAPTER 16. COMMERCIAL AGRICULTURE

CHAPTER INTRODUCTION

Agriculture is practiced in some form by virtually all of humanity but the range and types of practices are quite different. Commercial agriculture is largely a European invention and spread with colonization and the Industrial Revolution. The development of a global transportation network to support industrialization facilitated the flow of foodstuffs to the colonial powers who also introduced plantation agriculture in their colonies to produce luxury-crops. These systems still persist today and affect the well-being of many poorer countries. The following points should be noted when reading this chapter.

A Global Network

Modern commercial agriculture developed out of a global system of commodity exchange established by European colonial powers. As the era of global exploration and colonization by European countries unfolded, new products both agricultural and nonagricultural, from the colonial countries became available to a European population that was both growing and becoming more affluent as a result of the Second Agricultural Revolution and the Industrial Revolution. Products from an industrializing Europe made their way to colonies around the world. Transportation between source and market was handled by the shipping fleets of the major colonial powers, producing a global pattern of raw materials, manufactured products, and foodstuffs moving between colonies and colonial powers.

Plantations

Plantations—large land holdings devoted to the efficient production of a single tropical or subtropical crop for market—were first established in the 1400s by the Portuguese on islands off the west coast of Africa. Suitable natural environments and plentiful labor led colonial powers to establish plantation- and luxury-crop agriculture throughout the tropical regions. Such enterprises disrupted traditional practices of subsistence agriculture, displaced farmers, appropriated land, and generally created poverty and hardship for the indigenous population. This pattern remains today even though many plantations are owned not by colonial powers but by the governments of the countries where they are located. Their persistence is largely because poorer countries need the cash generated by these crops. In the late 1990s, the greatest concentration of plantations was in the American tropics.

Rice and Wheat

Most of humanity depends upon the *cereal grains* for their survival with rice and wheat feeding well over half of the world's population. In general, these two key grain crops represent different societies. Rice, originally domesticated in tropical Asia, and still the dominant crop in the south and east realms of that continent, is grown labor-intensively on small plots in poorer countries. Rice production by modern commercial methods is limited to a few countries and the cost of such production often makes it too expensive for many of the poorer countries who need it most.

Wheat, the second most important of the world's grain crops, was domesticated in several locations (see Table 14-1) and lends itself well to commercial production methods. It has come to be associated with Western cultures where it is grown on large landholdings by mechanized means in the richer countries. The principal grain moving in international trade, it is also grown at a subsistence level by millions of farmers as a first or second crop where environmental conditions are favorable.

Specialized Farming
The single most important factor in successful agricultural production is climate. Only one form of agriculture mentioned in the legend of figure 16-1 refers to a particular climate; Mediterranean agriculture. This is a specialized form of farming in a dry-summer climate (most climatic regions have wet summers). In the five world regions where this climate prevails a special combination of crops is grown, including grapes, olives, certain vegetables, and others. Many wines come from these areas and, along with other commodities, are exported to distant markets because Mediterranean products tend to be popular and command high prices.

CHAPTER QUIZ

MULTIPLE-CHOICE QUESTIONS

1. In which region do whole national economies depend on sugar exports.
   a. South Pacific
   b. Caribbean
   c. Pacific Rim
   d. East Africa

2. The colonial powers established cotton plantations in many different countries. Today these same countries:
   a. still export all their cotton production
   b. no longer grow any cotton
   c. have established factories to produce goods for the domestic market
   d. sell their cotton to each other instead of the developed countries

3. The beef industry of Argentina secured a global market when the invention of __?__ made possible the transporting of a highly perishable commodity over long distances.
   a. commercial canning
   b. refrigerated ships
   c. irradiation of food
   d. the steam engine

4. Today, 75 percent of the rubber produced comes from:
   a. South America
   b. Netherlands
   c. Southeast Asia
   d. lowlands of Florida

5. When the United States imposed an embargo on imports from Cuba in the 1960s, the principal Cuban export affected was:
   a. coffee
   b. cigars
   c. tea
   d. sugar

6. Coffee was first produced and is indigenous to:
   a. Columbia, South America
   b. Costa Rica in Central America
   c. Ethiopia
   d. South Africa

7. The world's tea plantations are concentrated in:
   a. Africa
   b. South America
   c. Asia
   d. the Caribbean

8. The world's largest exporter of rice is:
   a. China
   b. the United States
   c. Thailand
   d. Vietnam

9. The Third Agricultural Revolution came about because of:
   a. crop diversification in developing countries
   b. governments in developing countries giving farmers more money to grow more crops
   c. biotechnology
   d. global warming

10. The largest areas of commercial agriculture lie:
    a. within the tropics
    b. in Western Europe
    c. outside the tropics
    d. in the United States

TRUE/FALSE QUESTIONS

1. Refrigerated ships made it possible for Argentina to transport beef long distances. (TF)

2. Sugar producing and exporting countries set their own prices. (TF)

3. Cartels formed by countries producing the same produce are very successful. (TF)

4. More cotton is exported from developing countries than the United States. (TF)

5. Lately efforts have been made to establish rubber plantations in northern Brazil. (TF)

6. In contrast to coffee most tea is consumed in the countries where it is grown. (TF)

7. Much of interior China has turned into commercial-crop production zones. (TF)

8. Sub-Saharan Africa has increased their commercialized agriculture to the point that they are now exporting more than ever before. (TF)

9. From the southern prairie provinces of Canada south through the United States lies an extensive wheat growing region. (TF)

10. Grapes, olives, figs, dates, and some vegetables are grown in what is called the diversified tropical agriculture zone. (TF)

STUDY QUESTIONS

1. What are cartels and what is their purpose? Are they usually successful? Can they be used for both food and nonfood commodities?

2. Explain how and why rubber production shifted from its source region. Is the rubber industry as important as it once was? Why or why not?

3. Study Figure 16-1. Can you find climatic relationships in similar crop-growing areas around the world? If so, what does this tell you about the cultures in these regions?

4. Describe the Third Agricultural Revolution and how it has affected crop production. Where has this revolution has its greatest impact?

PART SIX: THE URBANIZING WORLD

CHAPTER 17. CIVILIZATION AND URBANIZATION

CHAPTER INTRODUCTION

The process of urbanization intensified the concentration of humanity that had already begun with agriculture. Cities are a relatively recent development of human culture made possible by a stable food supply. The need for central authority, organization, and coordination of effort produced the foundations for city formation. Social stratification was followed by the emergence of government, law, and the refinement of culture. The next challenge facing humanity is the success of cities with the opportunities and problems they present as we enter the twenty-first century.

Virtually everywhere in the world, people are moving from the countryside to towns and cities. This migration is happening so fast that the various agencies that monitor such movements cannot agree on the pace. The problem of undependable census data and inconsistent definitions make agreement all but impossible. There is, however, agreement on one point: in the twenty-first century, the world will be predominantly urban.

Early Development

The first agricultural settlements were true villages and remained so for several thousand years. They were small and did not vary much in size and there was apparently no governmental authority beyond the village. There were no public buildings and no workshops. These *egalitarian societies*—a society that is unstratified socially and all members have equal status—persisted long after agriculture was introduced. Urbanization and the formation of states transformed egalitarian societies into stratified, functionally specialized ones. This process occurred independently in several regions, probably first in the Fertile Crescent of Southwest Asia (see text Figures 3-3 and 17-3).

The period between about 7000 B.P. and 5000 B.P. is called the *formative era* for both the development of states and urbanization—the two obviously went hand in hand—in Southwest Asia. The egalitarian society had become a *stratified society*. Now there were priests, merchants, administrators, soldiers, farmers, and craftspeople. The city had become the focus of civilization.

Diffusion in the Mediterranean Region

Urbanization spread from Mesopotamia in several directions. On the Mediterranean island of Crete, more than 3500 years ago, Knossos was the cornerstone of a system of towns of the Minoan civilization. Ideas about city life may have reached Greece from several directions but whatever the case, during the third millennium B.P., Greece became one of the most highly urbanized areas on Earth. The ancient Greeks thus assimilated concepts of urban life from Mesopotamia as well as Minoa, and the urbanization of ancient Greece ushered in a new stage in the evolution of cities. Some 2500 years ago they had produced the most highly urbanized society of their time with a network of more than 500 cities and towns, not only on the mainland but also on the many Greek islands.

The Roman Urban System

The great majority of Greece's cities and towns were located near the Mediterranean Sea, linking peninsulas and islands. When the Romans succeeded the Greeks as rulers of the region, their empire incorporated not only the Mediterranean shores but also a large part of interior Europe and North Africa.

The ancient Romans combined local traditions with Greek customs in building an urban system that extended from Britain to Mesopotamia. The Roman *urban system* was the largest yet. The capital, Rome, was the apex of a hierarchy of settlements from small villages to large cities. A *transportation network* linked all of the urban centers of the Roman Empire together by a network of land and water routes. Efficiency was a Roman hallmark: urban places were positioned a modest distance from each other so that they could be reached in a reasonable amount of time. Some of their surface routes still serve European motorists today. The Roman road builders created a grid of communications to link the empire together.

Preindustrial Europe

Greek and Roman concepts of urbanization diffused into Western Europe, but Europe's preindustrial cities were poorly organized, unsanitary, overcrowded, and uncomfortable places to live for the majority of their inhabitants. The adage of "the good old days" hardly applies. More efficient weapons and the invention of gunpowder forced cities to develop more extensive fortifications; fortifications that could not simply be moved outward. The greater numbers of people could only be housed by building upward, and four-and-five-storied tenements began to appear. For the ordinary people, the overcrowded cities were no place to be. When the chance came, many decided to leave for America, Australia, and other parts of the world.

Urban Stages

Cities evolve in stages. The traders' mercantile city gave way to the factory-dominated manufacturing center, and the automobile enabled the evolution of the suburbanized modern city. Today's "post-modern" cities reflect the age of high technology.

CHAPTER QUIZ

MULTIPLE-CHOICE QUESTIONS

1. As early towns in a region started to grow and become interdependent a new development took place. This was the rise of the first:
   a. states
   b. identifiable specialization
   c. egalitarian societies
   d. counties

2. Stratification of society brought into being an urban elite. From them came the concept of writing and record keeping because they:
   a. were the smartest people in the cities
   b. had free time while others had to work
   c. could demand slaves write everything down
   d. owned so much they needed a method of record keeping

3. The early cities were not large by today's standards. The largest probably had populations of about:
   a. 20,000 to 25,000
   b. 30,000 to 35,000
   c. 40,000 to 45,000
   d. 10,000 to 15,000

4. By the middle of the third millennium B.P., Greece had the largest urban complex in the world. Its two largest cities were Athens and:
   a. Troy
   b. Sparta
   c. Volos
   d. Piraeus

5. The hallmark of the Roman culture was:
   a. their architecture
   b. their language
   c. their efficiency
   d. their clothing

6. The urban tradition on the Italian peninsula prior to the Romans came from the:
   a. Etruscans
   b. Trojans
   c. Minoans
   d. Carthaginians

7. In the early decades of the Industrial Revolution, which of the following countries had a region called the "black towns" because of soot.
   a. Holland
   b. Germany
   c. France
   d. England

8. The modernization of the American manufacturing city occurred in the late:
   a. seventeenth century
   b. nineteenth century
   c. eighteenth century
   d. sixteenth century

9. In the late nineteenth century, the introduction of which of the following transformed the geographical pattern of American cities.
   a. the electric trolley
   b. the affordable automobile
   c. coast-to-coast highways
   d. the diesel locomotive

10. The northern boundary of the Roman Empire in Britain was marked by:
   a. Caesar's Wall
   b. the Great Wall
   c. Hadrian's Wall
   d. the Thames River

TRUE/FALSE QUESTIONS

1. In the twenty-first century the world will still not be predominantly urban. (TF)

2. One of the world's earliest states developed in Mesopotamia. (TF)

3. Urbanization diffused directly from Mesopotamia to Greece. (TF)

4. To link their empire together, the Romans built roads. (TF)

5. The Roman forum was used only by the elite. (TF)

6. The Chinese city of Xian was known as the Rome of East Asia. (TF)

7. Late preindustrial cities around the world looked much the same. (TF)

8. Primate cities were usually the largest city in a state or urbanized region. (TF)

9. Developed during colonial times, the mercantile city is given credit for starting a downtown area, which had not existed in towns or cities before. (TF)

10. The early manufacturing cities offered good living conditions for their citizens. (TF)

STUDY QUESTIONS

1. Discuss how small early settlements went from egalitarian societies to being stratified cities. How did this transition lead to the development of the first states?

2. What role did function and location play in the development of the early cities? What basic factors were needed?

3. Why was the urbanization of ancient Greece different from past urbanizations? How were the cities laid out? How was the quality of live in these Greek cities? How did the Romans change the Greek city and its focus?

4. Discuss the development of cities in preindustrial Europe. How did they change with the development of new weapons? What was life like in these cities?

5. What are the characteristics of the primate city?

6. Describe the differences between mercantile cities, manufacturing cities, and the modern city.

CHAPTER 18. URBANIZATION AND LOCATION

CHAPTER INTRODUCTION

The site of a city is essential to early success and long-term survival. Many early cities would find themselves losing their early site advantage as civilizations and technology evolved and changed. Colonialization and industrialization would transform Western Europe and the world from rural to urban with varying results. People migrate to cities, now and in the past, in response to factors that are often more perceptual than real. Lifestyle may in fact be worse, not better, for those participating in rural-to-urban movement in many countries today. The birth of the world urban map of the late 1990s can be traced to the impact of the Industrial Revolution on the medieval and mercantile cities of Europe. In less than two centuries, Western Europe's population went from overwhelmingly rural to 85 percent urban. This astonishing transformation was the beginning of a worldwide process set in motion by colonialism and the diffusion of industrial know-how. Important key points you will encounter in this chapter are discussed below.

Urban Geography

The study of how cities function, their internal systems and structures and the external influences on them is the field of *urban geography*. Urban geographers want to know how cities are arranged, what they look like, how their circulation systems function, how commuting patterns develop and change, how and why people move from one part of the city to another. In short, how and why a city and its residents look, act, and change as they do. To do these studies, of course, you need to have urban places.

All cities are not equally successful. An urban center's location strongly influences its fortunes. its position in a large and productive *hinterland*—surrounding service area—can ensure its well-being. The hinterland reveals the *economic reach* of each settlement, the maximum distance at which people are still attracted for business purposes.

Locational Factors

The answer to the question of why some urban centers are more successful than others is geography. When it comes to explaining the growth and success of certain cities, *situation*—the external locational attributes of an urban center; its relative location or regional position with reference to other nonlocal places—is often the key. A city's situation can change, and the world's largest and most enduring cities have seen their situation improve with the times. Conversely, a city's situation can also deteriorate over time. Exhaustion of resources, repeated crop failures, climatic change, and political developments all can change a city's situation.

A second locational factor affecting the development of cities and towns is their *site*—the actual physical qualities of the place a city occupies. An urban center's site may have played a key role in its original and early survival, for example, as a defensive locale; but in modern times that same site may limit its growth and expansion. Air stagnation, depleted water supplies, or changes in transportation routes and means can reduce a previously advantageous site to a liability.

Urbanization In The 1990s

As a percentage of total population, urban dwellers are most numerous in the core areas of Western Europe, North America, Japan, and Australia. There are also remarkably high percentages of urbanization in several countries in the periphery (Figure 18-6). In addition, urbanization is currently occurring rapidly in many peripheral countries, especially Sub-Saharan Africa. Currently this region has both the lowest percentage of its population classed as urban **and** the fastest growing urban population in the world. Taking 70 percent and higher as the highest category, Mexico and Cuba are on a par with France, and Mexico's level of urbanization is higher than that of several Eastern European countries.

The culturally and economically diverse realm of Southwest Asia and North Africa displays remarkable variation in levels of urbanization. This variation is related to differences in national economics and cultures. Much of the realm, the Middle East and the Arabian Peninsula, is quite highly urbanized. *Nucleation* resulting from the oil industry has much to do with this situation.

Urbanization in South Asia remains low. For the realm as a whole, urbanization remains well below 30 percent. Southeast Asia, as a realm, is marked by low levels of urbanization (the city-state of Singapore is 100 percent urban; the only such country in the world). As a whole, East Asia is only about 36 percent urban, despite the rapid economic growth on the western Pacific Rim.

The Great Cities

More than 300 cities in the world have populations exceeding 1 million (text Figure 18-7). If you compare this map with text Figure 18-6, you will find that the former map shows the concentration of large cities in eastern North America, Western Europe, and Japan. Several of the great urban complexes in these regions are the products of megalopolitan coalescence. The fastest-growing megacities, however, are in South and East Asia.

Table 18-1 shows that many of the world's most populous cities are found in the poorer countries, and it also indicates how fast individual cities in poorer countries are growing compared to conurbations in richer countries. Despite wretched living conditions for many of their inhabitants, cities continue to attract new residents by the millions.

CHAPTER QUIZ

MULTIPLE-CHOICE QUESTIONS

1. This term describes the spatial process of clustering by commercial enterprises for mutual advantage and benefit
   a. specialization
   b. industrialization
   c. agglomeration
   d. urbanization

2. In ranking urban places, which of the following is at the bottom of the urban hierarchy.
   a. town
   b. hamlet
   c. village
   d. suburb

3. In some parts of the world, large metropolises are coalescing to create megacities called megalopolises. One such is the so-called Bosnywash in the United States. It is located:
   a. in southern Texas
   b. around Puget Sound in the Pacific Northwest
   c. on the Eastern Slope of the Rocky Mountains
   d. along the U.S. Northeast Coast

4. In the late 1990s, the world's fastest-growing urban area is:
   a. Shenzhen
   b. Hong Kong
   c. Mexico City
   d. Tokyo

5. The city of Paris is located on which of the following rivers.
   a. Rhine
   b. Thames
   c. Seine
   d. Marne

6. The capital city of Thailand has some of the most polluted air in the world. This city is:
   a. Singapore
   b. Gung How
   c. Djakarta
   d. Bangkok

7. Which of the following continents has the lowest level of urbanization.
   a. Africa
   b. Australia
   c. South America
   d. Asia

8. Outside North America and Western Europe, major megalopolitan development is occurring only in which of the following.
   a. China
   b. Japan
   c. Australia
   d. India

9. United Nations studies suggest that by 2025 there may be as many as __?__ cities with populations over 20 million.
   a. 15
   b. 20
   c. 25
   d. 30

10. Cities in poorer parts of the world generally lack enforceable laws to ensure the orderly use of space. Such laws are called __?__ laws.
    a. planning
    b. economic
    c. zoning
    d. population control

TRUE/FALSE QUESTIONS

1. Relative location played a big part in which cities grew during the industrialization of Europe. (TF)

2. While some hamlets may have no urban functions, all villages do. (TF)

3. The megalopolis of Bosnywash in the United States has a global economic reach. (TF)

4. All the fastest growing cities in today's world have benefitted from being located at a site which permits easy expansion. (TF)

5. South Africa's 57 percent urban level is representative of most other African countries. (TF)

6. Outside North American and Western Europe, only Japan has megalopolitan development. (TF)

7. Most of the world's largest, and still growing cities, are found in developed countries. (TF)

8. By careful planning, the fastest growing cities are meeting the needs of their fast growing population. (TF)

9. Cities in developing countries lack zoning laws. (TF)

10. Cities the world over are culturally regionalized. (TF)

STUDY QUESTIONS

1. List and define the ranking system for urban places. What is a hinterland and why is it important?

2. List the positive and negative factors found in and around a city's site. Do the same for a city's relative location (situation). Give two example cities and explain how these factors have affected them. Have their relative locations (situations) changed over time?

3. Discuss urbanization by continent and region using Figure 18-6, and the material in your text. Also look at Figure 18-7 and find the countries with the largest cities. Relating back to the text, which cities are growing the fastest? Which regions have the slowest growing cities? Why is this pattern emerging?

CHAPTER 19. URBAN PATTERN AND STRUCTURE

CHAPTER INTRODUCTION

From rather humble beginnings, the development of cities has produced a complex settlement pattern that is changing the face of the Earth and the way humans use and occupy it. A city's spatial organization reflects the culture that built it whether that culture is traditional or advanced. The common denominators of all cities are growth and change. While it is doubtful that the urbanization experiences of the industrialized Western countries can, or even should be duplicated, in much of the world there is no doubt that urbanization is the next step in human cultural evolution.

Geographer's have recognized that the relationships between cities and the surrounding countryside can be measured and mapped. Every city and town has an adjacent region within which its influence is dominant. Farmers in that region sell many of their products on the city's markets, and customers from smaller towns and villages come to the city to shop and to conduct other business. The city's dominance can be seen in many other areas of life as well, such as the surrounding trade zone or *hinterland*, the surrounding region from which people travel into the city for work, business, or pleasure. In general, large cities tend to lie farther apart than smaller ones; towns lie still closer together, and villages are separated by even shorter distances. Investigating the above patterns ultimately leads to the study of the anatomy of the city itself; its internal structure and functions.

Interurban Spatial Organization

The Industrial Revolution occurred almost a century later in the United States than in Europe. When it finally did cross the Atlantic in the 1870s, it progressed so robustly that only 50 years later America surpassed Europe as the world's mightiest industrial power.

The impact of industrial urbanization was felt at two levels. At the national level, there quickly emerged a network of cities specialized in the collection, processing, and distribution of raw materials and manufactured goods, and linked together by an even more efficient web of transport routes. The whole process unfolded so quickly that planning was impossible. Almost literally, near the turn of the twentieth century America awoke to discover that it had built a number of large cities.

In the United States, the urban system evolved through five stages of development determined by prevailing modes of transport and industry. Today's period of high technology, still in the process of transforming the modern city, dates from the 1970s.

Urban Functions

Every urban center has an economic base, with some workers employed in *basic* (that is, goods-producing) sectors that satisfy demand in the hinterland or markets even farther away. These activities produce goods for export and generate an inflow of money. On the other hand, workers who maintain city streets, clerks who work in offices, and teachers who teach in city schools are responsible for the functions of the city itself. This is the *nonbasic* (also called the service) sector. Some people who work in a city, of course, do some of each. A mechanic may serve customers from a village in the city's hinterland, where there are no repair facilities, while also serving city residents.

This employment structure—the number of people employed in various basic and nonbasic jobs—reveals the primary functions a city performs. You should note that all cities have multiple functions, and the larger the city, the larger the number of functions. Some cities, however, are dominated by one particular activity. This *functional specialization* was a characteristic of European cities even before the Industrial Revolution, but the Industrial Revolution gave it new meaning. This was once true in America as well, as Figure 19-1 reveals, but the situation revealed in these three maps no longer exists, at least to the extent shown on the maps. As urban centers grow, they tend to lose their specialization.

Central Places

The notion of a *hierarchy* of urban places, discussed earlier, identifies urban settlements ranging from hamlets to metropolises and is based not only on population but also on functions and services. These functions and services attract customers from both the urban areas and areas beyond the urban limits. Thus every urban center has a certain *economic reach* that can be used as a measure of its centrality—the strength of an urban center in its capacity to attract producers and consumers to its facilities.

In 1933, Walter Christaller laid the groundwork for *central place theory*. Christaller attempted to develop a model that would show how and where central places in the urban hierarchy (hamlets, villages, towns, and cities) would be functionally distributed, based on their respective provision of *central goods and services*—goods and services that a central place makes available to its consumers in a surrounding region—as opposed to those universally available. While not totally applicable in the real world, central place theory helps to explain why, under ideal circumstances, small urban places such as villages lie closer together while larger cities lie far apart (see text Figure 19-3).

Urban Structure

Cities are not simply random collections of buildings and people. They exhibit *functional structure*: they are spatially organized to perform their functions as places of commerce, production, education, and much more. Throughout the past century urban geographers have attempted to construct models that would account for the geographic layout of cities (see Focus on: Three Classic Models of Urban Structure). The task grew more complicated as manufacturing cities became modern cities and modern cities became postmodern. Today urban geographers identify superregions that they call urban realms, and they create models that show cities within cities (text Figure 19-5).

Models of urban structure reveal how the forces that shape the internal layout of cities have changed, transforming the single-center city with one dominant downtown into the polycentric metropolis with several commercial nodes.

CHAPTER QUIZ

MULTIPLE-CHOICE QUESTIONS

1. The area surrounding a village or town that depends on that urban place for services is called the:
   a. boondocks
   b. hinterland
   c. support region
   d. rural area

2. The Industrial Revolution crossed the Atlantic to America during the:
   a. 1850s
   b. 1860s
   c. 1870s
   d. 1880s

3. The *Iron Horse Epoch* of the evolution of the American urban system was dominated by the diffusion of the:
   a. steel industry
   b. automobile
   c. steam boat
   d. steam-powered railroad

4. The rank-size rule of urban places does not apply in countries with:
   a. dominant primate cities
   b. very long coast lines
   c. mainly urban populations
   d. Interstate Highway Systems

5. The *central place theory* of the urban hierarchy was developed by:
   a. Carl Sauer
   b. Walter Christaller
   c. Homer Hoyt
   d. Alfred Weber

6. In North America, the core of the city is called the:
   a. central city
   b. suburb
   c. CBD
   d. functional structure

7. In metropolitan Los Angeles how many discrete urban realms have emerged around the central city.
   a. eight
   b. seven
   c. six
   d. five

8. A number of large cities had been built in America by the turn of which century.
   a. twentieth
   b. nineteenth
   c. eighteenth
   d. seventeenth

9. New York became the primate city of America by:
   a. 1750
   b. 1850
   c. 1900
   d. 1950

10. In the 1940s, retail centers in America were concentrated in which of the following regions.
    a. the Northeast
    b. the South

c. the Great Plains
d. the West Coast

TRUE/FALSE QUESTIONS

1. One factor in the United States' ability to surge ahead of Britain in the Industrial Revolution was the immigration of millions European workers. (TF)

2. City planning was started early in the United States because of rapid growth.(TF)

3. Workers in manufacturing plants work in the nonbasic sector. (TF)

4. In a city, the number of nonbasic workers is never greater than the number of basic workers.(TF)

5. Today, functional specialization is no longer a major factor in American cities. (TF)

6. Christaller's central place theory was never proven to fit any place in the world. (TF)

7. The three classic models of urban structure, although quite different from each other, are used to explain the layout of post modern cities in different parts of the world. (TF)

8. In American cities most people live and work in the suburban city. (TF)

9. Studying cityscapes is useful in finding clues to how societies develop. (TF)

10. To study the urban morphology is to study the urban environment as a living organism because the city changes all the time.

STUDY QUESTIONS

1. Identify and define each stage of John Borchert's four-stage model of urban development. What stage has been proposed for the present? How is this stage affecting the United States?

2. Explain the rank-size rule. Where doesn't this rule apply?

3. Explain the difference between basic and nonbasic sectors. Give examples of jobs in each and their role in the urban environment.

4. When we talk about the primary functions of an urban place today, why is functional specialization no longer so important? Look at Figure 19-1 and compare it with what the text says about changes that have occurred since specialization was important.

5. What was Christaller's main contribution to geography?

CHAPTER 20. CHANGING CITIES IN A CHANGING WORLD

CHAPTER INTRODUCTION

The urban influences affecting the cultural geography of the modern world represent the end of a long evolutionary process resulting from the influences of different cultures with their goals and capabilities. A city, regardless of the culture where it develops, represents society, culture, opportunity, success, and failure. Europe and America are urbanized societies whose cities and cultures are changing within an urban environment, a condition not true in the developing world. The cities and urban places of the developing world represent the greatest challenge to traditional cultures as we approach the twenty-first century. Developing societies face the formidable task of retaining their cultural identities and traditional values in a rapidly changing world. On their success or failure rests the successful existence of much of humanity.

Two centuries ago demographers estimate less than 5 percent of the world's population was urbanized. Today the figure approaches 50 percent and some regional differences and changes are striking, as in such countries as Germany and Belgium where 90 percent of the population lives in cities and towns. In some parts of the world, megalopolises are evolving from formerly separate cities. In others, mega-cities are emerging with populations that exceed those of many countries. In this chapter we will discuss these regional changes and focus on several of the critical problems rapid urbanization has produced. As you will see, the problems of large cities are cross-cultural; they differ in degree, not in kind.

Urban America

The problems of urban America are especially severe in the *inner cities* and in the older *central business districts* (CBDs). While urban sprawl continues and cities are coalescing (text Figure 20-1), people have left the inner cities by the millions and moved to the suburbs. The CBD is being reduced to serving the inner-most portion of the metropolis. As manufacturing employment in the core are has declined, many large cities have adapted by promoting a shift toward service industries. Beyond the CBDs of many large cities however, the vast inner cities remain problem-ridden domains of low- and moderate-income people, most of whom live there because they have nowhere else to go.

In older industrial cities, the inner city has become a landscape of inadequate housing, substandard living, and widespread decay. Many of the buildings are now worn out, unsanitary, and many are infested by rats and cockroaches. These apartments are overfilled with people who cannot escape the vicious cycle that forces them to live there.

The Suburban City

For many decades the attraction of country life with city amenities, reinforced by the discomforts of living in the heart of many central cities, has propelled people to move to the suburbs and more distant urban fringes. Mass commuting from suburban residents to downtown workplaces was made possible in postwar times by the automobile. As a result, the kind of suburbanization that is familiar to North Americans and other Westerners became a characteristic of urbanization in mobile, highly developed societies.

Suburban cities are not just self-sufficient, but compete with the central city for leading urban economic activities such as telecommunications, high-technology industries, and corporate headquarters. In the current era of *globalization*, America's suburban cities are proving their power to attract such activities, thereby sustaining the suburbanizing process. Suburbanization has expanded the American city far into the surrounding countryside, contributing to the impoverishment of the central cities, and is having a major impact on community life.

The European City

European cities are older than North American cities, but they too were transformed by the Industrial Revolution. Indeed, industrialization struck many of Europe's dormant medieval towns and vibrant mercantile cities like a landslide. But there are differences between the European experience and that of North America.

In terms of population numbers, the great European cities are in the same class as major North American cities. London, Paris, Madrid, and Berlin are megacities by world standards. These are among Europe's historic urban centers, which have been affected but not engulfed by the industrial tide. The cities of the British Midlands and the megacities of Germany's Ruhr are more representative of the manufacturing era.

The industrial cities have lost much of their historical heritage, but in Europe's largest cities the legacy of the past is better preserved. Many European cities have a *Greenbelt*—a zone of open country averaging up to 20 miles wide that contains scattered small towns but is otherwise open country. This has the effect of containing the built-up area and preserving near-urban open space. For this reason, European cities have not yet experienced the dispersal of their U.S. counterparts, and remain more compact and clustered. Modern CBDs have emerged near the historic cores of these cities.

Colonial Legacies

South America, Southeast Asia, and Sub-Saharan Africa share a common imprint in their colonial heritage. Everywhere that urbanization is occurring, there is the imprint of the colonial era alongside the traditional culture. In these three realms, cities reflect their colonial beginnings as well as more recent domestic developments. In South and Middle America the fastest growth is where Iberian cultures dominate. Southeast Asian urban centers are growing rapidly, with foreign influences and investments continuing to play a dominant role. In Africa, the diversity caused by European influence in some, and decided lack of in others, makes it difficult to formulate a model African city that would account for all or even most of what is there.

CHAPTER QUIZ

MULTIPLE-CHOICE QUESTIONS

1. The urban core of big cities has changed mainly because:
   a. manufacturing plants have moved elsewhere
   b. middle-income people are taking over the area
   c. too many service sector businesses have moved in
   d. skilled laborers have moved to other part of the country

2. One of the big problems in trying to draw people and businesses to the central city is:
   a. lack of space
   b. fear of crime
   c. high cost of land and building space
   d. smog

3. In the city of Los Angeles, over __?__ manufacturing jobs were lost between the years 1978 and 1982.
   a. 60,000
   b. 70,000

c. 80,000
d. 96,000

4. In the 1980s, the suburban population grew by __?__ percent while population of central cities grew by only 6.6 percent.
a. 10.5
b. 12.3
c. 15.2
d. 17.2

5. Large Canadian cities:
a. suffer from a lack of good planning
b. are spread out
c. have a better tax base and offer better services
d. have slums larger than American cities

6. In many of Europe's largest dominant cities:
a. wars have wiped out the manufacturing areas
b. the past is better preserved
c. suburban areas compete with the central city
d. government planning has had 300 years to develop

7. Which of the following is **not** a characteristic of communist planned cities.
a. wide streets with little traffic
b. microdistricts
c. ugly apartment blocks
d. a vital central business district

8. In Middle and South America, the urban population had grown to __?__ percent by 1997.
a. 41
b. 55
c. 74
d. 80

9. The outer ring in both Latin American cities and Southeast Asian cities are usually the place where:
a. slums and squatter settlements are located
b. the rich live
c. markets are found
d. the industrial area is located

10. In African cities vertical growth occurs mainly in the __?__ part of the city.
a. outer
b. old colonial CBD
c. transitional business center
d. native CBD

TRUE/FALSE QUESTIONS

1. In the United States, many inner cities no longer have the financing to keep up adequate schools, housing, and many other city services. (TF)
2. Deglomeration is affecting many older downtowns, even in small cities. (TF)
3. Gentrification is the term used to describe areas outside the city where people move to enjoy a more relaxed lifestyle. (TF)
4. The new high-rise business buildings now found in many city downtowns are bringing many people back to the old central business districts (CBDs). (TF)
5. Many areas once called suburbs have become cities in their own right. (TF)
6. Canada's large cities are more compact and still have large numbers of high- and middle-income people living in the central city. (TF)
7. Many European cities have greenbelts surrounding the central city. (TF)
8. Communist planners attempted to create microdistricts in cities. This led to many cities not having a central downtown district. (TF)
9. The great Central and South American cities contain beautiful plazas usually surrounded by cathedrals, churches, and government buildings. (TF)
10. The African city quite often contains three central business districts. (TF)

STUDY QUESTIONS

1. List the problems in America's central (CBD) cities. Why do these problems exist? What efforts are being made to reverse this trend? How have the original suburbs evolved?
2. How do European cities differ from American cities? What are some of the factors that have made European cities different?
3. List the factors that make cities in Latin America, Southeast Asia, and Africa different from American and European cities. What is the prime reason these cities developed differently?

PART SEVEN: THE GEOGRAPHY OF MODERN ECONOMIC CHANGE

CHAPTER 21. CONCEPTS OF DEVELOPMENT

CHAPTER INTRODUCTION

In the last 200 years the benefits and influences of industrialization have spread, in varying degrees, to all parts of the Earth. In many countries this process has produced intraregional contrasts that tend to intensify the contrasts between urban and rural populations. This development is, unfortunately, often more symbolic than real for many countries and actually helps these societies very little. Industrialization is not the solution for many countries seeking to improve conditions for their citizens. Success is measured in many ways but should be judged based upon criteria and achievement applicable to the society involved. In the late 1990s poorer less industrialized countries must balance goals and ambitions with the needs of their populations.

Patterns of Development

The global economic picture is characterized by enormous gaps between rich and poor countries, but the geography of economic well-being also reveals regional disparities within countries at all levels of development. There are even areas within the industrialized countries themselves where change is slow in coming. Parts of the rural South in the United States still experience significant poverty and remain comparatively remote from the effects of national economic growth. Life has changed little in remote areas of western and northern Japan, and areas of isolation and stagnation persist in Europe.

In poorer less industrialized countries, there are places where clusters of industries have emerged and rapid urban growth is taking place, producing local conditions that differ sharply from those prevailing in surrounding areas. Recent economic growth on the Pacific Rim of East Asia has created huge regional disparities in economic conditions between some coastal provinces of China and distant interior provinces. Such regional contrasts have significant as well as political consequences. Regional economic disparities are increasing throughout the world.

Concepts and Approaches

Economists and geographers use a variety of approaches to describe the wide disparities in the global economy. Countries with high levels of urbanization and industrialization and high standards of living have long been referred to as *developed countries* (DCs), in contrast to *underdeveloped countries* (UDCs). This approach divides the world into two major categories, but also assumes that all countries are at some stage of development. But, the concept of development is a complicated one. How, for example, should development be measured? The GNP index provides one approach, but it has many shortcomings (see Focus on: Gross National Product). There are a number of things it does not measure, such as the informal economy and contrasts within countries. Other approaches provide a richer basis for thinking about development (see Focus on: Measurements of Development), but none of these approaches produces a clear dividing line between developed and underdeveloped countries. Since some countries that were classed as underdeveloped began to change, the term *developing country* came into use in the 1960s and 1970s, but problems still existed, not the least of which was no country wanted to be classed as "under-developed," and with good reason. The definition came from developed countries. Thus the developed-underdeveloped distinction was largely replaced by a developed-developing distinction. What all this showed is that while economic disparities are usually thought to be due to different levels of development, in reality development is much more complex and cannot be reduced to simple categories.

The Core-Periphery Model

Because of many criticisms and shortcomings in the "traditional" divisions of developed, developing, and underdeveloped system, a new approach to describing global economic disparities has been proposed. The new one is more sensitive to geographical differences and the relationships among development processes occurring in different places. The proposed *core-periphery model*, which is also used in discussions of political power, views the world as characterized by a *core*, *semi-periphery*, and *periphery*. Since the model focuses attention on the economic relationships among places, it is a key component of many theories that treat the global economy as a large system, and is actually quite different than the developed-developing-underdeveloped approach. The most important difference is the explicit identification of the power relationships among places, and it does not assume that socioeconomic change will occur in the same way in all places. This is important, because underlying economic disparities is a core-periphery relationship among different regions of the world. This affects how economies develop in both the core and the periphery.

A Changing World

As the twenty-first century approaches, some states are still subsistence-based and poor (*traditional*), whereas others are in the *takeoff* stage. These terms are part of a theory proposed by economist Walt Rostow in the 1960s, referred to as the *modernization model*. Rostow's model suggests that all countries follow a similar path through five stages of development. The model provides a useful view of how certain parts of the world have changed over time, but it has been criticized because it does not take into account the different constraints that regions face because it suggests a single development path that is not influenced by cultural differences. In the world of the late 1990s, rapid development is taking place under widely different political systems. It is often associated with democratization, but it is also occurring under authoritarian regimes. We should remember that there are many routes to development.

CHAPTER QUIZ

MULTIPLE-CHOICE QUESTIONS

1. The world's fourth most populous country is:
   a. India
   b. Canada
   c. Indonesia
   d. the Philippines

2. The core-periphery model focuses attention on the __?__ relationships among places.
   a. social
   b. economic
   c. military
   d. political

3. The World Bank groups states into four categories based on income. Which of the following is **not** one of the regions where low-income countries are concentrated.
   a. Africa
   b. South Asia
   c. East Asia
   d. South America

4. According to World Bank statistics, there are how many middle-income countries.
   a. 45
   b. 55
   c. 65
   d. 75

5. Europe had laid the foundation for its colonial expansion and global economic domination by the middle of which century.
   a. eighteenth
   b. sixteenth
   c. seventeenth
   d. nineteenth

6. Which of the following statements is correct concerning the world economic system.
   a. it works to the advantage of the periphery countries
   b. it works to the disadvantage of periphery countries
   c. it works to the advantage of both the core and periphery countries
   d. it works to the disadvantage of the core countries

7. Geographically, peripheral countries tend to be marked by:
   a. good regional developmental balance
   b. good site locations
   c. severe regional disparities
   d. good situation locations

8. In the *modernization model* of economic development as formulated by Walt Rostow, when a country reaches the *drive to maturity* stage, a majority of workers enter what sector of the economy.
   a. extractive
   b. service
   c. industrial
   d. managerial

9. In the world of the late 1990s, communism remained in control in three countries. Which of the following is **not** one of them
   a. Cuba
   b. China
   c. Panama
   d. North Korea

10. In the late 1990s, which of the following was **not** a low-income Western Hemisphere country.
    a. Ecuador
    b. Haiti
    c. Guyana
    d. Nicaragua

TRUE/FALSE QUESTIONS

1. In all the rich developed nations pockets of extreme poverty still exist. (TF)

2. Because of development On the Pacific Rim, all the Chinese people are now wealthier. (TF)

3. Gross national product figures for countries are not completely accurate because they leave out some sources of income. (TF)

4. The core-periphery model focuses on the economic relationships among places. (TF)

5. Middle-income states outnumber the poorer states. (TF)

6. The periphery countries cannot legitimately accuse developed countries of neocolonialism. (TF)

7. Tourism has been very beneficial to periphery countries by helping the poor. (TF)

8. The modernization model proposes that countries in the drive to maturity stage have sustained growth taking hold. (TF)

9. When many developing countries tried to adopt the communist state control method of economics the results were most often disastrous. (TF)

10. Politics and economics go hand-in-hand. (TF)

STUDY QUESTIONS

1. Why do you think there are such regional economic differences within a country?

2. Why are the seven measures of development in the Focus on box hard to apply in some countries?

3. Describe the core-periphery model. How is it different from other models?

4. Study Figure 21-1. List the conditions that put countries in the periphery. How do their industries differ in kind and dimension from core countries?

5. How does tourism affect the poorer countries? What contrasts are found?

6. List and explain the different models of development. Give some of the strong and weak points of each, if given. Do you think any one covers all the problems in deciding the development stage of a country? List some of the factors that helped or hindered a country in its economic development.

CHAPTER 22. INDUSTRIAL ACTIVITY AND GEOGRAPHIC LOCATION

CHAPTER OUTLINE

The Industrial Revolution was essentially a revolution in power and transportation. Goods, ideas, and humanity were transported across the Earth in a manner that would forever change our planet and its human occupants. Modern industry increased and intensified regional inequality while mushrooming demand for resources created new global patterns of movement. In the industrial-oriented world of the late 1990s success depended on the possession or control of resources. At a time when cultural differences should be reduced with benefits and technical capabilities shared for the good of all, our own innovations and abilities may work to hinder this end.

Location

Economic activities can be categorized according to their purpose, their relationship to the natural resources on which they are based, and their complexity. Economic geographers investigate the reasons behind the location of economic activity. Today, the world is a vast panorama of primary activity within which there are clusters of secondary industries symbolized by the great manufacturing belts of Japan, the United States, Europe, and Russia. What geographic factors created this arrangement and what will happen next? Answers to such questions come from the field of *location theory*, which attempts to explain the locational pattern of an economic activity in terms of the factors that influence this pattern. Location theory helps explain the spatial positioning of industries and their success or failure. The Industrial Revolution transformed the world's economic map, dramatically impacting certain areas while totally bypassing others. Understanding the forces and factors that shaped the world's industrial layout is a prime objective of economic geographers.

Location Decision

Industrial activity takes place in certain locations and not others. For primary industries, the location of resources is the determining factor. *Secondary industries* are less dependent on resource location because raw materials can be transported to distant locations if the resulting profits outweigh the costs. Any attempt to establish a model for the location of secondary industry, however, runs into complications because the location of secondary industries depends to a large extent on human behavior and decision making—cultural and political as well as economic factors, even on intuition or whim. In 1909, the German economist Alfred Weber developed a model for the location of manufacturing establishments. Weber's *least cost theory* accounted for the location of a manufacturing plant in terms of transportation (the most important), labor, and agglomeration (shared talents, services, and facilities). Despite numerous criticisms of the model, Alfred Weber set in motion a debate over the spatial aspects of economic activity that continues today (see Focus on: Industrial Location Theory).

Transportation

As Weber noted, *transportation* facilities and costs are crucial in industrial location. A huge market may exist for a given product, but if that market is not served by an effective transportation system, much of the advantage is lost. The maps in chapter 23 underscore the fact that highly developed industrial areas are also the places that are served most efficiently by transportation facilities. Industrialization and the development of modern transport systems go hand-in-hand.

In a sense, the Industrial Revolution was a transportation revolution—a revolution that is still going on. Transport costs played a key role in the location of heavy industries but raw-material acquisition and finished-product distribution determined the options. One of the first decisions faced by the capitalists who built the great iron works of Europe, for example, was whether to move either coal to iron ores sites or, iron ore to the coal fields. The iron smelters were built near the coal fields (it generally takes more coal than iron ore to make a ton of finished product). The same decision was made when the American iron industry located near Appalachian coal and hauled iron ore from the Great Lakes Mesabi Range.

Additional Factors of Location

Other factors influencing the location of industries also include labor costs, energy availability, and infrastructure. The availability of cheap semiskilled labor has had an immense impact on regional industrial development. Even in an era of automated assembly lines and computerized processing, the prospect of a large, low-wage, trainable labor force continues to attract manufacturers. Japan's postwar success was based in large measure on the skills *and* the low wages of its labor force. Taiwan and South Korea have successfully competed with Japan for the same reason. In the 1980s, China entered the Pacific Rim picture with its huge labor force and will, in turn, feel the impact of cheap labor when Vietnam enters the picture. The cost of labor still looms large in the location of industry.

The availability of an *energy* supply is another factor in the location of industry, but the factor used to be much more important than it is today. The early British textile mills were "site-tied" because they depended on falling water to drive the looms. Today, power comes from different sources and can be transmitted or transported over long distances. Exceptions occur when an industry needs very large amounts of energy, for example, certain metallurgical and chemical industries.

When Weber considered the role of agglomeration in location decisions, he could not foresee the dimensions of urban areas or industrial complexes a century hence. One of the most difficult problems that today's industrializing countries or regions face is providing adequate *infrastructure*—transportation and communication networks, banks, postal service, administrative assistance, energy distribution systems, social services, roads and highways. China has tried to slow industrialization in some regions because of a inadequate infrastructure. Thus many factors of industrial location are not accounted for by models. Even the growth of secondary industries is influenced by factors that are not accounted for in the models, such as political changes and even environmental fluctuations.

CHAPTER QUIZ

MULTIPLE-CHOICE QUESTIONS

1. In 1721, British textile makers rioted to protest the importation of foreign-made textiles from:
   a. India
   b. Egypt
   c. Japan
   d. Hong Kong

2. Before the Industrial Revolution, European industrial products suffered from:
   a. a lack of raw material
   b. depressed prices
   c. tariffs
   d. poor quality

3. The first steps in the Industrial Revolution involved:
   a. improved food supplies
   b. the use of electricity
   c. better machines
   d. importing foreign laborers

4. Weber's least cost theory to account for the location of a manufacturing plant considered which of the following to be the most important.
   a. power
   b. transportation
   c. raw material
   d. labor

5. The current economic boom on the Pacific Rim is based largely on:
   a. transportation advantages
   b. power supplies
   c. market proximity
   d. labor costs

6. The term *Black Towns* was applied to early industrial towns in the:
   a. British Midlands
   b. Ruhr in Germany
   c. Po Valley in Italy
   d. Saar region

7. The location of steel plants in which part of the United States was influenced by the need to import iron ore from overseas sources.
   a. the Ohio River Valley
   b. the Southern Appalachians
   c. the northeastern seaboard
   d. the Pacific Northwest

8. Which of the following Asian counties, by using the example of Britain's control of the sources of industrial raw material through colonization, followed a similar path of colonial expansion.
   a. China
   b. Japan
   c. India
   d. Thailand

9. In a sense, the Industrial Revolution was a revolution in:
   a. power sources
   b. technological application
   c. labor utilization
   d. transportation

10. For most industrial goods, which method of transport is cheapest over short distances.
    a. truck
    b. railroad
    c. barge
    d. ships

TRUE/FALSE QUESTIONS

1. Hong Kong could have developed a superior economy based on primary industry. (TF)

2. No industries of any kind existed before the Industrial Revolution. (TF)

3. Transportation, not location, is the determining factor for primary industries. (TF)

4. In Weber's least cost theory, transportation and labor availability play a large role. (TF)

5. In the United States, steel mills are located along the northeastern seaboard because they use imported iron ore. (TF)

6. Colonization did **not** give the controlling countries access to many raw materials. (TF)

7. When labor in Japan began to cost more, Taiwan and South Korea surged ahead in the production and export of low cost products. (TF)

8. Certain industries will generally shift from country to country as long as low cost labor is available. (TF)

9. China has tried to slow the rate of industrialization on the Pacific Rim because of a lack of available raw materials. (TF)

10. A close source of energy is necessary for industrial development. (TF)

STUDY QUESTIONS

1. Why is it accurate to describe the world today as being in the modern age of industrial intensification? Did the Industrial Revolution affect all regions in Europe? Why or why not?

2. Why are secondary industries less dependent on resource location? What factors are taken into account in site location?

3. Describe Weber's least cost theory.

4. List and describe the factors that are considered in industrial site location. Why is Japan a prime example of the role of transportation with relationship to industrialization?

CHAPTER 23. WORLD INDUSTRIAL REGIONS

CHAPTER INTRODUCTION

The future of the world is today being shaped by industrialization. The remarkable achievements that began in a single nation have not yet been shared equally by all humanity but this may be about to change. Modern industry is largely a phenomenon of countries in the mid-latitudes of the Northern Hemisphere with few peripheral countries as yet members of this rather exclusive club. As the world approaches the twenty-first century much has changed concerning industrialization and the resources that support it. Industry is presently undergoing a global shift which portends a new era for the world as we have come to know it.

When the Bolsheviks took control of the Russian Empire, they found themselves in charge of a vast realm with a mainly agricultural economy. There was nothing in the Soviet Union of the 1920s to rival what was happening in Europe or North America. Soviet communist rulers were determined to change this. They wanted to transform the Soviet economy into an industrial one. The human cost of this gigantic scheme was dreadful, but the desired transformation was accomplished. The Soviet Union became a major industrial power with vast manufacturing complexes.

Outside the Soviet Union, industrial development took a very different course. Market forces, not state planning propelled the Industrial Revolution in Europe and North America, and industrial economies on both sides of the Atlantic Ocean rose to global prominence. Because of the imposition of Soviet ideology and economic planning on Eastern Europe's industrial development, for more than four decades after World War II, East Europe's economic geography was constrained. Western Europe's industrial growth proceeded more freely, and in the postwar period Japan, Taiwan, and South Korea industrialized under free-enterprise rules as well. China, on the other hand, collectivized its agriculture and put its industries under state control.

Major Industrial Regions

Whatever the ideological basis (market-commercial, communist-state, or some combination), the world map of major regional-industrial development reveals that only a small minority of countries have become major industrial economies. Four major industrial regions have developed, all in the Northern Hemisphere: Western and Central Europe (Figure 23-1), Eastern North America (Figure 23-3), Russia-Ukraine (figure 23-4), and Eastern Asia (Figure 23-5). Each consists of core areas with subsidiary clusters some distance away.

While the older manufacturing regions are quite entrenched, notable shifts are occurring. This dispersal is especially evident in East Asia, where Japan's dominance is being challenged by the "Four Tigers" of East Asia (see Focus on: "The Four Tigers" in Chapter 24). In addition, the entrance of China into the global manufacturing economy in the 1980s is certain to gain in significance in the twenty-first century.

Europe

The location of Europe's primary industrial regions still reflects the spatial diffusion of the Industrial Revolution. An axis of manufacturing extends from Britain to Poland and the Czech Republic, and onward to Ukraine. The explanation of this pattern lies in the location of coal fields in Britain and the European continent. Britain's coal fired industries produced a pattern of functional specialization that, for a time, had no equal in the world, for it was coal that fired the Industrial Revolution.

Europe's coal deposits lie in a belt across northern France, Belgium, north-central Germany, the northwestern Czech Republic, and southern Poland—and when the Industrial Revolution diffused from Britain onto the mainland it was along this zone that Europe's major concentrations of heavy industry developed. Europe's industrial success also depended on the skills of its labor force and the high degree of specialization achieved in various industrial zones.

North America

In North America, industrialization occurred first in the East. Served by a wide array of natural resources and supported by networks of natural as well as artificial transportation systems, remote from the destruction caused by wars in other industrial regions, and on the doorstep of the world's richest market, North American manufacturing developed rapidly. Today, this complex, anchored by the American Manufacturing Belt—from the northeastern seaboard to Iowa, and from the St. Lawrence Valley to the confluence of the Ohio and Mississippi Rivers—is the largest in the world (Figure 23-3).

Ukraine and Russia

The most important country detached from the Soviet Empire (after Russia itself) was Ukraine. In the new Europe, Ukraine would be the largest territorial state and one of the most populous. It was a major manufacturing center before the end of the nineteenth century, having been strongly affected by the Industrial Revolution. Coal from its Donetsk Basin (Donbas) and iron ore from the Krivoy Rog reserve and later from Russia's Kursk Magnetic Anomaly allowed Ukraine to grow into one of the world's largest manufacturing complexes. Today, despite Ukraine's political separation from the former Soviet Union (and hence from Russia), Ukrainian and Russian industries are interdependent: Ukraine needs Russian fuels and Russia needs Ukrainian raw materials.

Eastern Asia

Two centuries after the onset of the Industrial Revolution, East Asia is the cauldron of industrialization. From japan to Guangdong and from South Korea to Singapore, the islands, countries, provinces, and cities fronting the Pacific Ocean are caught up in a frenzy of industrialization that has made the term *Pacific Rim* synonymous with economic opportunity. Industrial regions in East Asia are the fastest growing in the world. The Asian Pacific Rim, from Japan to Indonesia, includes several of the most rapidly expanding economies, recent setbacks notwithstanding.

CHAPTER QUIZ

MULTIPLE-CHOICE QUESTIONS

1. Which of the following is <u>not</u> a major industrial region
   a. Eastern Asia
   b. South Asia
   c. West Europe
   d. Russia

2. One reason London is now considered a key industrial district is:
   a. nearby new coal deposits were discovered
   b. the government shut down older plants in the Midlands because of pollution
   c. the supply of coal ran out in the Midlands
   d. coal has decreased in importance

3. Europe's greatest industrial region is called:
   a. the Paris Triangle
   b. Saxony
   c. Silesia
   d. the Rühr

4. The United States is one of the world's largest __?__ producers.
   a. coal
   b. petroleum
   c. oil shale
   d. hydroelectric

5. Industrial growth in the Upstate New York district started with the:
   a. discovery iron ore deposits
   b. building of the Erie Canal
   c. large ships using Lake Erie
   d. invention of electrical appliances

6. The Northwest district from Portland, Oregon to Vancouver, Canada is noted for its:
   a. agricultural products
   b. timber industry
   c. aerospace industry
   d. optical industry

7. After 1900 Ukraine produced as much as __?__ percent of all coal mined in the then Soviet Union.
   a. 55
   b. 70
   c. 80
   d. 90

8. One of Russia's oldest and still thriving manufacturing areas is:
   a. the Volga
   b. Urals
   c. St. Petersburg
   d. Vladivostok

9. With its Pacific Rim development, China now ranks as the world's __?__ largest economy.
   a. third
   b. second
   c. fourth
   d. first

10. Japan's dominant industrial district is the:
    a. Kansai
    b. Kanto Plain
    c. Kitakyushu
    d. Toyama

TRUE/FALSE QUESTIONS

1. Manufacturing cities in Britain's Midlands are modernizing and are still the dominate industrial region in Britain. (TF)
2. Paris's relative location was one factor that helped it to become a major industrial center. (TF)
3. New York is one of the world's major break-of-bulk locations. (TF)
4. The manufacturing region known as the Erie Horseshoe encompasses both the United States and Canada. The international border keeps the countries from being interdependent. (TF)
5. Because of hurricanes, little industrial activity takes place along the Gulf Coast. (TF)
6. Ukraine is divided between a large very productive agrarian region and a Russianized industrial region located in the east. (TF)
7. Russia's Volga industrial region was originally started when the Russians felt threatened by the Germans before and during World War II. This region has not progressed much since that time because of a lack of available power. (TF)
8. The Pacific Rim of East Asia is a region of varying industrialization depending on the country involved. (TF)
9. Japan has three major industrial areas. (TF)
10. China's northeast industrial district is suffering some of the same effects that plague older United States' industrial areas. (TF)

STUDY QUESTIONS

1. When you look at Figure 23-1, what do almost all of Europe's industrial and urban areas have in common? Read the text. Which regions lie on coal fields? Besides resources, what other factors help to create the industrial regions?
2. Referring to figures 36-2 and 36-3 can you find a correlation between the location of fossil fuel and manufacturing regions? Is energy readily availability in the major manufacturing belt? Identify the other manufacturing areas and what they produce. What are maquiladora plants, where are they located, and what do they produce?
3. Looking at Figure 23-4, what connects all of Russia's manufacturing regions? List the regions and their products.
4. Identify manufacturing regions in East Asia and their products using Figure 23-5. Where is the Pacific Rim? What do these regions produce? How are they changing?

CHAPTER 24. DEINDUSTRIALIZATION AND THE RISE OF THE SERVICE SECTOR

CHAPTER INTRODUCTION

Ever since the Industrial Revolution, the growing demand for resources, the expansion of manufacturing and trade, and the technological innovation have worked to produce an increasingly interconnected global economy. Almost all places are in some way part of the web of production, exchange, and consumption that make up that economy—and their position in that web has significant social consequences. Those in the developed core tend to be in the driver's seat, whereas those in the periphery have far less control. Tracing the historical geography of industrialization can tell us much about why some areas are in a more advantageous position that others, but that is not the entire story.

Changing Patterns

The declining cost of transportation and communication, along with changes in the production process, have led to an enormous expansion of the service sector (activities such as transportation, banking, retailing, administration, and decision making are some examples). Activities do not generate an actual tangible product. This transition has primarily occurred in the industrialized core. The service sector is sometimes broken down into three categories: tertiary, quaternary, and quinary industries. Over the past 30 years this growth in service-related activities has been accompanied by significant deindustrialization in the core industrial economies. This shift had its roots in dramatic decreases in the cost of transporting goods, the increasing mechanization of production, the growth of the public sector, and the rise of new information and communication technologies.

The changes of the past three decades have not fundamentally altered global patterns of economic well-being, but they have produced significant new spatial orders. They have caused shifts in the locus of production, altered patterns of regional specialization, and fostered new centers of economic growth. Deindustrialization in the core has also led to the growth of labor-intensive manufacturing in the periphery where labor costs are dramatically lower and profits thus higher. Such manufacturing ranges from shoes and apparel to computers, automobiles, and television sets. The next time you purchase such items, check and see where they were manufactured or assembled.

Global Dimensions of Economic Activity

To understand the economic shifts that have occurred over the past few decades we must look beyond individual places to the global scale, for both the core and periphery have been significantly changed. The phrase *new international division of labor* refers to the set of relationships that define the contemporary world economy. Whereas earlier in the twentieth century economic relationships were defined by an industrialized core and a resource-exporting periphery, today the geography of the global economy is far more complex. The countries and regions outside the core that have increased their manufacturing output most rapidly in recent decades are shown in text Figure 24-1. Lying behind the patterns shown is a set of developments that give meaning to the phrase "new international division of labor." In the traditional core, the shift away from heavy industry and toward the service sector has been accompanied by the rise of labor-intensive manufacturing in new locations. More labor-intensive manufacturing, particularly assembly activities, is likely to be located in peripheral countries where labor is not only cheap, but regulations (including environmental controls) are few, and tax rates low. Elaborate trading networks and financial relations support the economic web at the heart of the new international division of labor. This new pattern has linked the world's economies more closely together, but it carries with it patterns of interaction that favors some areas over others.

Specialized Patterns
Developments discussed so far—the growing connections between the developed core and the newly industrialized countries, the decline of the older industrial areas, and the emergence of assembly-style manufacturing in the periphery—are not the only significant changes that have shaped the new global economic picture. One change that is altering the economic landscape of the contemporary world is the development of a set of links between *world cities*—major urban centers of multinational business and finance; the control centers of the world economy. These cities are not necessarily the largest in terms of population, nor are they the greatest centers of manufacturing. Instead, they are the places where the world's most important financial and corporate institutions are located and where decisions are made that divide the world economy. The basic pattern is shown in text Figure 24-3, which shows that most of the major world cities are located in the developed core. Thus a global economic geography dominated by nation-states is giving way to one in which world cities and multinational corporations play an increasingly significant role.

Time-Space Compression
A key theme of the last few decades is captured by the phrase *time-space compression*—a set of developments that have dramatically changed the way we think about time and space in the global economic arena. The rise of the World Wide Web plays into the time-space compression. It is too early to know what the full impact of the Web might be, but its role in reducing the importance of distance is self evident. It also clearly plays a role in the decentralization of economic activity.

<u>CHAPTER QUIZ</u>

MULTIPLE-CHOICE QUESTIONS

1. The mass-production assembly line was pioneered by:
   a. J.P. Morgan
   b. Henry Ford
   c. Andrew Carnegie
   d. Henry Kaiser

2. Service industries are commonly referred to as:
   a. secondary industries
   b. tangible industries
   c. primary industries
   d. tertiary industries

3. One of the fastest-growing segments of the tourist industry is:
   a. golfing
   b. fishing
   c. cruising
   d. birding

4. In the late 1990s, five regions accounted for well over 75 percent of the world's total output of manufactured goods. Which of the following **is** one of these.
   a. western Russia and Ukraine
   b. southeastern Australia
   c. Eastern Europe
   d. South Asia

5. A number of so-called newly industrialized countries now have emerged as contributors to the global manufacturing base. Two are in the Americas and these are:
   a. Chile and Brazil
   b. Brazil and Mexico
   c. Argentina and Chile
   d. Mexico and Venezuela

6. Commercial production of television sets began after:
   a. the Korean War
   b. World War I
   c. World War II
   d. the Vietnam War

7. The American ideal of the university town originated in:
   a. Italy
   b. England
   c. France
   d. Germany

8. Maquiladora plants are an example of special economic zone development; these particular ones are located along the border between:
   a. the United States and Canada
   b. Mexico and the United States
   c. Spain and Portugal
   d. Italy and France

9. For many decades the Rühr Valley was associated with what kind of industry.
   a. iron and steel
   b. textiles
   c. footwear
   d. computers

10. Which continent has none of the World Cities that are becoming dominant in the global economy.
    a. South America
    b. Asia
    c. Africa
    d. Australia

TRUE/FALSE QUESTIONS

1. The mass-production assembly line, pioneered by Henry Ford, did not affect any other industries except the making of cars. (TF)

2. Service industries belong in the tertiary industry category. (TF)

3. One factor causing older industrial districts to decline is newer factories building elsewhere. (TF)

4. The rise of new core industrial regions has not shifted the relative importance of older regions. (TF)

5. Research and development activities tend to be concentrated in the periphery. (TF)

6. Singapore's industrial growth can largely be traced to its geographical location. (TF)

7. Many service industries do not need raw materials nor use large amounts of energy. (TF)

8. World cities are the largest in terms of population, and are the places where decisions are made that drive the world economy. (TF)

9. California's "Silicon Valley" is an example of a high-technology corridor. (TF)

10. The World Wide Web is playing a role in the decentralization of economic activity. (TF)

STUDY QUESTIONS

1. What event of the 1970s changed the role of core industrial regions? Discuss the service sector and its three categories, also discuss the largest service industry and its impact on countries.

2. Discuss the global shift in industrial production including the tertiary sector—where and why. How and why has location changed in these industries? Discuss foreign investment and its role in location.

3. How do world cities fit into the picture of today's global economy? Where are they located (Figure 24-3)?

4. List and define the different kinds of specialized economic zones. Where are they located? Why have they been created?

5. What is meant by time-space compression? How has it affected the world? What is the World Wide Web and how has it already affected the world?

PART EIGHT: THE POLITICAL IMPRINT

CHAPTER 25. POLITICAL CULTURE AND THE EVOLVING STATE

CHAPTER INTRODUCTION

Political activity is very much a part of human culture and could probably be traced to competition for space or leadership in groups of early humans. Thus emerged history's first politicians. Political acti-vity possesses spatial expression that can be mapped, a fact that interests geographers (*political geography* is the study of political activity in spatial context). The most common line on a map is a political bound-ary and such boundaries represent a long evolutionary process, but the world political map is relatively new to human history. Perhaps no political map will ever be permanent, as events in the 1990s have shown us, but there is hope that political activity may yet lead to a lessening of tensions and conflict between the Earth's inhabitants.

The present-day layout of the world's political map is a product of humanity's endless politico-geographic accommodations and adjustments. A mosaic of more than 200 states and territories separated by boundaries, makes the world looks like a jigsaw puzzle (text Figure 25-1). The map depicting that jigsaw puzzle is the most familiar and widely used map of the world—so widely used that we often fail to think about the pattern it contains. Valuable insights can be obtained from even a brief examination of the na-ture and significance of the patterns on the political map. It shows, for example, that in terms of territory there are vast inequalities ranging from subcontinental giants to microstates. What the map cannot show is that only a minority of the world states are nation-states, the ideal form to which most nations and states aspire—a political unit wherein the territorial state coincides with the area settled by a certain national group of people (see Focus on: Defining the Nation-State). The population of such a country would thus possess a substantial degree of cultural homogeneity and unity—and, hopefully, political stability.

Rise of the Modern State

The concept of statehood spread into Europe from Greece and Rome, where it lay dormant until feudalism began to break down. The Norman invasion of 1066 was perhaps the most significant event in this pro-cess. The Normans destroyed the Anglo-Saxon nobility, created a whole new political order, and achieved great national strength under William the Conqueror. On the European mainland, the continuity of dynastic rule and the strength of certain rulers led to greater national cohesiveness. At the same time, Europe experienced something of an economic revival, and internal as well as foreign trade increased. The lifestyles of many disadvantaged people improved and crucial technological innovations occurred. The so called Dark Ages were over and a new Europe was emerging.

From a political-geographic perspective, the Peace of Westphalia can be seen as the first major step in the emergence of the European state. The treaties signed at the end of the Thirty Years' War (1648) contained language that recognized statehood and nation-hood, clearly defined boundaries, and guarantees of security. Europe's politico-geographical evolution was to have enormous significance, because the European state model was exported through migration and colonialism, but it has not always worked well in the non-Western world.

Territory
No state can exist without territory, although the United Nations does recognize the Palestinians as a stateless nation. Within the state's territory lie the resources that make up the state. The territorial character of states has long interested geographers, who have focused on *territorial morphology*—territorial size, shape, and relative location. There is no question that the nature of a state's territory can have social and political significance, but focusing just on territory without considering other aspects of a state's geographical context can be misleading. Being small and compact can mean very different things for a state in the economic core than for one in the periphery.

Different territorial characteristics can present opportunities and challenges, depending on the historical and political-economic context. For the United States, large size, large population, and abundant resources meant emergence as a global power. For the former Soviet Union, the vast distances over which people and resources were distributed presented a serious obstacle and contributed to its collapse. Similar problems can result because of a state's shape—as in the case of the *fragmented* Philippines; the *elongated* Chile or Thailand with its southern *protruded* area. These and other states' shapes can often cause problems of political control, defense, transportation, or access.

Boundaries
The territories of individual states are separated by international boundaries that mark the limits of national jurisdiction. Boundaries may appear on maps as straight lines or twist and turn to conform to physical or hydrologic features. A *boundary* between states is actually a vertical plane that cuts through the rocks below (called the *subsoil* in legal papers) and the *airspace* above—defined by the atmosphere above a state's land area as marked by its boundaries, as well as what lies at higher altitude (text Figure 25-4). Only where this vertical plane intersects the Earth's surface (on land or at sea) does it form the line we see on a map.

When boundaries were established, things were much different and the resources below the surface were much less well-known than they are today. Many mineral deposits extend from one country to another, provoking arguments about ownership and use. This includes everything from coal deposits and petroleum reserves to groundwater supplies (aquifers). Since aircraft had not yet been invented, little attention was paid to the control of the air above—an issue that is of considerably greater importance today. The control of airline traffic over states' territory may someday be extended to satellite orbits and air circulates from one airspace to another carrying pollutants of one state across the vertical plane to another state.

CHAPTER QUIZ

MULTIPLE-CHOICE QUESTIONS

1. A country that is *landlocked* is a country that:
   a. has developed only land transportation
   b. has far more land than people to populate it
   c. has no coast on the open sea
   d. has only one coast on the open sea

2. In the Middle east, the Golan Heights were captured in the 1967 war from:
   a. Syria
   b. Lebanon

c. Jordan
d. Egypt

3. Which of the following is **not** a connation of the term "nation".
   a. ethnic
   b. linguistic
   c. religious
   d. political

4. The Kurds, a stateless nation, form the largest minority in:
   a. Iraq
   b. Turkey
   c. Iran
   d. Pakistan

5. Which of the following is **not** currently a parliamentary democracy in Europe.
   a. the United Kingdom
   b. the Netherlands
   c. Germany
   d. Sweden

6. Which of the following **cannot** presently be designated as a nation-state
   a. Belgium
   b. France
   c. Denmark
   d. the Czech Republic

7. Which of the following is currently the world's largest state territorally.
   a. India
   b. China
   c. Canada
   d. Russia

8. Which of the following is a good example of an elongated or attenuated state.
   a. Thailand
   b. Chile
   c. France
   d. Mexico

9. The international boundary between the United States and Canada west of the Great Lakes is classified as a __?__ boundary.
   a. superimposed
   b. natural-political
   c. geometric
   d. antecedent

10. Which of the following is **not** an example of a generic political boundary type.
    a. cultural-political
    b. superimposed
    c. antecedent
    d. relic

TRUE/FALSE QUESTIONS

1. The terms country and state are **not** interchangeable. (TF)

2. States tend to jealously guard their territory. (TF)

3. The Kurds are a stateless nation. (TF)

4. Europe in the mid-seventeenth century was a patchwork of ill-defined political entities. (TF)

5. The European nation-state model was adopted around the world. (TF)

6. Elongated and protruded states have basically the same shape. (TF)

7. All landlocked states are surrounded by other states but have access to the sea by rivers. (TF)

8. When state boundaries are established, demarcation is the third stages and all states demarcate their boundaries. (TF)

9. The boundary between the United States and Canada west of the Great Lakes, is a geometric boundary. (TF)

10. Boundary disputes generally take five principal forms. (TF)

STUDY QUESTIONS

1. Define state and nation. List the main historic events that led to development of the modern European state and nation-state. Why have most other states followed this model?

2. List the different territorial shapes of states and give examples of each. What problems have been attributed to a state's shape?

3. Why are political boundaries considered to be on a vertical plane? How do boundaries evolve? List the different types of boundaries and what they represent. List and explain the genetic boundary classification pioneered by Hartshorne.

4. What are the functions of boundaries, and how have they changed over time?

5. What are the major reasons for boundary disputes?

CHAPTER 26. STATE ORGANIZATION AND NATIONAL POWER

CHAPTER INTRODUCTION

A state cannot exist without territory and this component can be expressed spatially on a map in several ways. Careful study of such a map tells us much about world political units even at the scale of a world map, and raises intriguing questions. Organizational ability and preference are intrinsic cultural attributes of humans and the political map of the world states expresses this quite clearly. The forces at work in the shaping of a state provoke both unity and division and some states may fracture, but cooperation and tolerance can produce success under almost any circumstances. That fact offers the best hope for solving the problems of humanity as we approach the twenty-first century.

Most political geographers believe that in the near future the total number of independent states will surpass the some 200 existing today. These 200 plus countries will occupy the surface of a small planet of which over two-thirds is covered by water or ice. With such a large number of entities, some large and others very small, some well-endowed and some poor, it is inevitable that equality will remain a mirage. We turn now to a consideration of the human and organizational dimensions of the state.

Cores and Capitals

A well-developed primary core area and a mature capital city are essential components of a well-integrated state. *Core* refers to the center, heart, or focus. The core of a nation-state is constituted by the national heartland—the largest population cluster, the most productive region, the area with the greatest centrality and accessibility, probably containing the capital city as well. Countries without recognizable cores (Chad, Mongolia, Bangladesh) may have notable capitals, but these alone do not produce a well-integrated state. Some states possess more than one core area, and such *multicore states* confront particular problems. If the primary core is dominant, as in the United States, such problems may be slight but in a country like Nigeria, where three core areas—none truly dominant— mark ethnically and culturally diverse parts of the state (text Figure 26-1), serious problems arise.

The core area is the heart of the state; the *capital city* is the brain. This is the political nerve center of the country, its national headquarters and seat of government, and the center of national life. This special status is often recognized by using the name of a country's capital interchangeably with that of the state itself. The primacy of the capital is yet another manifestation of the European state model, one that has diffused worldwide. In general, the capital city is the pride of the state, and its layout, prominent architectural landmarks, public art, and often its religious structures reflect the society's values and priorities. It is the focus of the state as a political region.

Unitary and Federal Systems

All states confront divisive forces—some strong enough to threaten their very survival. The question is how best to adjust the workings of the state to ensure its continuity. When the nation-state evolved in Europe, this was not a problem. Democracy as we know it today had not yet matured; governments controlled the use of force and could suppress dissent by forceful means. There seemed to be no need to accommodate minorities or outlying regions where the sense of national identity was weaker. The European state model was a *unitary state* and its administrative framework was designed to ensure the central government's authority over all parts of the state.

European notions of the state diffused to much of the rest of the world, but in the New World and former colonies elsewhere these notions did not always work well. When colonies freed themselves of

European dominance, many found that conditions in their newly independent countries did not lend themselves to unitary government, and such situations led to the emergence of the *federal state*. Federalism accommodated regional interests by vesting primary power in provinces, States, or other regional units over all matters except those explicitly given to the national governments. The Australian geographer K.W. Robinson described federation as "the most geographically expressive of all political systems... federation enables unity and diversity to coexist." Canada, Australia, Brazil, Nigeria, and India are examples of federal governments existing today.

Opposing Forces

All states suffer in some measure from disruptive forces, and all states possess unifying bonds. Strengthening these bonds to overcome divisions is a principal task of government. States are held together by *centripetal forces* such as nationalism, education, circulation (the system of integration of and movement through language, education, transportation, and transportation), and the institutions of government. By manipulating the system, many countries have managed to enhance the centripetal forces that shape unity.

States must also deal with divisive or *centrifugal forces* in the form of ethnic disunity, cultural differences, or regional disparities. When these centrifugal forces outweigh the centripetal ones described above, the state will collapse. In recent times we have witnessed the disintegration of the world's largest colonial empires, including, in the late 1980s, the Soviet Union. Yugoslavia collapsed when a quasi-federal system failed to withstand the forces of division. In the late twentieth century, centrifugal forces seem to be on the rampage.

Power Relationships

Just as some states are large and others are small, some are rich and others poor, so there are powerful states and weak ones. Measuring the power of states is a complex and imprecise business. There can be no doubt, however, that a state's power is directly related to its capacity for organization. *Geopolitics*, a century-old part of political geography, studies the power relationships among states. Current developments in the states of the Pacific Rim fuel an old debate on Eurasian power relationships.

CHAPTER QUIZ

MULTIPLE-CHOICE QUESTIONS

1. In the late 1990s, the third largest global economy belonged to:
   a. India
   b. Japan
   c. Germany
   d. China

2. Over half the world's states have populations below:
   a. 5 million
   b. 4 million
   c. 3 million
   d. 2 million

3. The state of Nigeria has __?__ core areas.
   a. four
   b. two

c. three
d. five

4. In the late 1990s, which of the following countries was building a new, multi-billion dollar capital city to symbolize its rapid economic growth and modernization.
   a. Brazil
   b. Malaysia
   c. the Philippines
   d. China

5. Which of the following is **not** a federal state.
   a. Nigeria
   b. Germany
   c. Brazil
   d. Ghana

6. In newly independent countries throughout Africa the divisive force that has threatened "national" unity is:
   a. tribalism
   b. language
   c. religion
   d. economic development differences

7. Outside the European realm two countries built colonial empires. These were:
   a. India and Pakistan
   b. Japan and Russia
   c. China and Japan
   d. Russia and China

8. The continent which had the greatest number of different colonial powers represented was:
   a. South America
   b. Africa
   c. Asia
   d. North America

9. The originator of the *heartland theory* was:
   a. Karl Haushofer
   b. Friedrich Ratzel
   c. Nicholas Spykman
   d. Halford Mackinder

10. In the United States, the capital city was built on federal territory originally taken from which two states.
    a. Maryland and Virginia
    b. Virginia and North Carolina
    c. Maryland and Delaware
    d. Delaware and Virginia

TRUE/FALSE QUESTIONS

1. The ideal population for a state is one in which all the people can have jobs. (TF)

2. The term forward capital, refers to a capital city that is moving ahead economically. (TF)

3. A federal state creates unity by accommodating regional differences. (TF)

4. Education is a centrifugal force because educated people begin to think for themselves. (TF)

5. Alaska was originally part of Russia's colonial empire. (TF)

6. Mackinder's heartland theory proposed land-based power, not ocean dominance, would rule the world. (TF)

7. At the end of World War II, the world was bipolar. (TF)

8. Multicore states are more stable than those states having only one core. (TF)

9. There are signs a multipolar world is again forming. (TF)

10. Some governments create artificial crises to bring the people together and lessen internal conflict. (TF)

STUDY QUESTIONS

1. Explain why economic success and political power are closely linked. What role did colonialization play in the establishment of today's states?

2. How do core areas influence a state's success? What are the functions of capital cities within a core area and those outside the core area?

3. What is the difference between unitary and federal systems? List the unifying and divisive forces of each. What role does nationalism play in unifying a state, and how do governments manipulate this feeling? Why is the Nigerian government having problems keeping the country unified?

4. List the events that led the world to become multipolar during the nineteenth and early twentieth centuries. How did World War II change this? List the main reasons we will be living in a multipolar world again.

CHAPTER 27. MULTINATIONALISM ON THE MAP

CHAPTER INTRODUCTION

The world today presents a complex map of political entities outlined by lines representing political boundaries. Such lines show the geographic limits of the political unit but actually represent much more. Originally serving primarily as trespass lines to indicate the limits of claim to a portion of the Earth by a group or culture, time and technology have combined to demand that they be quite precise, a condition fairly new in human history. Most boundaries were established before much was known about the interior of the earth and the resources that lay hidden there. Add to this the increasing activity of many states in controlling adjacent areas and you begin to appreciate the enormity of the problems. Like other components of human culture, boundaries represent a history of adjustment, evolution, and experience which must adjust to new conditions and circumstances if they are to be beneficial to humanity.

Ours is a world of contradictions. At every turn we are reminded of the interconnections of nations, states, and regions, yet separatism and calls for autonomy are rampant. In the 1990s, we appear to be caught between the forces of division and unification. Despite these conflicts and contradictions there is today hardly a country in existence that is not involved in some multinational association. There is ample proof that such association is advantageous to the partners and that being left out can have serious negative effects on state and nation.

Supranationalism

The phenomenon of interstate cooperation is quite old. In ancient Greece, city-states formed leagues to protect and promote mutual benefits. This practice was imitated many centuries later by the cities of Europe's Hanseatic League. But the degree to which this idea has taken root in the modern world is unprecedented. The twentieth century has witnessed the establishment of numerous international associations in political, economic, cultural, and military spheres, giving rise to the term *supranationalism* (technically, the efforts by three or more states to forge associations for mutual benefit and in pursuit of shared goals).

Supranational unions range from global organizations such as the United Nations and its predecessor, the League of Nations, to regional associations such as the European Union. All signify the inadequacy of the state system as a framework for dealing with important issues and problems in the world as it approaches the twenty-first century. In the late 1990s, there are more than 100 supranational organizations, counting subsidiaries. The more states participate in such multilateral associations, the less likely they are to act alone in pursuit of a self-interest that might put them at odds with neighbors.

League of Nations to United Nations

The modern beginnings of the supranational movement came with the conferences that followed the end of World War I. The concept of an international organization that would include all the states of the world led to the creation of the League of Nations in 1919. The league was born of a worldwide desire to prevent future aggression, but the failure of the United States to join dealt the organization a severe blow. It collapsed in the chaos of the beginning of World War II, but it had spawned other organizations such as the Permanent Court of International Justice which would become the International Court of Justice after World War II. It also initiated the first international negotiations on maritime boundaries and related aspects of the law of the sea.

The United Nations was formed at the end of World War II to foster international security and cooperation. Representation of countries in the United Nations has been more universal than it was in the League (text Figure 27-1). In 1998, there were 185 member states with only a handful of states still not members. It is important to remember that the United Nations is not a world government; member states participate voluntarily but may agree to abide by specific UN decisions.

Among the functions of the United Nations the imposition of international sanctions and mobilization of peacekeeping operations are the most high-profile. Peacekeeping has become a costly and controversial responsibility, with the UN active militarily in more than a dozen countries in 1998. The organization's peacekeeping function provides major benefits to the international community. Another arena in which the United Nations has accomplished much is the *law of the sea* through which are channeled the extension of national claims over the oceans (see text Figure 27-2).

Regional Multinational Unions

The global manifestation of international cooperation is most strongly expressed at the regional level. States have begun to join together to further their political ideologies, economic objectives, and strategic goals. Among many regional multinational associations, the European Union is the most complex and far reaching. Originally known as *Benelux* it was formed by Belgium, the Netherlands, and Luxembourg before the end of World War II. Today, the 15 member states (text Figure 27-4) are likely to be joined by others within a decade.

Economic, military, cultural, and political forces are today affecting the activities of more than 60 major international organizations. The main motives for supranational cooperation are economic, but they are not the only ones. Along with economic prosperity, a shared military threat (the North Atlantic Treaty Organization [NATO] for example), appears to be equally strong in promoting international cooperation.

CHAPTER QUIZ

MULTIPLE-CHOICE QUESTIONS

1. The beginnings of the supranational movement came with the conferences that followed the end of:
   a. WW I
   b. WW II
   c. the Korean War
   d. the Gulf War

2. Which of the following functions of the United Nations has become the most costly and controversial.
   a. maintaining its own armed force
   b. boundary demarcation
   c. peacekeeping
   d. refugee control

3. By 1998, how many members were there in the Unrepresented Nations and Peoples Organization (UNPO).
   a. 65
   b. 49
   c. 15
   d. 39

4. Which of the following countries was the first to announce that it claimed not only the continental shelf adjacent to its coast but also the waters lying above it.
   a. Chile
   b. Peru
   c. the United states
   d. Argentina

5. The Territorial Sea designation allows countries to claim state sovereignty for a distance of __?__ nautical miles from their shorelines.
   a. 12
   b. 18
   c. 24
   d. 30

6. In 1998 there were more than __?__ multinational unions in the world.
   a. 40
   b. 50
   c. 60
   d. 70

7. The original name of the group that would ultimately become the European Union was:
   a. the Common Market
   b. Benelux
   c. the European Community
   d. the European Free Trade Union

8. Which member of the European Union is a concern for other members because of a possible dominance of the organization.
   a. England
   b. France
   c. Sweden
   d. Germany

9. Which member of the European Union joined as a result of legislative action rather than a referendum of the people of the country.
   a. England
   b. Denmark
   c. France
   d. Germany

10. Progress toward European unification depends on:
   a. military alliances
   b. agreements on refugee questions
   c. economics
   d. a common currency decision

TRUE/FALSE QUESTIONS

1. Supranationalsim is a twentieth century phenomenon. (TF)
2. International sanctions are designed to praise a country for its good behavior. (TF)
3. The WHO is a part of the United Nations. (TF)
4. The Truman Proclamation territorially claimed the continental shelves of the United States, and the sea above them. (TF)
5. Benelux was the first interstate economic union. (TF)
6. Today, interstate cooperation is widespread all around the world. (TF)
7. Germany dominates the current EU. (TF)
8. Any European country can join the EU. (TF)
9. Political motives lie behind the forming of most all interstate unions. (TF)
10. NATO is a military alliance between states, and membership is now spreading eastward in Europe. (TF)

STUDY QUESTIONS

1. Define supranationalism. Why is it important?
2. Why did the League of Nations fail? Did it accomplish anything?
3. What was the primary reason for the formation of the United Nations? List and describe its subsidiaries and their purposes.
4. List the main points in the process that led to ratification of the law of the sea, include the history. How does this law affect an ocean fronting country's boundaries?
5. Discuss the history leading to the formation of the EU. What problems does this organization face? In what other parts of the world are international associations being formed to reduce economic barriers?
6. Beside economic concerns, what other kinds of alliances are being formed around the world today? Where are these located?

PART NINE: SOCIAL GEOGRAPHIES OF THE MODERN WORLD

CHAPTER 28. A GEOGRAPHY OF NUTRITION

CHAPTER INTRODUCTION

Humans must have food to survive. Hunting and gathering provided a precarious existence, but with the development of agriculture, surpluses of food could be produced. Concerns about food supplies and population appear periodically but predicted global shortages have not materialized. Yet there is hunger, even in an affluent country like the United States. This chapter examines the geography of nutrition, and should cause you to consider not the success of the past, but the question of a hungry world of the future.

Just twenty years ago, predictions of regional famines in countries with large populations and high growth rates regularly made headlines, and the warnings seemed to have a sound basis: population growth was outpacing the Earth's capacity to provide enough food, let alone distribute it where it was most needed. Today, daily caloric consumption still varies from high levels in the richer countries such as the United States, Canada, European states, Japan, and Australia to very low levels in poorer countries of Africa. Yet the overall situation has improved markedly over conditions two decades ago. How was this accomplished in light of the rapid growth of population?

The Green Revolution

The "miracle" that was seen as the only solution for a hungry world, with rapidly increasing population numbers, in the 1970s came in the form of *miracle rice* and other high-yielding grains developed by technicians working in agricultural research stations. Crop yields rose dramatically, especially in Asia's paddies, but also on wheat fields throughout the world. As fast as the world's population grew, food production grew faster, and the gap between demand and supply narrowed. In countries such as India and China the threat of famine receded. The threat of global food shortages seemed gone. Or is it?

The "miracle" of increased food production was the result of the so-called *Green Revolution* (the introduction of new, more productive strains of grains and the resulting harvest increases), also called the Third Agricultural Revolution. Actually underway since at least the 1950s, the biogenetic advances in the 1970s appeared to have permanently solved the world's food shortages. But this may no longer be true.

Some researchers believe that the Green Revolution has run its course. Lack of commercial fertilizers, water for irrigation, and additional farm land may revive the threat of widespread malnutrition or worse. In addition, the Green Revolution primarily increased the yields of wheat, rice, and some other cereals but not **all** grains or food production. It also had far greater affect in Asia and the Americas than in Africa—currently the continent with the fastest rate of population growth. Finally, there is more to the issue of adequate food supplies than supply alone. Food availability is also a matter of geography. Even with adequate supplies, people are deprived of food because of inadequate transportation systems. In today's world, starvation results from human shortcomings, not nature's shortfalls.

Distribution of Dietary Patterns

The map of average daily calorie consumption (Figure 28-1) is based on data that are not always reliable, so it gives only a general impression of the global situation. Statistical information about caloric intake, especially for countries in the periphery, is often based on rough estimates rather than on accurate counts. Nevertheless, the map reveals rather clearly the world distribution of hunger and *malnutrition*—conditions of ill health resulting from the deficiency or improper balance of essential foodstuffs in the diet. Compare Figure 28-1 and Table 28-1 to the map of world population distribution in Figure 4-1 and it will be apparent that malnutrition still afflicts and shortens the lives of hundreds of millions of people, especially children, who are often the first victims in villages when food supplies dwindle. It is also worth mentioning that the scale of Figure 28-1 precludes identifying pockets of malnutrition which occurs even within many of the better-nourished countries, where pockets of poverty still exist.

A Future Global Food Emergency?

Although global food production is sufficient to feed the world's people (if it were evenly distributed), concerns are rising that a food emergency may develop. Among the factors and circumstances that may contribute to future food emergencies, the most serious are population growth, climatic change, and rising energy costs.

Population growth is a major factor in any consideration of future food supplies, particularly in Africa where the Green Revolution has had a minimum impact and some of the highest population growth rates are found. Add to this the political turmoil, widespread poverty, the poor status of women, and threat of drought and the concerns become very real. For the world as a whole, some 90 million people are added to the population each year, creating the need to produce even more food just to keep pace.

Climatic change is also a risk factor. If some predictions are true, the primary environmental problem of the first quarter of the twenty-first century may be wide fluctuations in weather conditions, producing extremes capable of destroying crops and farmland. If this were to be the case, sustaining food production, let alone increasing it, may be difficult.

There is a good chance that the cost of energy may rise again, as it did during the 1970s. If it does so will the cost of fertilizers and fuel for equipment. For farmers in many countries, this would be disastrous.

A More Secure Future

The mitigation of a future food crisis depends on policies and practices ranging from family planning and women's rights to improvement of distribution systems and expansion of farm lands. These and other issues would require cooperation on a global scale that may be difficult, if not impossible, to achieve. Yet the food crisis of the 1970s was a harbinger of the future. In time, a rising tide of world hunger may again threaten world order. All humanity has a stake in the war on malnutrition.

CHAPTER QUIZ

MULTIPLE-CHOICE QUESTIONS

1. Today marine food webs are being disrupted by:
   a. changing ocean currents
   b. rising water temperatures
   c. pollution
   d. overfishing

2. Yields of these two crops have been dramatically improved globally by hybridization.
   a. corn and soybeans
   b. rice and wheat

c. sorghum and wheat
d. wheat and millet

3. Which continent has the lowest average daily per capita calorie consumption.
   a. Asia
   b. South America
   c. Africa
   d. Australia

4. Which of the following is **not** one of the factors that determine people's diets.
   a. personal preference
   b. economic circumstances
   c. traditions
   d. what the soil and climate can produce

5. The *food chain* is a sequence of consumption that starts with:
   a. herbivores
   b. humans
   c. green plants
   d. carnivores

6. Which of the following countries has the lowest food availability.
   a. Mexico
   b. Uruguay
   c. Brazil
   d. Haiti

7. Which of the following is most vital to a child in the first three years of life.
   a. carbohydrates
   b. proteins
   c. fats
   d. minerals

8. Which of the following continents has benefitted the least from the Green Revolution.
   a. Asia
   b. South America
   c. Europe
   d. Africa

9. In which of the following countries has male life expectancy **dropped below** 60 years.
   a. Ukraine
   b. India
   c. Russia
   d. France

10. It takes as __?__ times as much soil, water, and fertilizer to sustain a person in the United States as it does to feed someone in India.
    a. 5
    b. 10
    c. 15
    d. 20

TRUE/FALSE QUESTIONS

1. One of the main reasons people do not have adequate food in poorer countries is the lack of good transportation. (TF)

2. In the country of Haiti, food availability has risen sharply in the last few years. (TF)

3. In poorer countries, even if enough food is available malnutrition is common. (TF)

4. Adult males in poorer countries suffer more from malnutrition than children because they cannot work. (TF)

5. Africa received less benefit from the Green Revolution than Asia. (TF)

6. Today, people in Middle and South America have an overall higher caloric intake because their rate of population growth has decreased. (TF)

7. Fish harvests from oceans are growing and feed people in poorer countries with access to them. (TF)

8. Cash-crop plantations in former colonial countries continue to make money that allows people to buy needed food. (TF)

9. Japan has lost more than half its farmland since 1950. (TF)

10. There are nine key areas that can be addressed to help prevent another world food crisis. (TF)

STUDY QUESTIONS

1. What constitutes a balanced diet? Why are some people suffering from malnutrition when their diet is over 2000 calories a day? How does a dietary deficiency affect children?

2. Looking at Figure 28-1, which continent has the worst fed countries? List the problems encountered by these countries that contribute to their food shortages.

3. What areas of the world have improved their caloric intake and why? Discuss the regional variations found within many countries. List conditions that cause such regional variations.

4. List and explain the possible causes for a future global food emergency.

5. List and discuss ten areas that need to be addressed in possibly preventing another world food crisis.

CHAPTER 29. SPATIAL PATTERNS OF HEALTH AND DISEASE

CHAPTER INTRODUCTION

Americans take good health for granted. It may be expensive, but the capacity for good health is present in our society, as it is in all developed countries. For much of the world's population, especially those residing in tropical areas and other poorer countries, the situation is quite different. Good health, like adequate food is unevenly distributed. Patterns of health show even greater regional differences than those for the distribution of food. When people are inadequately fed they are susceptible to many debilitating diseases. Similarly, women who are healthy tend to bear healthy babies, but women who suffer from malnutrition and related maladies are less fortunate. In many poorer countries people, especially children, are visibly malnourished. The resulting disadvantages will be with them for life—if they survive childhood.

The study of health in geographic context is called *medical geography*. Many diseases have their origin in the environment. They have source (core) areas, spread (diffuse) through populations along identifiable routes, and affect clusters of populations (regions) when at their widest distribution. Mapping disease patterns can provide insights into relationships between diseases and environment and sometimes give clues to source regions.

Malnutrition and Child Mortality

It is difficult to identify the specific effects of malnutrition on people's susceptibility to disease, because so many other factors are present. However, there is little doubt about the effects of malnutrition on growth and development. The impact on children is especially important, who are often the first to be affected when food supplies become inadequate.

Infant and child mortality reflect the overall health of a society. *Infant mortality* is recorded as a baby's death during the first year following its birth; *child mortality* records death between ages 1 and 5. The map showing the world distribution of infant mortality (Figure 29-1) reveals the high rates in many poorer countries. The map also clearly shows the relationship between social disorder and high IMRs. Conflict, dislocation, and refugee movements produce high IMRs, and the map reflects this.

Even if there is general adequacy of available calories, *protein deficiencies* still have a devastating affect on children, as they do for entire populations. In tropical areas especially, dietary deficiencies inhibit the development of young bodies and the resultant problems follow children through their entire lives.

Life Expectancy

Figure 29-2 maps *average* life expectancies as of the late 1990s. The map is important in understanding the world population because life expectancy is another key measure of the well-being of a population. Life expectancies have increased significantly over the past half-century, as the map suggests and it does underscore the aging of many populations, but the map does not show a number of other important aspects about a population.

For example, women have far greater life expectancies than men virtually everywhere. In the late 1990s, the world average life expectancy was 68 for women and 64 for men, and the map reveals huge regional contrasts. Most African countries fell well short of these averages. The figures represented on the map are actually averages that take into account the children who die young and the people who survive well beyond the average. Thus the dramatically lower figures for the world's poorer countries primarily reflect high infant mortality. These figures should change as improvements in medical facilities, hygiene, and drug availability suppress death rates.

Types and Patterns of Disease

The incidence and types of diseases that affect a population, like life expectancy, also reveal the conditions in which people live. Certain kinds of environments harbor dangerous disease carriers, and diseases have ways of spreading from one population to another. Medical geographers are interested in both the regional distribution of diseases and the processes and paths whereby diseases spread of diffuse.

Tropical areas, wherein are located many of the world's people (see text Figures 3-7 and 4-1), are zones of intense biological activity and hence are the sources of many disease-transmitting viruses and parasites. Certain major diseases remain contained within tropical or near-tropical latitudes (much of this is due to limited environment tolerance by these diseases), but others have spread into all parts of the world. Before European exploration and colonization, many diseases were limited to region outbreaks (called *epidemics*) and only took on global significance when they were carried to all parts of the globe (termed *pandemics*). As transportation improved and human movement on a global scale increased, so did the spread of many diseases. AIDS, for example, originated in tropical Africa and is now a global pandemic.

In the rapidly expanding urban areas of periphery countries today, densely populated shantytowns with inadequate sanitation and contaminated water supplies are highly susceptible to outbreaks of disease. In December 1990, a cholera outbreak began in the slums of Lima, Peru and by early 1995 had killed more than 10,000 people with more than a million cases reported in every country in the Western Hemisphere. And cholera is a disease who causes are known and prevention and treatment possible.

Dramatic as are the global pandemics of AIDS, influenza, or cholera, the number of cases of heart disease, cancer, stroke, and lung ailments are far greater. These *chronic diseases* (also known as degenerative diseases and generally associated with old age) have always been the leading causes of death and remain so today in the United States (see Table 29-1) and throughout the Western world. Problems of chronic diseases are as heavily concentrated in the urban, industrial core as some of the major infectious diseases prevail in the periphery (text Figure 29-14).

CHAPTER QUIZ

MULTIPLE-CHOICE QUESTIONS

1. In 1990, there was an outbreak of which of the following diseases in Peru that killed 10,000 people.
   a. influenza
   b. cholera
   c. yellow fever
   d. malaria

2. Which of the following is **not** one of the leading causes of death in the Western world.
   a. AIDS
   b. cancer
   c. heart diseases
   d. strokes

3. The continent with the highest infant mortality rate is:
   a. Asia
   b. Australia

c. North America
d. Africa

4. The lowest infant mortality rate among larger populations has long been reported by:
   a. the United States
   b. Sweden
   c. Japan
   d. France

5. In the late 1990s, the world average life expectancy was __?__ for women and 64 for men.
   a. 62
   b. 66
   c. 68
   d. 70

6. In the late 1990s, which region had one-fifth of its population age 60 and over.
   a. North America
   b. Western Europe
   c. Eastern Europe
   d. East Asia

7. Chronic diseases are the diseases of:
   a. longevity
   b. youth
   c. males only
   d. females only

8. Which two continents suffer the most from yellow fever.
   a. Asia and Africa
   b. Australia and Africa
   c. Africa and South America
   d. Asia and Europe

9. Influenza originally came from:
   a. China
   b. India
   c. Brazil
   d. South Africa

10. In Southeast Asia, the country of __?__ has the highest incidence of AIDS.
    a. Myanmar
    b. Vietnam
    c. Cambodia
    d. Thailand

TRUE/FALSE QUESTIONS

1. Medical geographers can map diseases as they diffuse from their core area. (TF)

2. Poor sanitation is the key factor in high infant mortality rates. (TF)

3. Average life expectancy may vary from rich to poor countries, but in all cases women outlive men. (TF)

4. When a disease spreads around the world it is called an epidemic. (TF)

5. Malaria, yellow fever, sleeping sickness, and bilbarzia are vectored diseases caused by mosquitos, or flies. (TF)

6. Cholera has never been a problem in the United States. (TF)

7. Influenza is a virus transmitted from birds, to pigs, to humans and originates in China. (TF)

8. Chronic diseases tend to be associated with an older aging population found mostly in the richer developed countries. (TF)

9. In India, about 80 percent of the population has some lactose intolerance. (TF)

10. There were over 20.8 million cases of AIDS in Africa in 1997. (TF)

STUDY QUESTIONS

1. How are infant and child mortality defined in the text? What are the causes of kwashiorkor and marasmus?

2. What are the main factors that contribute to infant mortality? Looking at Figure 29-1, which countries are shown in the highest category of infant mortality? Discuss infant mortality in the different world regions and variations within each region.

3. What are the three major types of disease? Discuss the major vectored diseases: what is the vector, how do they spread, are they worldwide, how do they affect people? Use the Figures in your text to help you find the core area of these different diseases.

4. How are nonvectored infectious diseases spread? Which of these has reached the pandemic stage many times? Using the Focus on, explain how the cause of this disease was discovered. Discuss the spread of AIDS. Where are infection rates the highest?

5. Briefly discuss chronic and genetic diseases. In what sector of the population are most chronic diseases found? What causes genetic diseases?

CHAPTER 30. GEOGRAPHIES OF INEQUALITY: RACE AND ETHNICITY

CHAPTER INTRODUCTION

All humans belong to the *human race*. For a variety of reasons human groups do differ physically from one another (there are physical differences *within* the human race, not *between* races) and, unfortunately, it is these differences that have become synonymous with "race." Many societies have used these differences to create distractions in status and opportunity among individuals.

Ours is a world of inequalities—of unequal opportunities, advantages, privileges. The disparities apply across the board, to entire countries, to majorities and minorities within those countries, and to individuals in those societies. Dominant majorities in multicultural states create and sustain systems designed to protect their privileges. Members of minority groups find their upward path blocked by racial or ethnic discrimination. Women the world over suffer from mistreatment in male-dominated societies.

This chapter should be studied carefully, for with the many problems facing humanity in the twenty-first century, racial conflict is an unneeded burden, and there is no doubt about the biological unity of the human species. We also need to keep in mind that what is often called "racial" conflict is nothing of the sort. Take the case of the recent disastrous breakdown of order in Rwanda. The Western press implied a genuine difference exists between the Tutsi and the Hutu "races." In fact, no one can discern a Tutsi from a Hutu just by physical appearance. The war was over status, advantage, and opportunity. The conflict was cultural or ethnic, not "racial." Yet hundreds of thousands died.

A Geography of Race

Humans may think that they look quite different but it is not appearance that is the key. Rather, it is the *genetic* makeup of the individuals. Within a species, the chromosomes of reproducing organisms are identical in number and size, and they carry very similar groups of *genes* (see Focus on: Genetics). Groups of individuals *within* a species display certain physical characteristics that tend to set them apart from others. In the human species, these groups (sometimes called *subspecies* or *populations*) exhibit regional variation. This results *not* from differences in the fundamental genetic makeup of each group but from differences in *gene frequency* among populations. So what is often called a race is in fact a combination of physical attributes in a population, the product of a particular inheritance that dominates in that population. This possibly results from a long history of adaptation to different environments.

So human populations vary and their differences are, in part, matters of physical appearance. Appearances, together with a variety of related biochemical factors, have led some anthropologists to argue that there are four basic human stocks (see text page 421). Even such seemingly straightforward classifications are controversial because some groups do not fit into any of the categories. The groups are based on the assumption that some physical differences are more important than others. And for the group to have survived in their particular environment this may have be true. But it does not necessarily hold true for others, thus producing a totally inappropriate conclusion.

Race As A Social Category

Many societies around the world treat race as significant and a large number of people believe that those of different races—however defined—are in some way inferior. *Racism* is, therefore, part of human condition, and it has both geographic expression and geographic consequences. When guestworkers are attacked in a country, it is the product of a flow of people from one part of the world to another. Such attacks are concentrated in areas where social problems are more acute and nationalism has taken root among the young. In these and many others instances, racism influences the organization of people and place in ways that have significant impacts on possibilities and opportunities.

Racism is often associated with a degree of segregation that promotes stereotypes and influences where people go and what they do. Race is a particularly notable feature of the internal geography of many American urban areas, and some large cities are remarkably segregated along urban lines. But the significance of segregation goes beyond who lives where; it can promote stereotypes of racial neighborhoods and foster arrangements and perceptions that affect what people do and where they do it. Understanding racial patterns at various scales can reveal important aspects of the way human beings create communities and relate to one another.

Ethnicity

Ethnicity defies easy definition or description (*ethnic* is defined as a combination of a people's culture [traditions, customs, language, and religion] and racial ancestry), but in actual practice its defining characteristics differ from place to place. A map showing all recognizable ethnic areas might be no larger than a neighborhood or as large as an entire country.

But size is no measure of the intensity of ethnic pride and solidarity. Such feelings are deepened by shared cultural traits, a common history, a treasured cultural landscape, or a real or potential threat to language or faith. So-called "racial" ancestry may or may not play a part in this, and ethnicity should not be equated with race-consciousness. Ethnic conflict intensifies when hostile groups perceive themselves to be of different ancestry, but it is culture, not race that dominates in shaping the world's ethnic patterns and processes. Ethnicity is of very real significance in the contemporary world.

Ethnic Conflict

Territory is at the root of ethnic conflict. The global political order is organized around nation-states whose governments theoretically control the territory of the state in the name of the nation. But the concept of the nation itself is often tied to a particular sense of ethnic identity, which in turn can lead members of different ethnic groups to resist the control of national governments. This is particularly true when ethnic groups living in political territories that are defined and governed by the national ambitions of other ethnic groups face frustration because of a real or perceived slighting by the central government.

CHAPTER QUIZ

MULTIPLE-CHOICE QUESTIONS

1. Humanity is sometimes divided into __?__ different racial stocks.
   a. 2
   b. 4
   c. 6
   d. 8

2. What is often called a race is in fact a combination of __?__ attributes in a population.
   a. cultural
   b. ethnic
   c. economic
   d. physical

3. Skin color is a matter of pigmentation. This pigment is called:
   a. DNA
   b. epithelial
   c. melanin
   d. caratin

4. The highest intensity of skin pigmentation is found in the:
   a. tropics and subtropics
   b. middle and high latitudes
   c. subtropics and high latitudes
   d. tropics and middle latitudes

5. The United States Civil Rights Act was passed in:
   a. 1984
   b. 1974
   c. 1954
   d. 1964

6. The term *ethnic* comes from the ancient Greek word *ethnos,* meaning:
   a. state
   b. people or nation
   c. race
   d. culture

7. Which of the following urban areas has an ethnic neighborhood called Little Havana.
   a. Houston
   b. Atlanta
   c. Miami
   d. New Orleans

8. The root of most ethnic conflict is:
   a. territory
   b. economics
   c. food shortages
   d. skin color

9. Perceptual regions are called __?__ regions at larger scales.
   a. functional
   b. popular
   c. folk
   d. vernacular

10. The largest Canadian province is:
    a. Prince Edward Island
    b. Quebec
    c. Alberta
    d. Ontario

TRUE/FALSE QUESTIONS

1. The term race focuses on differences rather than on similarities. (TF)

2. The different outward appearance of humans can be attributed gene frequency. (TF)

3. People with dark skin have less melanin pigment than those with light skin. (TF)

4. Conflicts between groups are actually cultural not racial. (TF)

5. Because of the interaction between different ethnic groups in today's world. Ethnicity is not the issue it used to be. (TF)

6. When many ethnic groups came to America, they tried to settle in places that resembled their home country. (TF)

7. Ethnic groups that seem to have been completely assimilated may experience a cultural revival if people from their ethnic group are being threatened elsewhere. (TF)

8. The Quebec Parliament passed a law compelling all businesses to demonstrate they functioned in French. (TF)

9. The first thing people notice about another person is the shape of their nose. (TF)

10. Jews and Palestinians are easily identified as being different because of skin color. (TF)

STUDY QUESTIONS

1. Discuss the use of the word race. When differences are noted in a person's physical appearance, what are you actually seeing? Why do the proposed four basic stocks of humans cause controversy?

2. Discuss the different physical traits that make people appear different. What does Bergmann's Rule say about the size and height of people?

3. How is the term ethnic used? How does ethnicity fit with culture? Briefly describe the situation in former Yugoslavia with regard to race, ethnicity, culture, and religion. How does acculturation affect ethnic identity?

4. Briefly, using the major points in your text, describe the history and current situation in Quebec, Canada.

CHAPTER 31. GENDER AND THE GEOGRAPHY OF INEQUALITY

CHAPTER INTRODUCTION

Women slightly outnumber men in the world. In other words, numerically, men and women are almost equal. The "equality" stops there, however. In virtually every country of the world the position and status of women is less than men. We have already seen that ours is a world of racial diversity, cultural variety, and economic disparity. The inequality between men and women is another kind of inequality; inequality between the sexes, sometimes referred to by the term *gender*—a term that connotes social situation, not just biology. The plight of women is undefendable in much of the world and is a subject that demands our attention.

A Geography of Gender

When topics such as population growth, migration, or food production arise, they tend to be discussed in the aggregate. When a country's high population growth rate is cited as a possible threat to its future stability or its development potential, we may not consider the situation of the women who bear children, and raise them, then are confined to a village—possibly for life. Men suffer no such constraints, and men and women born and raised in the same village live in completely different worlds.

Demographic statistics for individual countries (or divisions within countries) tend to conceal gender gaps—differences between females and males ranging from life expectancy to literacy rates. Often times this is deliberate on the part of a government, but it may also be due simply to conditions within the country. In poorer countries the majority of the population may be rural dwellers, and in contrast to wealthy developed countries, little attention is paid to rural areas. Since taking an accurate census is difficult and expensive, it is not a high priority of many governments. When you add to this the perceived lower status of women in many traditional societies, accurate information becomes impossible.

Modernization and economic development reduce inequalities between men and women, but they do not eliminate them. In Western Europe, the United States, and Japan equality has not been achieved. Large wage differences remain, and barriers to social and economic advancement persist. In corporate, political, and many other settings, maps of inequality can still be drawn. Despite the persistence of gender inequality, however, women in urban, industrial societies have made enormous progress during the twentieth century, in stark contrast to what has occurred in more traditional societies.

life Expectancy

In all but three countries of the world (Bangladesh, India, and Pakistan), women outlive men for periods ranging from less than one year to ten years or more—termed the *longevity gap*. Population pyramids (Chapter 5) show that for certain countries women outnumber men, especially in the higher age categories. The average gender-longevity gap is about four years, but this differential varies spatially (Figure 31-1). In countries where life is especially difficult for women the closing of the longevity gap reflects this.

Figures on life-expectancy say nothing about quality of life. During their lifetimes, women's health problems and concerns differ from those of men. According to a UN study, pregnant women in the poorer realms face health risks 80 to 600 times greater than those faced by women in the richer countries (Figure 31-2). South Asian women suffer the highest *maternal mortality,* but the risk for African women is nearly as high. Inadequate medical services, an excessive number of pregnancies, and malnutrition are among the leading causes of maternal death in poorer countries.

Population-Control Policies

Women may live longer than men, and in the upper age categories women may outnumber men, but in early life it is another story. Female infanticide and the abortion of female fetuses (aborted after gender detection tests) occur widely in India, China, and other countries where tradition and economics combine to threaten girls and women. Many thousands of female infants are killed each year according to a UNICEF report, but the modern techniques of prenatal gender detection contribute far more to the imbalance between male and female.

Both India and China have a traditional preference for male offspring, and India, like China has begun to experience an imbalance between men and women as a result of the practices described above. In 1994, the UN reported that India as a whole had 133 single men for every 100 single women and some Indian states report wider differences. But there is an important difference between the problems in China and India. In India, female infanticide appears to be most prevalent in remote rural areas and the same is true in China. But the one-child policy introduced by the Chinese government in the past has been most effective in urban and near-urban areas. Thus female infanticide has increased substantially in China's more developed areas, where the scarcity of female marriage partners has now become acute.

Economy and Production

Work performed by women as unpaid labor in households and on the land would, if measured in monetary value, increase the world's total paid production by about one-third. In the poorer countries women produce more than half the food (70 percent in Africa), transport water and firewood, build dwellings, and perform numerous other tasks. From a purely practical point of view, ignoring the economic contribution of women in a culture (or denying them the opportunity) makes poor fiscal sense.

Despite these conditions, the number of women in the "official" workforce is rising. All but one geographic realm showed increases between 1970 and 1990 (in Sub-Saharan Africa, the percentage of women in the labor force actually declined). It is sad but true that women continue to be the last to benefit from job expansion and the first to suffer from job contraction—particularly in the stagnant or declining economies of Africa, Latin America, and the Caribbean.

CHAPTER QUIZ

MULTIPLE-CHOICE QUESTIONS

1. All three of the countries in which men live as long as women are located in:
   a. East Asia
   b. South Asia
   c. Africa
   d. Eastern Europe

2. In this region of the world women suffer the highest maternal mortality rate.
   a. East Asia
   b. Africa
   c. South America
   d. South Asia

3. During their reproductive years, women need nearly __?__ times as much iron in their diet as men.
   a. four
   b. five

c. three
d. six

4. In __?__ over 70 percent of girls are married by age 15.
a. Mauritania
b. Bangladesh
c. Turkey
d. Japan

5. In this country, the victorious Islamic Taliban movement in 1997 resulted in severely restricted rights for women.
a. Afghanistan
b. Iraq
c. Pakistan
d. Sudan

6. Equal educational opportunities are still lagging for girls in:
a. South and East Asia
b. Sub-Saharan Africa and South America
c. North Africa and South Asia
d. Sub-Saharan Africa and South Asia

7. In Africa south of the Sahara, it is estimated that women produce __?__ percent of the food.
a. 100
b. 70
c. 80
d. 90

8. Which continent has the highest women's education as a ratio to mens.
a. South America
b. Europe
c. North America
d. Asia

9. Between 1970 and 1990 women in the labor force increased in all but which geographic realm.
a. Southwest Asia
b. Eastern Asia
c. Sub-Saharan Africa
d. South Asia

10. The first country to grant women the right to vote was New Zealand. The second was:
a. Australia
b. the United States
c. Switzerland
d. Sweden

TRUE-FALSE QUESTIONS

1. Modernization and economic development has given women equal status in society. (TF)

2. India has laws against female infanticide and dowry payments, but they are not enforced. (TF)

3. Islamic women are now allowed to wear modern dress in public as well as in the privacy of their own homes. (TF)

4. In India's southern State of Kerala, women are better educated, enjoy better health, and have fewer children. (TF)

5. In Middle and South America illiteracy rates are highest in urban areas because most people migrating from rural areas are not able to afford to send children to school. (TF)

6. Women produce more than half the food in periphery countries. (TF)

7. Women in Africa can gain title to land when they are the head of a household. (TF)

8. Quality of life is lowest for women in South Asia. (TF)

9. Many women in poorer countries engage in "informal" activities to advance above the subsistence level. (TF)

10. Switzerland did not give women the right to vote until 1971. (TF)

STUDY QUESTIONS

1. Despite the fact that women tend to live longer in most of the world's countries, what factors affect their quality of life? Looking at Figure 31-2, which countries have the highest maternal mortality?

2. According to your text, what two countries practice female infanticide and female fetus abortion? Is this legal in both countries? What are the affects of these practices? How do these countries differ in where these practices occur?

3. Discuss the treatment of women in India and in all Muslim countries. How do they differ?

4. What is the woman's role in the economy of poorer countries? Reading the text and looking at Figure 31-3, note which realms and their countries have increased the number of women in the labor force. Which realm has decreased? Why? What have women done to try and advance beyond subsistence level in Asia and Africa?

5. Have women achieved total equality in the wealthier developed regions of the world? How do women fair in the political scene? How is this beginning to change? Are you surprised at how late women were finally allowed to vote in some developed countries?

PART TEN: COPING WITH A RAPIDLY CHANGING WORLD

CHAPTER 32. HUMAN ALTERATION OF THE PHYSICAL ENVIRONMENT

CHAPTER INTRODUCTION

As Earth's population continues to climb, there is more and more concern about the stress humanity places on the global environment. Resources, after all, are finite (nonrenewable) in many cases, and even those that are renewable have limits. Water, for example, is more likely than oil to be the cause of the next conflict in the Middle East. We face a new millennium with a world that is changed politically, economically, socially, and technologically from just a few decades ago. Much of this so-called advancement has been achieved with an extraordinary increase in the utilization of resources and environmental impact.

Consider how much the world has changed in just the past ten years during which the world map has been redrawn. New countries have arisen from old ones. New names by the hundreds have appeared on regional maps. New economic and political alliances have been formed. New industrial regions and new trade routes have emerged.

All this is going on against a background of global environmental change whose future is uncertain but troubling. A combination of natural cycles and human impacts may produce unprecedented climatic extremes. Climatic change, sometimes severe and dramatic, has been a natural part of Earth's cycles over time, but never before have these changes taken place with some 6 billion human beings present who depending upon a hospitable environment for survival.

Alteration of Ecosystems

Human alteration of the environment has been taking place for millennia, beginning with the use of fire to kill entire herds of animals, or the hunting to extinction of entire species of large mammals. Native populations from New Zealand to the Pacific Islands did significant damage to the flora and fauna long before the appearance of Europeans. Europeans, in turn, ravaged species ranging from Galapagos turtles to Arctic seals, North American Bison, and African species from snakes to leopards. Traditional as well as modern societies have had devastating impacts on their *ecosystems* (ecological units consisting of self-regulating associations of living and nonliving natural elements) as well as on those areas into which they migrate.

For the first time in history the combined impact of humanity's destructive and exploitive actions is capable of producing environmental changes at the global scale. Early human societies had relatively small populations, and their impacts on the physical environment were limited in both duration and intensity. Over the last 500 years, however, both the rate and scale at which humans modify the Earth have increased dramatically. Particularly during the last half-century, the very character of human alterations of the physical world have taken on global dimensions.

Water

Water is a renewable resource, but water shortages threaten in many parts of the world, including portions of the United States. Water is a renewable resource, but the available supply of fresh water is not distributed evenly across the globe as Figure 1-5 (pages 10-11) shows. The largest totals are recorded in tropical areas of the world. The distribution is sustained through the *hydrologic cycle*, which brings moisture from the oceans to the landmasses (Figure 32-1). Despite what you might think, the supply of water is anything but plentiful for the world as a whole, and chronic water shortages afflict farmers in Africa, city dwellers in Southern California and Florida, and in Spain. In many areas of the world people have congregated in places where water supplies are insufficient of undependable, and as human populations have expanded, people have increasingly settled in arid regions. Since nearly three-quarters of all the fresh water used annually is consumed in farming, the implications are considerable as a comparison of text Figures 1-5 and 4-1 reveals. Future conflicts over water supplies may come to rival recent conflicts over oil supplies. The next war in the Middle East, for example, could well be over water.

The Atmosphere

The Earth has only one *atmosphere*, a thin layer of air directly above the lands and oceans that we depend on for our survival. The atmosphere has a truly amazing capacity to cleanse itself, at least from some pollutants as it has done in the past after violent volcanic eruptions, but human pollution of the atmosphere may result in long-lasting, possibly even permanent damage. Some of the waste pouring into the atmosphere may be producing irreversible change to both the lower-level *troposphere* and the upper-level *stratosphere*. Human activity has produced an unprecedented concentration of greenhouse gases in the atmosphere, raising concerns about the prospects for significant global warming (referred to in Part One) and the full effect may not be felt until well into the twenty-first century.

The Land

Over the centuries human population growth has put increasing pressure on the land surface. The human impact on the Earth's land surface has several key aspects. One of the most significant is *desertification* which is the encroachment of desert conditions on moister zones along the desert margins (Figure 32-5). A second critical impact is *deforestation* as the world's forests yield to human population pressure. Population pressure has also produced *soil erosion* which has been called a "silent crisis" of global proportions. Finally, it is a sign of the times that the rapid accumulation of solid, toxic, and radioactive wastes in the technologically advanced countries is producing an increasingly serious disposal problem. As we approach the twenty-first century the Earth is under human assault as never before and the well-being of humanity may well depend on how these, as well as other, critical issues are addressed.

CHAPTER QUIZ

MULTIPLE-CHOICE QUESTIONS

1. Biologists estimate that there may be as many as __?__ types of organisms on Earth.
   a. 40
   b. 30
   c. 25
   d. 35

2. Human alteration of the physical world has become truly global during the past __?__ years.
   a. 25
   b. 50
   c. 75
   d. 100

3. Which of the following is **not** one of the world regions with the highest precipitation totals.
   a. South Asia
   b. Middle America
   c. Southeast Asia
   d. South Africa

4. In the Unites States, it is estimated that there is 50 times as much water stored in __?__ as falls as precipitation on the land surface.
   a. aquifers
   b. reservoirs
   c. lakes
   d. rivers

5. For the world as a whole, the greatest use of water is for:
   a. urban dwellers
   b. industry
   c. farming
   d. recreation

6. The lowest layer of the atmosphere is called the:
   a. ionosphere
   b. stratosphere
   c. tropopause
   d. troposphere

7. This body of water in the former Soviet Union has been virtually destroyed by irrigation diversion.
   a. the Aral Sea
   b. the Black Sea
   c. the Caspian Sea
   d. Lake Baikal

8. The United States enacted legislation establishing minimal clean-air standards in:
   a. 1950
   b. 1970
   c. 1960
   d. 1980

9. Which continent has the largest percent of its area threatened by desertification.
   a. North America
   b. Africa
   c. Australia
   d. Asia

10. Which of the following is **not** a region where the largest areas of forest still survive.
    a. South America
    b. Southeast Asia

c. Africa
d. North America

TRUE-FALSE QUESTIONS

1. Humankind had **not** altered the environment until the start of the Industrial Revolution. (TF)

2. Water is a renewable resource. (TF)

3. The hydrologic cycle is the process that fills Earth's lakes and streams. (TF)

4. The atmosphere will probably still be able to clean itself even with all the human pollution pouring into it. (TF)

5. In the United States and Western Europe, reduced emissions into the air are not having any positive affect on reducing acid rain damage in forests or lakes. (TF)

6. Desertification can result from both human and natural causes. (TF)

7. Old trees in forests should be harvested first so the younger second growth trees can provide habitat for birds and animals. (TF)

8. As the world's population grows, more marginal land is farmed. This practice leads to more soil erosion. (TF)

9. The United States produces more solid waste than any other country in the world. (TF)

10. The category of toxic waste includes radioactive waste. (TF)

STUDY QUESTIONS

1. When did humankind begin altering the environment? Human need for fresh water is putting great stress Earth's available supply. List the ways human's are creating this stress. What are the results? Read the Focus on: Water and Politics in the Middle East. Using this information and other examples in the text, list places conflict might occur over water rights and usage.

2. How is pollution affecting our atmosphere? Can we reverse this process?

3. List the stresses put on the land by humans. What are the consequences listed? Do you think we can reverse this process. Be sure to cover desertification, deforestation, and soil erosion.

4. What problems have waste disposal created? Discuss toxic and radioactive waste disposal problems.

5. How has human impact affected the biodiversity on Earth? Is this a new phenomenon?

CHAPTER 33. CONFRONTING HUMAN-INDUCED ENVIRONMENTAL CHANGE

CHAPTER INTRODUCTION

Human alteration of the environment is nothing new. The ancient Greeks and Romans cut down many of the trees of the Mediterranean region and herds of goats decimated the lesser vegetation of the same area. Spanish invaders harvested the forests of Mexico for building materials and firewood. The difference is that in the modern era the combined impact of expanded human populations, increased consumption, and technological advances has led to environmental changes that some experts view as *irreversible*.

Environmental change has natural as well as human causes, and changes in the physical world are not always wrought by humans. Nature has its own cycles of change, and it is sometimes difficult to determine whether an observed change is attributed to nature or to humans. Current concerns over environmental change reflect humanity's role in accelerating the pace and extent of environmental change. For all the power of nature, humans are now the dominant species on the planet, and observed changes in Earth's physical systems are being influenced, if not driven by, human activities.

Understanding Environmental Change

Geography is one of the few academic disciplines in which the relationship between humans and the environment is a primary concern. In the past, text books and conferences involving geographers have focused primarily on local and regional changes, since these were perceived as the principal concerns. Today, things are different. A recent symposium led by geographers on "The Earth as Transformed by Human Action" addressed global environmental change as the now-recognized focus of concern. The geographer's concern with how things are organized on the Earth and how they are connected in space provides a useful platform from which to consider human-induced environmental change.

One important lesson that has been learned as the study of environmental change has moved forward is that the global environmental systems are interconnected at numerous temporal and spatial scales. Human actions—the activities we undertake individually and collectively—are increasingly important factors in all sorts of global environmental changes. In the past, many of the environmental problems that drew our attention occurred at local or regional levels. Recent global environmental changes have forced us to recognize the larger spatial scales at which many processes operate.

Several interrelated factors are responsible for the accelerated impact of humans on the environment over the past two centuries. There can be little doubt, for example, that the fourfold increase in the *human population* in the twentieth century has had significant environmental impact. Another is *consumption*, which has increased dramatically in parts of the modern world. Finally, *technology* has both expanded the human capacity to alter the environment and brought with it increasing energy demands.

Patterns of Consumption

While the population of countries in the developed core are often smaller than those in the periphery, per capita consumption of resources in the rich countries is far greater. Maps of world population fail to convey the relative demands made by different peoples on the Earth's resources. Consequently, it is important to keep in mind that many societies consume resources at a level and rate that far exceed basic subsistence needs, a level many times that of people in poorer countries. Thus rapid population growth in the poorer countries tends to be a local or regional matter, keeping rural areas mired in poverty. But population growth in the richer countries is also a matter of concern, one whose impact is not just local or regional but global. This underscores the importance of thinking geographically about humans and the environment.

Transportation
Globally, consumption is tied to technology and modes of transportation represent some of the most important technological advances in human history. As stated earlier, the Industrial Revolution was, essentially, a revolution in transportation and the innovations in transportation that began with the invention of the steam engine and intensified with the internal combustion engine have required increased resource use. Resources are needed not only to make the actual vehicles that move people and goods, but also to build and maintain the related infrastructure—roads, railroad tracks, repair facilities, and the like. And with each innovation the impacts seem to widen. Moreover, transportation innovations offer access to remote areas of the planet and these places, in turn, have been altered by human activity. Modern transportation devices thus contribute to environmental change not just by consuming energy, producing pollution, and indirectly contributing to alteration of even remote areas, but by facilitating global trade networks that fuel consumption in the developed core.

Policy Responses to Environmental Change
A major challenge in confronting environmental problems is that many of these problems do not lie within a single jurisdiction. Environmental problems frequently cross political boundaries, complicating regulation and management efforts. Designing policy responses is thus complicated by the fact that the political map does not reflect the geography of environmental issues. There are few international policy-making bodies with significant authority over multinational environmental spaces. Those that do exist often have limited authority and must heed the concerns of member states. Nonetheless, increasing recognition of the gravity of certain problems have resulted in a number of international accords being adopted on issues ranging from biodiversity to climatic change.

CHAPTER QUIZ

MULTIPLE-CHOICE QUESTIONS

1. Approximately __?__ of all the species that have ever existed on our planet have evolved and become extinct.
   a. 65
   b. 85
   c. 95
   d. 75

2. Because of humans, the current rate of the extinction of species is estimated to be __?__ times as faster than natural extinction rates.
   a. 2,000 to 8,000
   b. 1,000 to 10,000
   c. 3,000 to 9,000
   d. 4,000 to 12,000

3. In the twentieth century the human population has increased:
   a. twofold
   b. eightfold
   c. tenfold
   d. fourfold

4. It is estimated that a baby born in the U.S. today will consume __?__ times as much energy over a lifetime as a baby born in Bangladesh.
   a. 250
   b. 350
   c. 450
   d. 750

5. Globally, the consumption of resources is tied to:
   a. population numbers
   b. technology
   c. local availability
   d. cost

6. To produce 1 kilogram of beef requires __?__ liters of water.
   a. 50,000
   b. 70,000
   c. 100,000
   d. 200,000

7. In 1993, the production of global energy was __?__ percent greater than in 1973.
   a. 80
   b. 20
   c. 60
   d. 40

8. Chlorofluorocarbon gases (CFCs) which have been found to damage the Earth's ozone layer have only been in use since the:
   a. 1950s
   b. 1960s
   c. 1970s
   d. 1980s

9. Modern societies may draw resources from all over the world, yet it is estimated a hunter-gatherer could subsist on the resources found within an area of about __?__ square kilometers.
   a. 13
   b. 26
   c. 54
   d. 67

10. Consumption of material goods is closely linked to consumption of:
    a. raw materials
    b. water
    c. energy
    d. food stuffs

TRUE-FALSE QUESTIONS

1. Regional environmental changes can have global effects. (TF)

2. Because wealthier countries consume more of the world's resources, population growth in these countries has a greater impact on the environment than it does poorer countries. (TF)

3. The demand for hamburger meat in the United States has a direct impact on the cutting of forests in Central and South America. (TF)

4. Technology has played a large role in destroying the environment around the world. (TF)

5. Transportation has allowed access to remote places causing erosion because of dirt roads. (TF)

6. Ships unintentionally transport different species of sea life from one part of the world to another. (TF)

7. Fossil fuels are a renewable resource. (TF)

8. Remote sensing is a valuable tool in helping to monitor what is happening on the Earth's surface. (TF)

9. The ozone layer over Antarctica has thinned and now has a hole in it that is growing. (TF)

10. The UNCED has gotten the agreement of the developed nations to reduce CO_2 released into the atmosphere. This agreement also includes the developing countries. (TF)

STUDY QUESTIONS

1. There are many things to consider when we try to understand humanity's role in environmental change. List the factors involved and give examples of each. Include the damage done.

2. Look at Figures 33-1 and 33-2. Can you understand why oil slicks appear in this pattern? What causes these oil slicks? What are some alternative sources for energy besides the use of fossil fuels?

3. Pollution is a worldwide problem. What organizations are trying to address this problem? What progress is being made? What issues are being addressed? What are some of the results that could be seen from global climate change? Why must these problems be addressed now?

CHAPTER 34. POLICY RESPONSES TO DEMOGRAPHIC CHANGES

CHAPTER INTRODUCTION

Population is at the center of any consideration of global change. Despite some reduction in birth rates, population continues to grow very rapidly in some parts of the world, creating social and economic challenges. Not all challenges, however, involve population growth because in some parts of the world little or no population growth is placing strains on economic and social systems. This situation calls attention to the fact that population growth varies from realm to realm, from region to region, and even from province to province within individual countries. Some 30 years ago the world's highest rates of natural increase were in South Asia and Middle America, but in the 1970s tropical Africa took the lead and retains it today. Still farther back in history, Europe underwent a population *explosion* that was mitigated by emigration.

Today, things are quite different. In two dozen European countries fertility rates are below replacement level and Europe's population will decline in coming years (this is sometimes referred to as a population *implosion*), a decline that will be accompanied by difficult social problems. A population that is not replacing itself also becomes a population of older people who require pensions, social services, and other forms of support that must be paid for from a dwindling tax base. Because not enough younger people are available to take jobs, immigrant workers are needed and this, too, can lead to social problems.

Population decline is a two-edged sword. How do governments react to demographic problems, and what have been the results of past policies and actions? In the late 1990s, France is the only Western European country that is officially encouraging its citizens to have large families. Japan is in similar straits, but Japanese policy bars immigration of foreign workers. A population-control program in Singapore was so successful that the population stopped growing and started aging. Now Singapore's government is urging families to have three or even four children. Clearly, balanced population growth is not easily achieved.

Geography of Demography

For practical purposes population data are reported by country (see Figures 5-6 and 5-7). But demographic variation *within* countries can be very large as, for example, in India (Figure 34-2). At first glance this might not seem to be a problem, but closer examination indicates otherwise. Take, for example, the situation in Quebec (Figure 34-1). Quebec has long had the lowest birth rate among all of Canada's provinces. In 1990 the Quebec *provincial* government offered women a subsidy for every child born after the first two. Quebec's leaders want to encourage the rate of natural increase for political as well as economic reasons.

The Canadian example reminds us of the spatial variations within countries, especially larger countries, that do not appear in national statistics. It also indicates that national population policies may not be appropriate, or even acceptable, in particular regions of a country. As in all federations, the objectives of one region may diverge from those of the state as a whole.

Population Policies

Many of the world's governments have instituted policies designed to influence the overall growth rate or ethnic ratios within the population. Certain policies directly affect the birth rate via laws that range from subsidization of abortion to forced sterilization. Others influence family size through taxation or subvention. These policies fall into three groups: expansive, eugenic, and restrictive.

The former Soviet Union and China under Mao Zedong led other communist societies in *expansive population policies*, which encourage large families and raise the rate of population growth. Sometimes these policies have unanticipated effects, as in the case of Romania where, after the communist regime was toppled in 1991, it was found that many parents had abandoned children to state orphanages. In the past, some governments engaged in *eugenic population policies*, which were designed to favor one section of the population over others. The ultimate example of this type was Nazi Germany, but other countries also pursue such strategies through more subtle ways such as discriminatory taxation, allocation of resources, or other forms of racial favoritism. Today most countries seek to reduce the rate of natural increase through *restrictive population policies*. These policies range from toleration of official unapproved means of birth control to outright prohibition of large families. Societies have experimented with a variety of techniques for achieving demographic goals, with varying results.

International agreements on population policies are difficult to reach, in part because religious doctrines, cultural practices, and governmental goals may be incompatible. Subsistence agricultural societies need large families to provide the labor to work the land, regardless of possible government goals to reduce family size (in rural societies children do not present the economic burden associated with urban-industrial development). Many religions oppose artificial birth control for any reason, governmental goals notwithstanding. Achieving acceptable population-control in non-totalitarian societies is difficult in itself, let alone attempting such goals on the international level.

CHAPTER QUIZ

MULTIPLE-CHOICE QUESTIONS

1. In the late 1990s, the world region with the highest rates of natural population increase is:
   a. South Asia
   b. tropical Africa
   c. Middle America
   d. East Asia

2. In which of the following countries has the government introduced a campaign to urge families to have three or even four children.
   a. Thailand
   b. Japan
   c. Bangladesh
   d. Singapore

3. Which Canadian province wants to encourage larger families as a political move.
   a. British Columbia
   b. Ontario
   c. Quebec
   d. Manitoba

4. UN population conferences are held every __?__ years.
   a. 5
   b. 10
   c. 15
   d. 20

5. Asia's only Roman Catholic country is:
   a. the Philippines
   b. Sri Lanka
   c. Bali
   d. Myanmar

6. In the Muslim world, the most successful family planning program is found in:
   a. Iraq
   b. Pakistan
   c. Indonesia
   d. Saudi Arabia

7. The country of Japan is about the size of which U.S. state.
   a. Delaware
   b. Texas
   c. Nebraska
   d. Montana

8. Sometime during the first half of the twenty-first century demographers predict that the most populous country will be:
   a. China
   b. India
   c. Brazil
   d. Nigeria

9. China launched their one-child policy in:
   a. 1979
   b. 1969
   c. 1989
   d. 1959

10. India is a federation of __?__ States and 7 so-called Union Territories.
    a. 15
    b. 20
    c. 25
    d. 30

TRUE-FALSE QUESTIONS

1. Today, Africa's overall population growth rate is approaching 4 percent. (TF)

2. A country's TFR must be above 2.1 to sustain a population at its current levels. (TF)

3. Germany is the only Western European country encouraging its citizens, through subsidies and services, to have larger families. (TF)

4. Japan's low population growth rate has caused the country to encourage immigration of needed workers. (TF)

5. Catholic Quebec has the highest birth rate of all of Canada's provinces. (TF)

6. The economic gains made by developing countries is wiped out by their high birth rates. (TF)

7. The ultimate example of eugenics was Nazi Germany. (TF)

8. Indian State governments are using advertising and persuasion to encourage families to have fewer children. (TF)

9. Families in rural China defied the government's one-child policy because they needed more children to help produce crops. (TF)

10. It is estimated that during China's one-child policy surviving male children exceeded females by 400,000 annually. (TF)

STUDY QUESTIONS

1. What problems face countries with a below replacement growth rate? What kinds of different measures are some countries taking to raise the natural population growth rate?

2. Briefly describe the different meetings held by the United Nations on population control. Start with 1974. How did different countries react at each meeting?

3. List and define the three different population policies as presented in your text. How do Japan, India, and China handle their different population problems? Discuss why each country handles its problem differently. What role does culture play in these differences?

CHAPTER 35. TOWARD A NEW WORLD ORDER? THE CHANGING GLOBAL POLITICAL LANDSCAPE

CHAPTER INTRODUCTION

The world at the end of the twentieth century is a world of contradictions. Hopes for peace and cooperation are often countered by the reality of division resulting from national self-interest, economic factors, human rights issues, and many other concerns. The hopes for a so-called New World Order shaped by forces that interconnect nations and states by supranational blocks capable of balancing the force of the major powers, and multinational action should any state violate rules of communal conduct, are already clouded by doubts and uncertainties. The world today is burdened by a weakening state system and devolution, which afflicts a growing number of countries.

In this final chapter the focus is on the forces that are changing the global political landscape. These are forces with which governments, businesses, and individuals must contend. To be aware of these forces is to be better prepared to cope with them. When we study the changes taking place in the world's political framework, we enter the field of *geopolitics*. This field combines geography with some aspects of political science but geography brings cultural, environmental, and spatial perspectives to the field. As such, geopolitics is a wide arena that helps us understand the forces that are transforming the world map.

Forces of Devolution

Devolution, the disintegration of a state along regional lines, is occurring in a growing number of countries, old and young, large and small, wealthy and poor. States are the result of political-geographical evolution that may have spanned millennia (China) or centuries (many European states). Still others have evolved from colonial empires only a few decades ago, as in much of Africa. Revolution, civil war, and international conflict accompany the evolution of states. Even the oldest and apparently most stable states are vulnerable to a process that is the reverse of evolution, propelled by forces that divide and destabilize. That process is called *devolution.*

Devolution results from many factors, and rarely is the process propelled by a single one, but the primary ones are *cultural*, *economic*, and *spatial*. In Europe, devolutionary forces threaten a large number of older as well as younger states (Figure 35-1). Several of these have cultural bases, as in Spain, Belgium, and the former Yugoslavia. Economic *and* cultural devolutionary forces are present in Catalonia, but purely economic forces are at work in Italy and France (which is often cited as the model nation-state). In this case the problem is the island of Corsica where the activists want power and money. Europe is not alone in confronting economic forces leading to devolution. During the 1990s a devolutionary movement arose in Brazil that was rooted in economics. It seems that no country is immune from devolutionary pressures.

If devolutionary events have one feature in common, it is that they occur on the margins of states. Note that every one of the devolutionary-infected areas shown in Figure 35-1 lies on a coast or a boundary. Distance, remoteness, and peripheral location are allies of devolution. In many cases the regions adjoin neighbors that may support separatist objectives. As stated previously, the basic reason for almost all devolutionary forces is territory under one guise or another.

In most instances of devolution, the problem remains domestic; that is, it has little or no impact on the world at large. One notable exception is the devolution of the former Soviet Union by a powerful combination of political, cultural, and economic forces (Figure 35-3). When this occurred, the world was transformed. The former Soviet empire is left with a political-geographic legacy that will remain problematic for generations to come. Visions of local or regional autonomy, notions of democracy and participation, concepts of religious fundamentalism, and economic globalization are changing the map of the modern world.

The State In The New World Order

The state is the crucial building block in the global international framework, yet the world today is burdened by a weakening state system and an antiquated boundary framework. The state's weaknesses are underscored by the growing power of regions, provinces, States, and other internal entities to act independently of the national government. The European state system, born more than 350 years ago and exported globally with Europeanization in autocratic form, later modified in many instances to a federal system, was at best tenuous in non-European areas. Many boundaries in existence today are the result of colonial control and decision with little regard for the impact on indigenous populations. With the end of colonialism, the legacy of such decisions has produced devolution and conflict. Supranationalism may be a solution to at least some of these problems but the state system did not evolve quickly or painlessly and it is doubtful its successor, whatever that may be, will proceed more smoothly.

A New World Order is said to be in the making following the end of the Cold War, but its geographic outlines cannot yet be discerned. It is likely to involve a multipolar rather than a bipolar configuration (as existed before the devolution of the former Soviet Union) and it is unclear how orderly it will be or who the key players will be.

CHAPTER QUIZ

MULTIPLE-CHOICE QUESTIONS

1. The common currency of the European Union is the:
   a. lira
   b. euro
   c. dollar
   d. mark

2. In 1997, which of the following European countries is **not** facing serious devolutionary pressures.
   a. Scotland
   b. Belgium
   c. Italy
   d. Germany

3. The region of province of Catalonia is a part of which country.
   a. Spain
   b. France
   c. Italy
   d. Portugal

4. In the past decade, which two East European countries have succumbed to devolutionary pressures.
   a. Bulgaria and Yugoslavia
   b. Poland and Hungary
   c. Czechoslovakia and Yugoslavia
   d. Poland and Czechoslovakia

5. In this South Asian country the Sinhalese majority has been unable to suppress the demands of the Tamil minority for an independent state.
   a. India
   b. Sri Lanka
   c. Indonesia
   d. Bangladesh

6. In the United States the first real brush with devolution may come in which state.
   a. Alaska
   b. Florida
   c. Washington
   d. Hawaii

7. Before the Soviet Union devolved, it was composed of how many Soviet republics.
   a. 10
   b. 15
   c. 20
   d. 25

8. Which of the following Muslim countries is actually a secular state.
   a. Syria
   b. Bulgaria
   c. Turkey
   d. Romania

9. Which of the following is **not** one of the likely candidates to be included as dominating state in a New World order.
   a. Canada
   b. China
   c. India
   d. Europe

10. The so-called *domino theory* first arose during which armed conflict.
    a. Indochina
    b. World War II
    c. Gulf War
    d. Korean War

TRUE-FALSE QUESTIONS

1. State devolution is the reverse of state evolution. (TF)

2. In Italy devolution is caused by economic problems between the north and south. (TF)

3. Devolutionary processes tend to occur in the middle of states. (TF)

4. The removal of the Berlin Wall was a result of the devolution of the former Soviet Union. (TF)

5. The 15 new independent former Soviet republics suffer from centrifugal forces. (TF)

6. The new Russia is a unitary state. (TF)

7. Today, politics are being conducted on a global scale making state boundaries less important. (TF)

8. In some countries, religious fundamentalism appeals to people where prospects for democracy are dim or oppression seems inescapable. (TF)

9. The ability of small countries to acquire nuclear weapons poses a serious danger to the whole world. (TF)

10. A New World Order will probably be established very early in the twenty-first century. (TF)

STUDY QUESTIONS

1. Explain the devolution process. Does culture always play a role in this process? How have devolutionary factors affected particular European countries? Name the countries and list the factors involved.

2. List the factors involved in the break-up of Yugoslavia. Why was this such a tragic and complicated situation? Has it been resolved?

3. Spatially, where does devolution usually occur? Why? Where does the United States have devolution forces at work today?

4. Explain the devolution of the former Soviet Union. What devolutionary factors are now being faced in the newly independent republics?

5. How is the position of the state changing in today's world? Are we heading for a New World Order? What are the options this new world order might take?

STUDY GUIDE ANSWER SECTION

CH#	MULTIPLE-CHOICE	TRUE/FALSE
1.	1c, 2c, 3a, 4a, 5a, 6c, 7d, 8c, 9a, 10b,	1T, 2F, 3F, 4T, 5F, 6F, 7T, 8F, 9F, 10F
2.	1b, 2c, 3a, 4c, 5c, 6b, 7b, 8c, 9b, 10c	1F, 2F, 3F, 4F, 5F, 6F, 7F, 8F, 9T, 10F
3.	1b, 2c, 3d, 4b, 5c, 5a, 7c, 8c, 9d, 10b	1T, 2F, 3T, 4F, 5T, 6F, 7T, 8F, 9T, 10F
4.	1c, 2c, 3d, 4a, 5d, 6a, 7d, 8b, 9a, 10b	1F, 2T, 3T, 4F, 5T, 6T, 7T, 8T, 9T, 10F
5.	1b, 2a, 3b, 4c, 5c, 6b, 7b, 8d, 9b, 10b	1T, 2T, 3T, 4F, 5F, 6T, 7T, 8F, 9F, 10F
6.	1c, 2a, 3b, 4c, 5c, 6b, 7b, 8d, 9b, 10b	1T, 2T, 3T, 4F, 5F, 6T, 7T, 8F, 9F, 10F
7.	1c, 2c, 3d, 4b, 5a, 6c, 7d, 8a, 9b, 10c	1F, 2F, 3T, 4F, 5T, 6F, 7F, 8F, 9T, 10F
8.	1c, 2a, 3b, 4c, 5c, 6b, 7a, 8d, 9a, 10b	1F, 2F, 3F, 4F, 5F, 6T, 7T, 8T, 9F, 10F
9.	1c, 2c, 3d, 4a, 5b, 6c, 7d, 8b, 9a, 10c	1T, 2F, 3F, 4T, 5T, 6F, 7T, 8F, 9T, 10T
10.	1a, 2b, 3a, 4b, 5c, 6d, 7d, 8a, 9c, 10c	1T, 2F, 3T, 4T, 5T, 6F, 7F, 8T, 9T, 10T
11.	1b, 2c, 3d, 4a, 5c, 6b, 7a, 8d, 9c, 10b	1T, 2F, 3T, 4T, 5T, 6F, 7F, 8T, 9F, 19F
12.	1d, 2a, 3c, 4b, 5d, 6b, 7a, 8c, 9c, 10a	1F, 2T, 3F, 4T, 5F, 6T, 7T, 8T, 9T, 10T
13.	1c, 2d, 3b, 4c, 5a, 6b, 7d, 8c, 9a, 10b	1F, 2T, 3F, 4F, 5T, 6T, 7T, 8T, 9F, 10T
14.	1c, 2c, 3b, 4d, 5b, 6c, 7a, 8d, 9b, 10b	1F, 2F, 3T, 4T, 5F, 6T, 7F, 8T, 9F, 10T
15.	1a, 2c, 3d, 4d, 5a, 6c, 7b, 8c, 9a, 10b	1F, 2F, 3T, 4T, 5T, 6T, 7F, 8F, 9T, 10T
16.	1b, 2c, 3b, 4c, 5d, 6c, 7c, 8b, 9c, 10c	1T, 2F, 3F, 4F, 5T, 6T, 7F, 8F, 9T, 10F
17.	1a, 2b, 3d, 4b, 5c, 6a, 7d, 8b, 9a, 10c	1F, 2T, 3F, 4T, 5F, 6T, 7F, 8F, 9T, 10F
18.	1c, 2b, 3d, 4a, 5c, 6d, 7a, 8b, 9a, 10c	1T, 2T, 3T, 4F, 5F, 6T, 7F, 8F, 9T, 10T
19.	1b, 2c, 3d, 4a, 5b, 6c, 7d, 8a, 9b, 10c	1T, 2F, 3F, 4F, 5T, 6F, 7F, 8T, 9T, 10T
20.	1a, 2c, 3b, 4c, 5c, 6b, 7d, 8c, 9a, 10b	1T, 2T, 3F, 4F, 5T, 6T, 7T, 8T, 9T, 10T
21.	1c, 2b, 3d, 4c, 5a, 6b, 7c, 8b, 9c, 10a	1T, 2F, 3T, 4T, 5T, 6F, 7F, 8F, 9T, 10T
22.	1a, 2d, 3c, 4b, 5d, 6a, 7c, 8b, 9d, 10a	1F, 2F, 3F, 4T, 5T, 6F, 7T, 8T, 9F, 10F
23.	1b, 2d, 3d, 4a, 5b, 6c, 7a, 8c, 9a, 10b	1F, 2T, 3T, 4F, 5F, 6T, 7F, 8T, 9F, 10T

CH#	MULTIPLE-CHOICE	TRUE/FALSE
24.	1b, 2d, 3c, 4a, 5b, 6c, 7d, 8b, 9a, 10c	1F, 2T, 3T, 4F, 5F, 6T, 7T, 8F, 9T, 10T
25.	1c, 2a, 3d, 4b, 5c, 6a, 7d, 8b, 9c, 10a	1F, 2T, 4T, 4T, 5T, 6F, 7F, 8F, 9T, 19F
26.	1d, 2a, 3c, 4b, 5c, 6a, 7b, 8c, 9d, 10a	1F, 2F, 3T, 4F, 5T, 6T, 7T, 8F, 9T, 10T
27.	1a, 2c, 3b, 4d, 5a, 6c, 7b, 8d, 9a, 10c	1T, 2F, 3T, 4F, 5T, 6T, 7T, 8F, 9F, 10T
28.	1d, 2b, 3c, 4a, 5c, 6d, 7b, 8d, 9c, 10a	1T, 2F, 3T, 4T, 5T, 6T, 7F, 8F, 9T, 10F
29.	1b, 2a, 3d, 4c, 5c, 6b, 7a, 8c, 9a, 10d	1T, 2F, 3T, 4F, 5F, 6F, 7T, 8T, 9T, 10T
30.	1b, 2d, 3c, 4a, 5d, 6b, 7c, 8a, 9d, 10b	1T, 2T, 3F, 4T, 5F, 6T, 7T, 8T, 9T, 10T
31.	1b, 2d, 3c, 4b, 5a, 6d, 7b, 8c, 9c, 10a	1F, 2T, 3F, 4T, 5F, 6T, 7F, 8F, 9T, 10T
32.	1c, 2b, 3d, 4a, 5c, 6d, 7a, 8b, 9c, 10d	1F, 2T, 3T, 4F, 5F, 6T, 7F, 8T, 9T, 10F
33.	1c, 2b, 3d, 4a, 5b, 6c, 7d, 8a, 9b, 10c	1T, 2T, 3T, 4T, 5F, 6T, 7F, 8T, 9T, 10F
34.	1b, 2d, 3c, 4b, 5a, 6c, 7d, 8b, 9a, 10c	1F, 2T, 3F, 4F, 5F, 6T, 7T, 8T, 9T, 10F
35	1b, 2d, 3a, 4c, 5b, 6d, 7b, 8c, 9a, 10a	1T, 2T, 3F, 4T, 5T, 6F, 7F, 8T, 9T, 10F

TAKE NOTE!

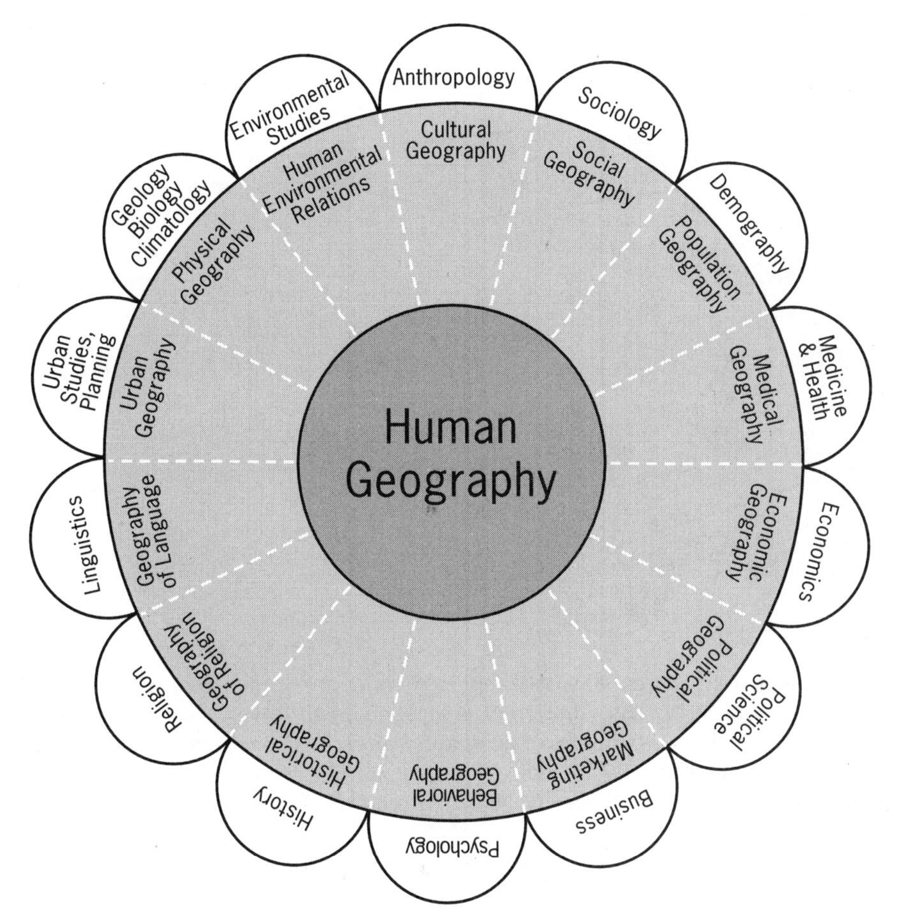

Figure 1-1 Fields of Human Geography. A schematic diagram showing the relationships among the fields of human geography and related fields outside the discipline. *Source: From authors' sketch.*

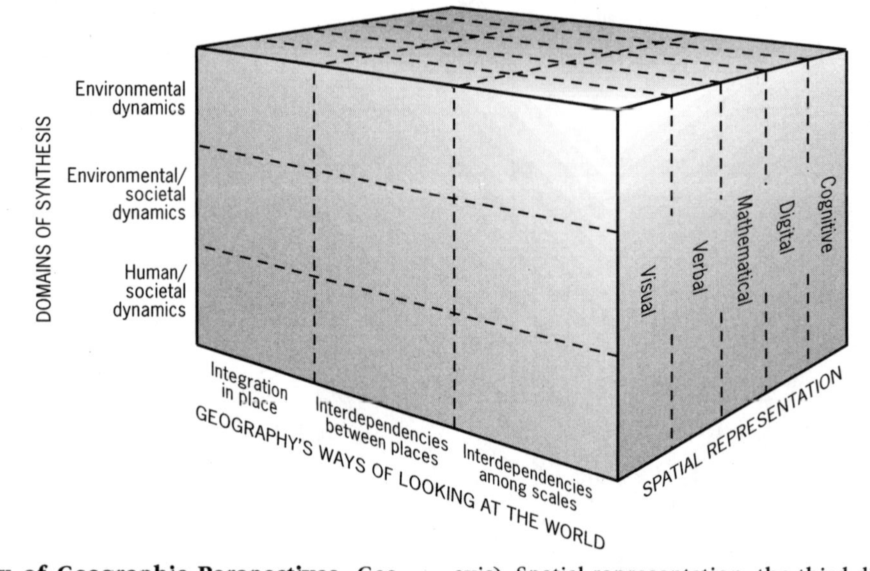

Figure 1-2 Matrix of Geographic Perspectives. Geography's ways of looking at the world—through its focus on place and scale (horizontal axis)—cuts across its three domains of synthesis: human-societal dynamics, environmental dynamics, and environmental-societal dynamics (vertical axis). Spatial representation, the third dimension of the matrix, underpins and sometimes drives research in other branches of geography. *Source: National Research Council, 1997.* Rediscovering Geography: New Relevance for Science and Society. *Washington, D.C.: National Academy Press.*

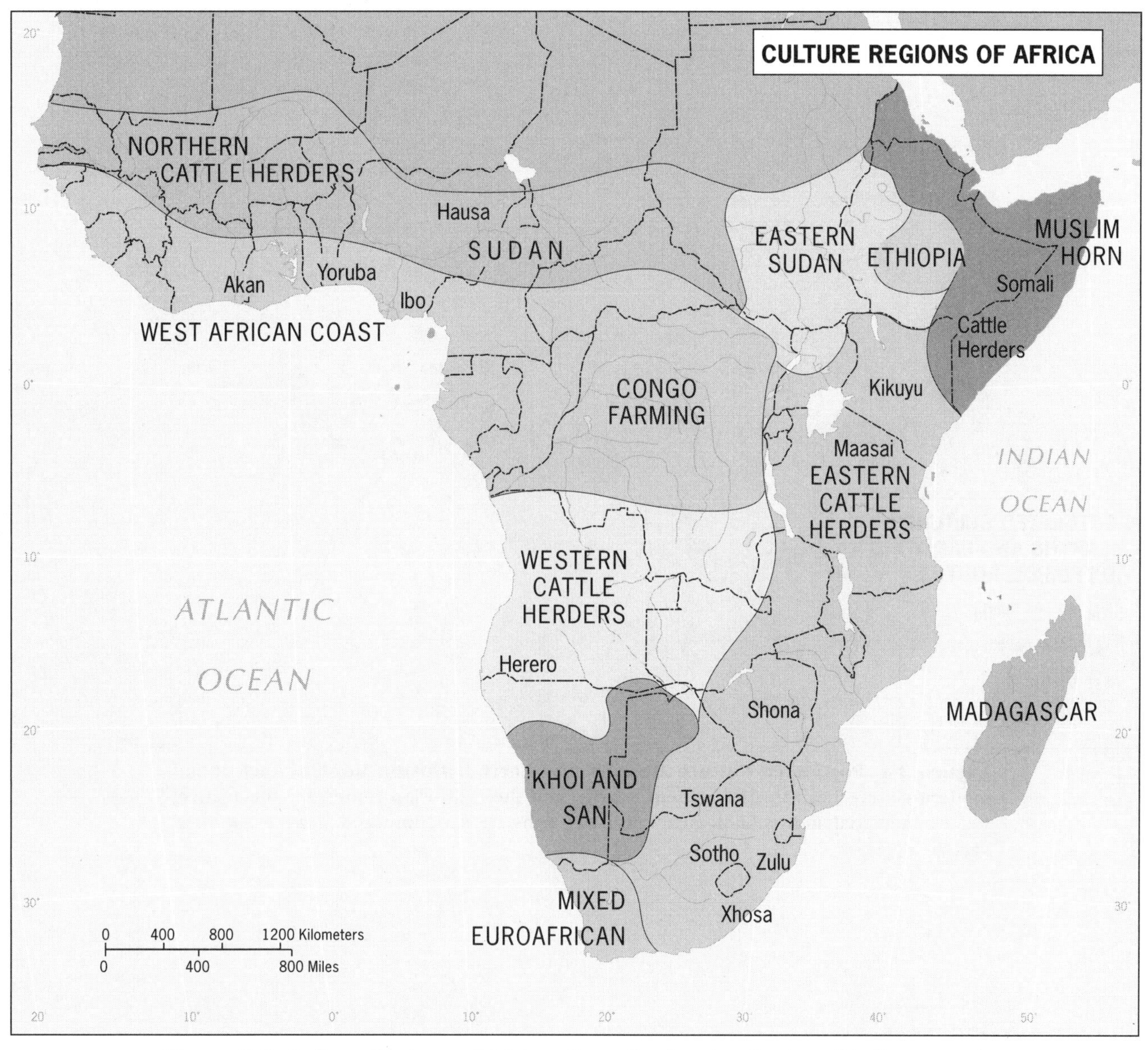

Figure 2-2 Culture Regions of Africa. Generalized regionalization of indigenous cultures in mainland Africa south of the Sahara.

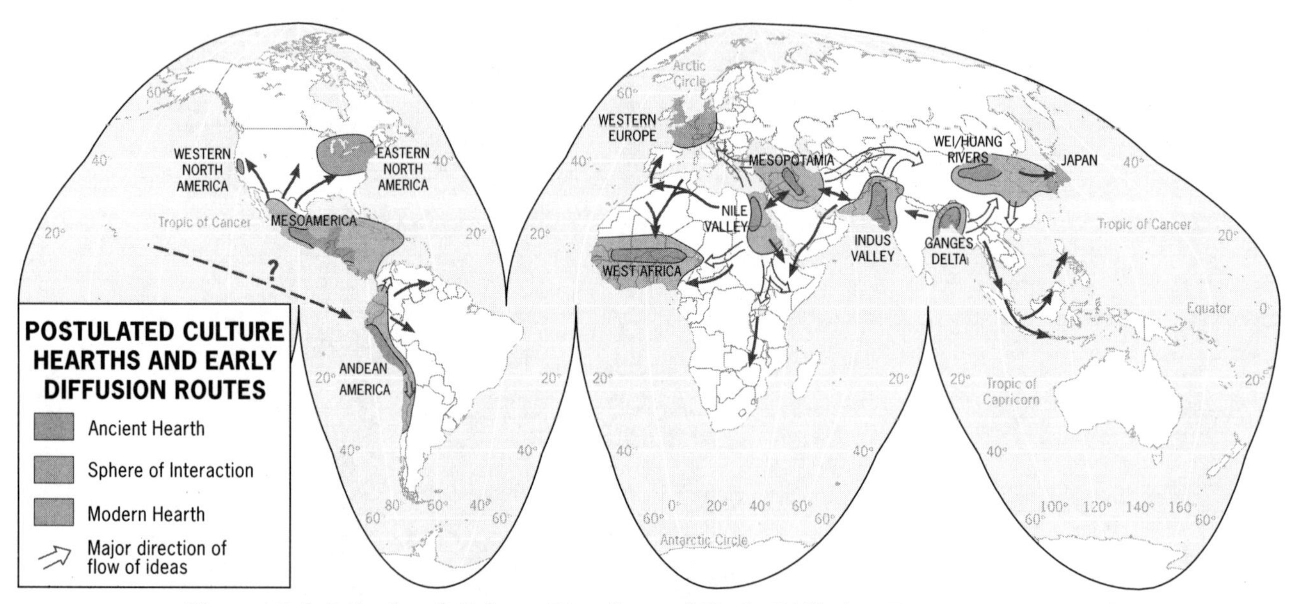

Figure 2-4 Postulated Culture Hearths and Early Diffusion Routes. Ancient and modern culture hearths. The ancient hearths and their diffusion routes are speculative; today's industrial and technological culture hearths are superimposed. *Source: Authors' sketch.*

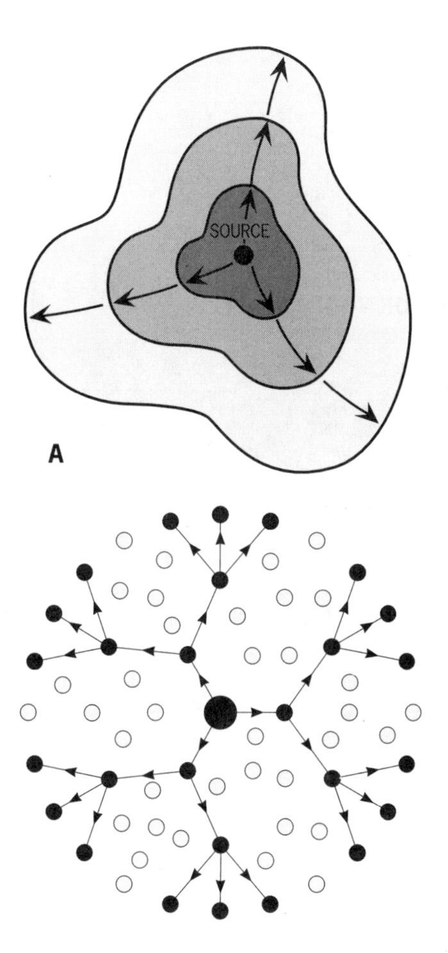

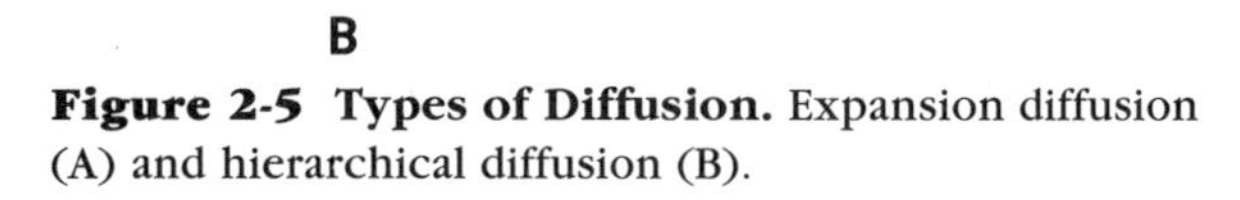

Figure 2-5 Types of Diffusion. Expansion diffusion (A) and hierarchical diffusion (B).

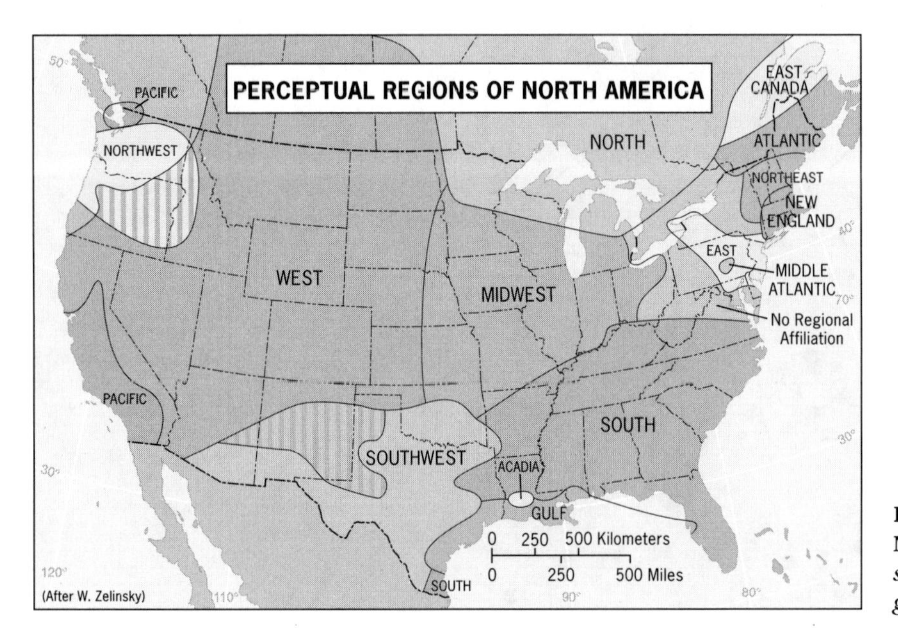

Figure 2-8 Perceptual Regions of North America *Source: From W. Zelinsky, "North America's Vernacular Regions,"* Annals of the AAG, *1980, p. 14.*

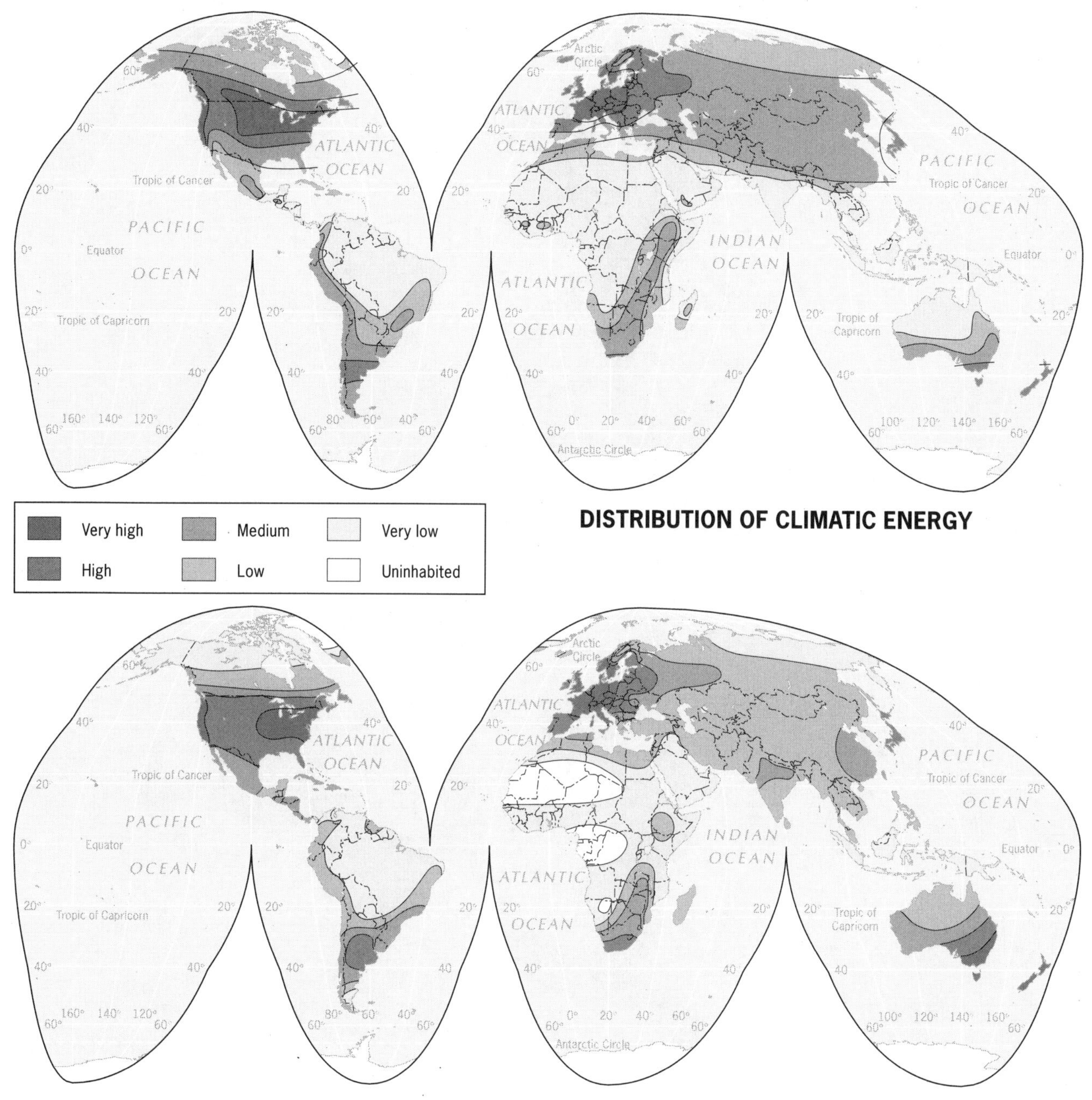

Figure 2-9 Distribution of Climatic Energy and of Civilization. This is how E. Huntington viewed climate and civilization. Below these maps, the author states that they are "based on the opinion of fifty experts in many countries." *Source: E. Huntington,* Principles of Human Geography. *New York: Wiley, 1940, p. 352.*

Figure 3-6 Global Terrain. Despite centuries of technological progress, the influence of terrain as an element of the overall natural environment still is reflected in world population distribution. Mountains and high plateaus do not generally support large or dense population clusters.

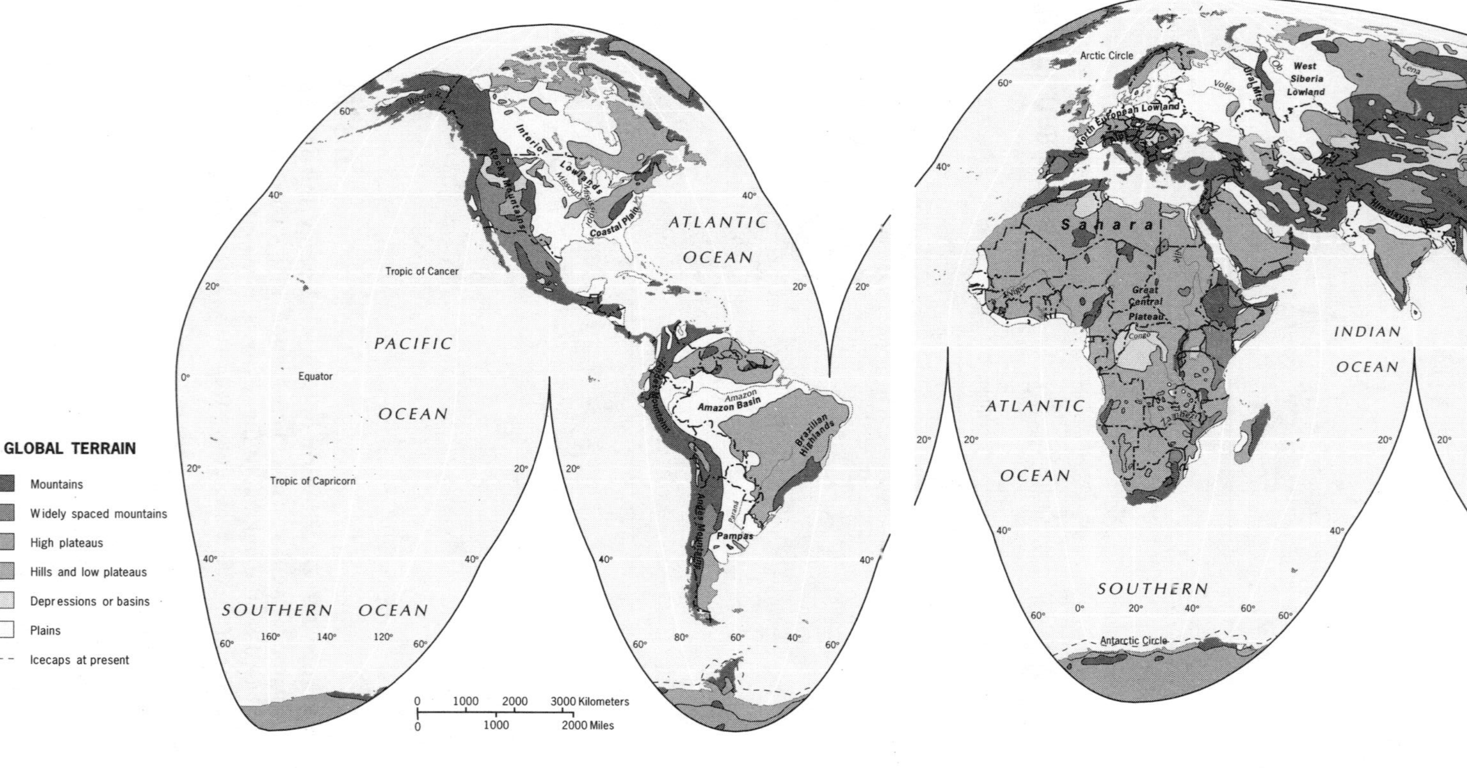

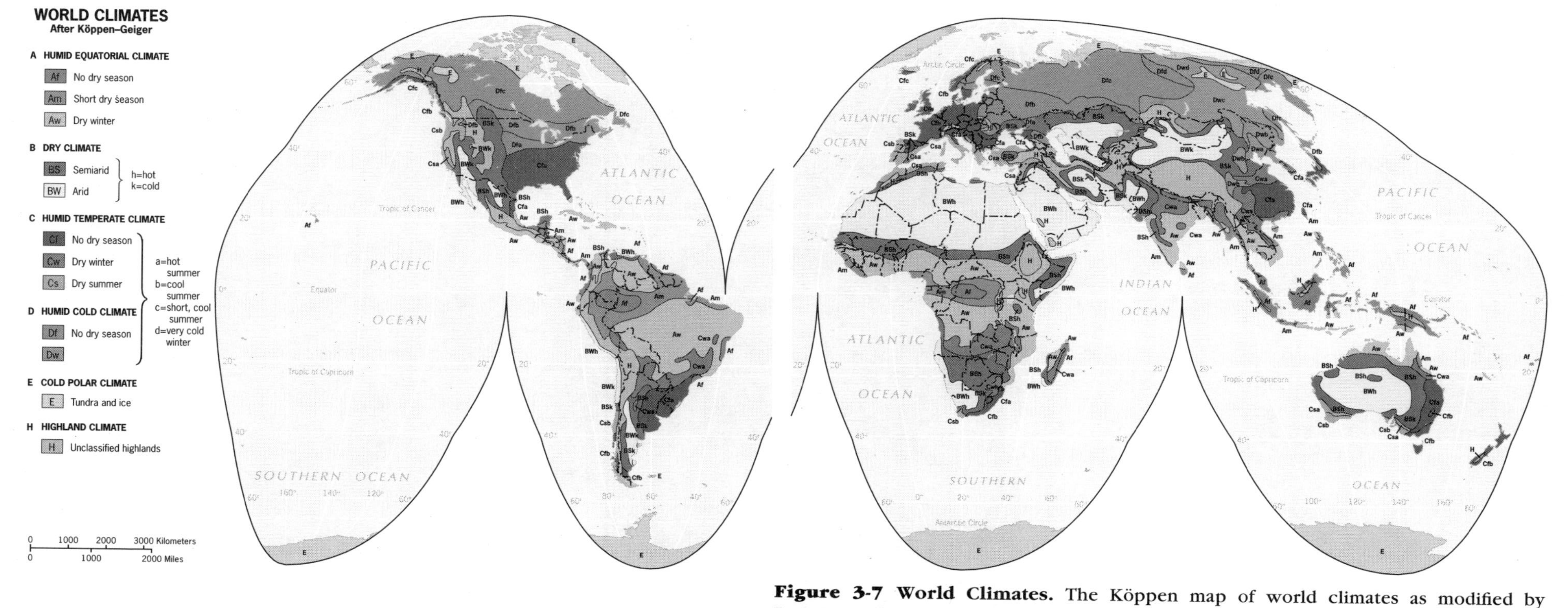

Figure 3-7 World Climates. The Köppen map of world climates as modified by R. Geiger. These, of course, are macroclimatic regions; microclimates are set within these but cannot be shown at this scale.

Table 4-1 Population Densities for Selected Countries, 1998

Country	1995 Population (millions)	Area (thousand sq mi/km)	Arithmetic Density (sq mi/km)	Physiologic Density (sq mi/km)
Egypt	66.2	386.7/1001.6	172/66	8161/3150
Japan	126.5	145.7/377.4	870/335	6788/2620
Netherlands	15.6	15.9/41.2	981/379	4431/1711
Bangladesh	124.6	55.6/144.0	2478/956	3779/1459
Colombia	38.2	439.7/1138.8	87/34	1709/660
India	988.1	1237.1/3204.1	798/308	1491/576
Nigeria	110.3	356.7/923.9	309/119	901/348
Argentina	36.0	1068.3/2766.9	34/14	689/266
United States	269.3	3787.4/9808.4	71/27	367/142

Sources: Calculated from World Population Data Sheet published by the Population Reference Bureau, Inc., from data on agriculture in the Encyclopaedia Britannica *Book of the Year* 1997, and from the United Nations Food and Agriculture Organization (FAO) *Production Yearbook* 1996. Note that population data in this table may not correspond to statistics drawn from other sources. (See "Focus on: Reliability of Population Data.")

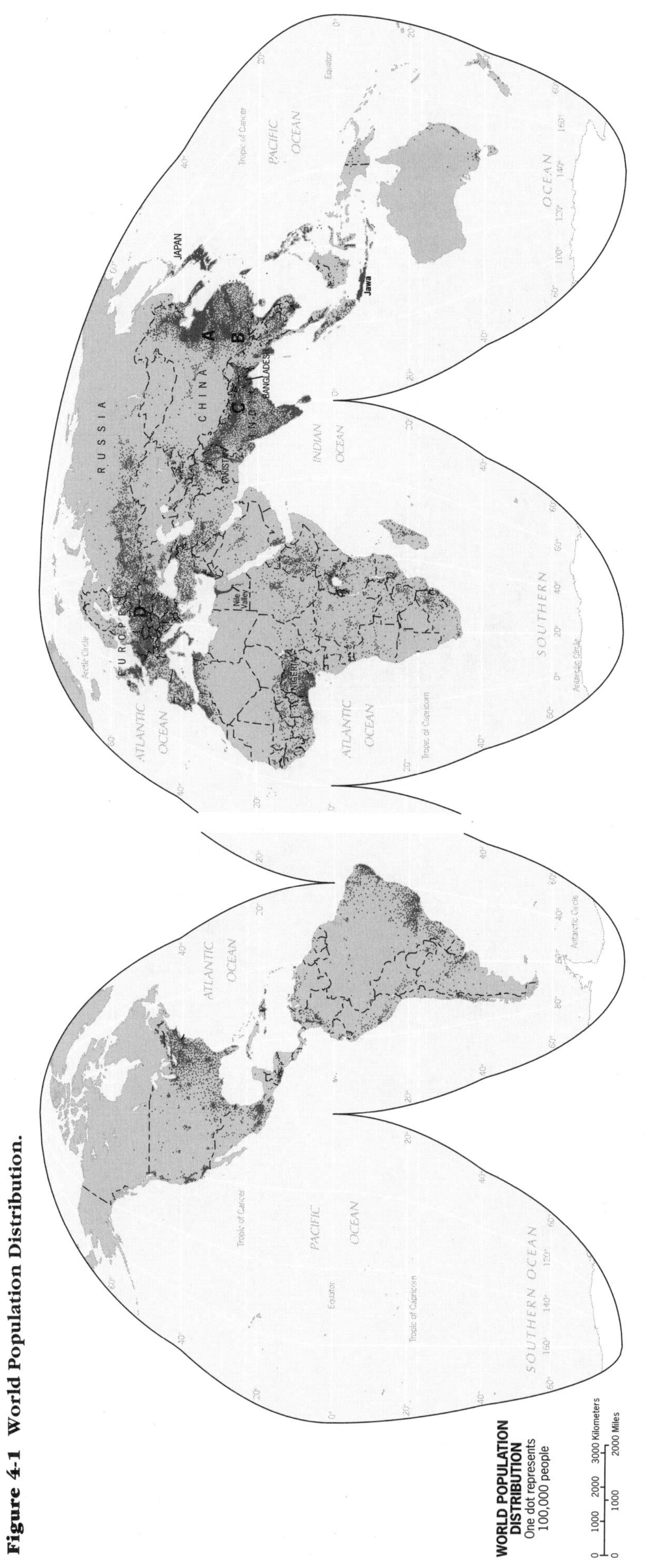

Figure 4-1 World Population Distribution.

Figure 4-2 World Population Density.

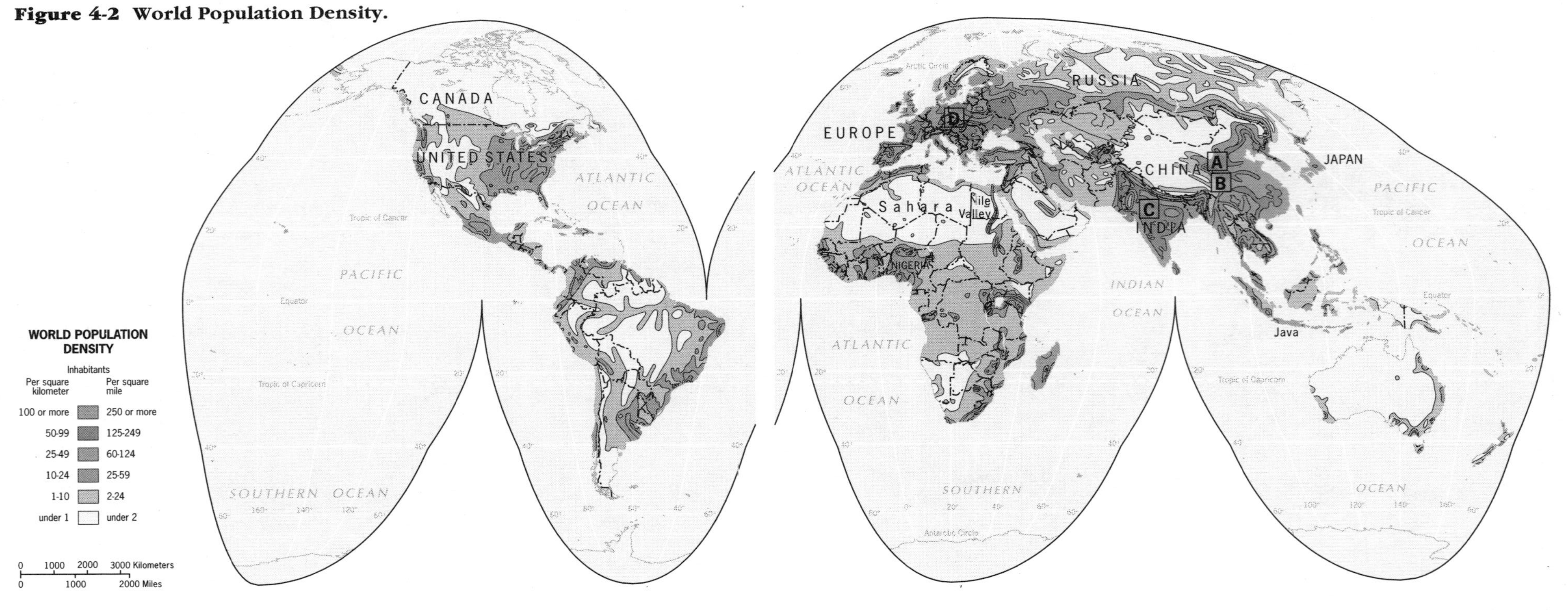

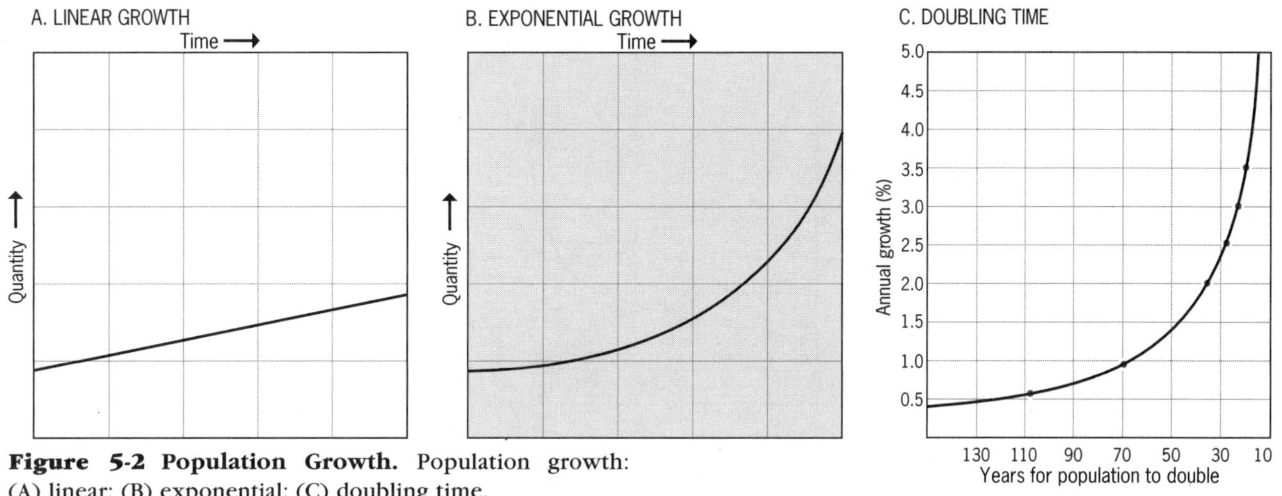

Figure 5-2 Population Growth. Population growth: (A) linear; (B) exponential; (C) doubling time.

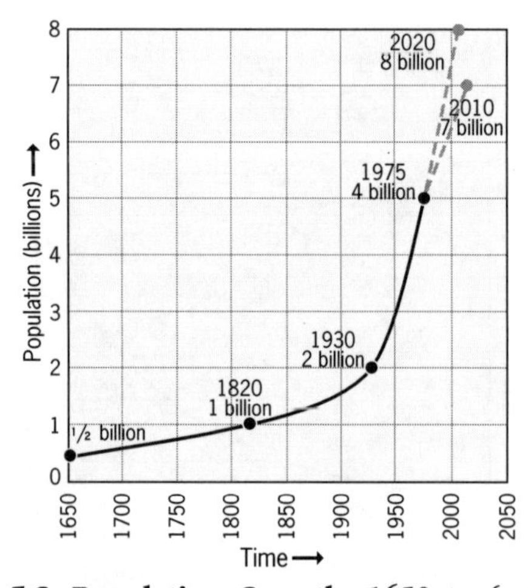

Figure 5-3 Population Growth, 1650 to (estimated) 2020. The dotted lines indicate different scenarios depending on birth rate trends in the coming decades.

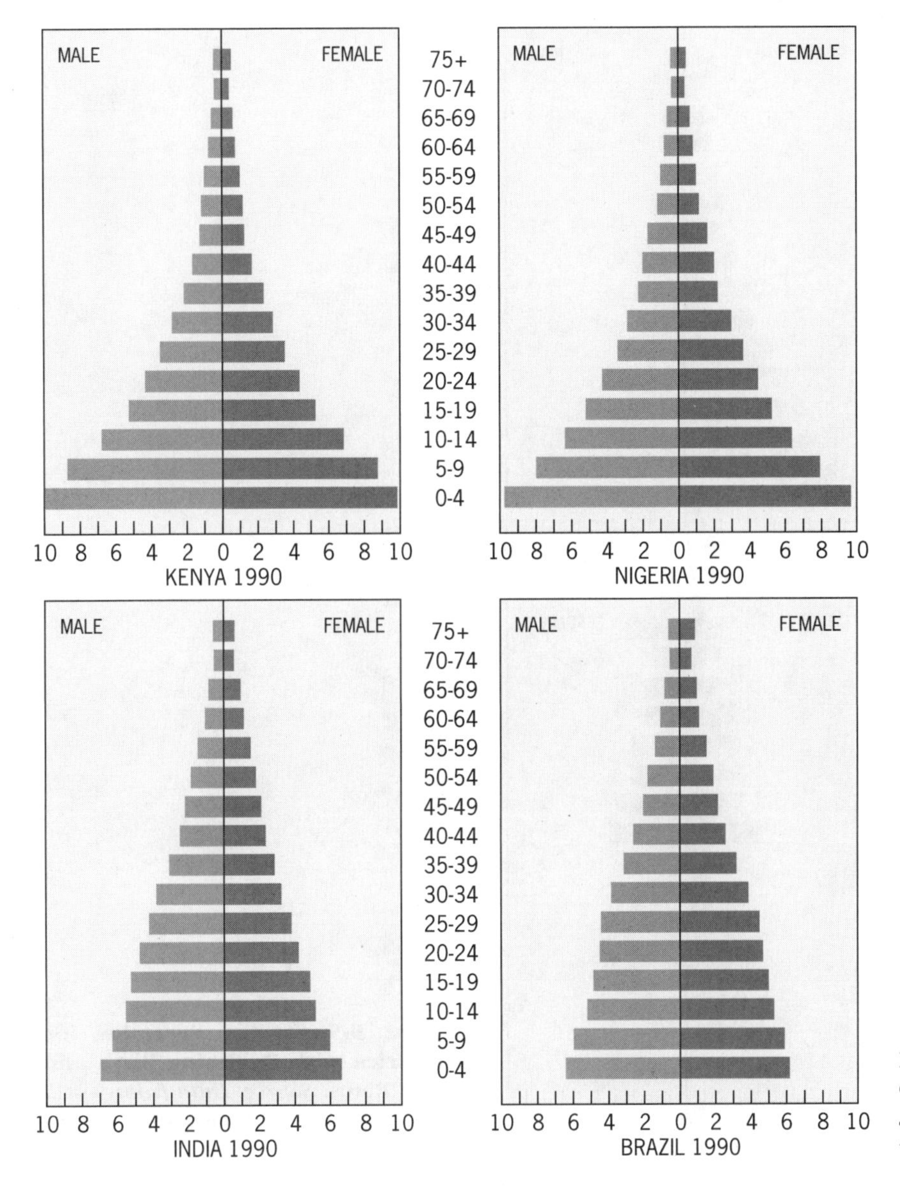

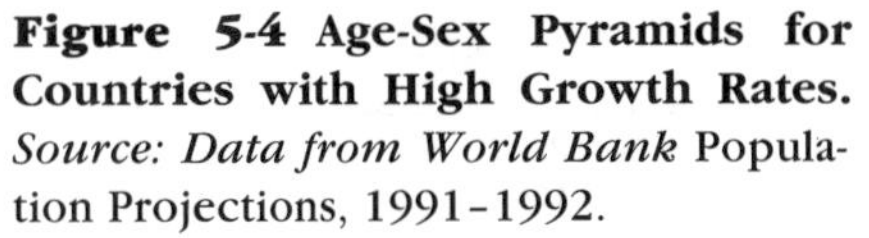
Figure 5-4 Age-Sex Pyramids for Countries with High Growth Rates. *Source: Data from World Bank* Population Projections, 1991–1992.

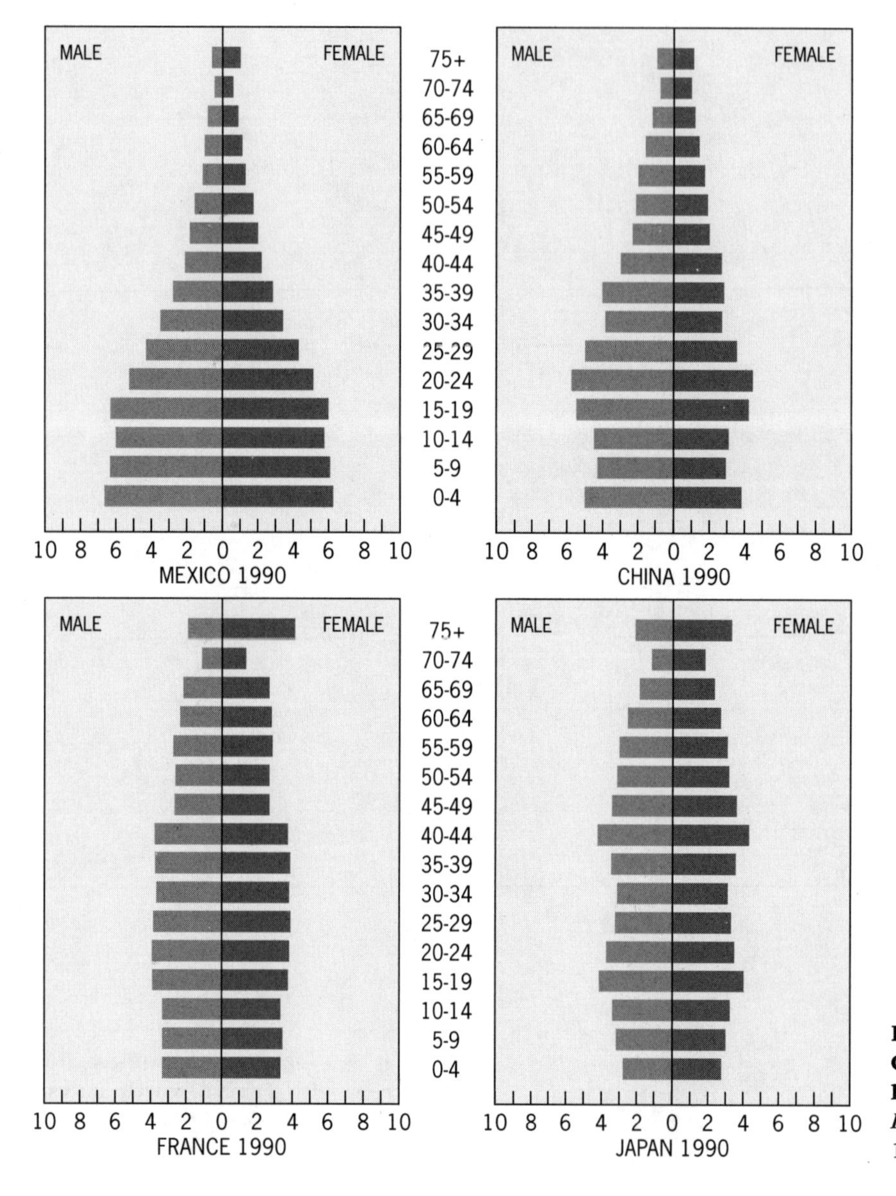

Figure 5-5 Age-Sex Pyramids for Countries with Declining Birth and Death Rates. *Source: Data from World Bank* Population Projections, 1991–1992.

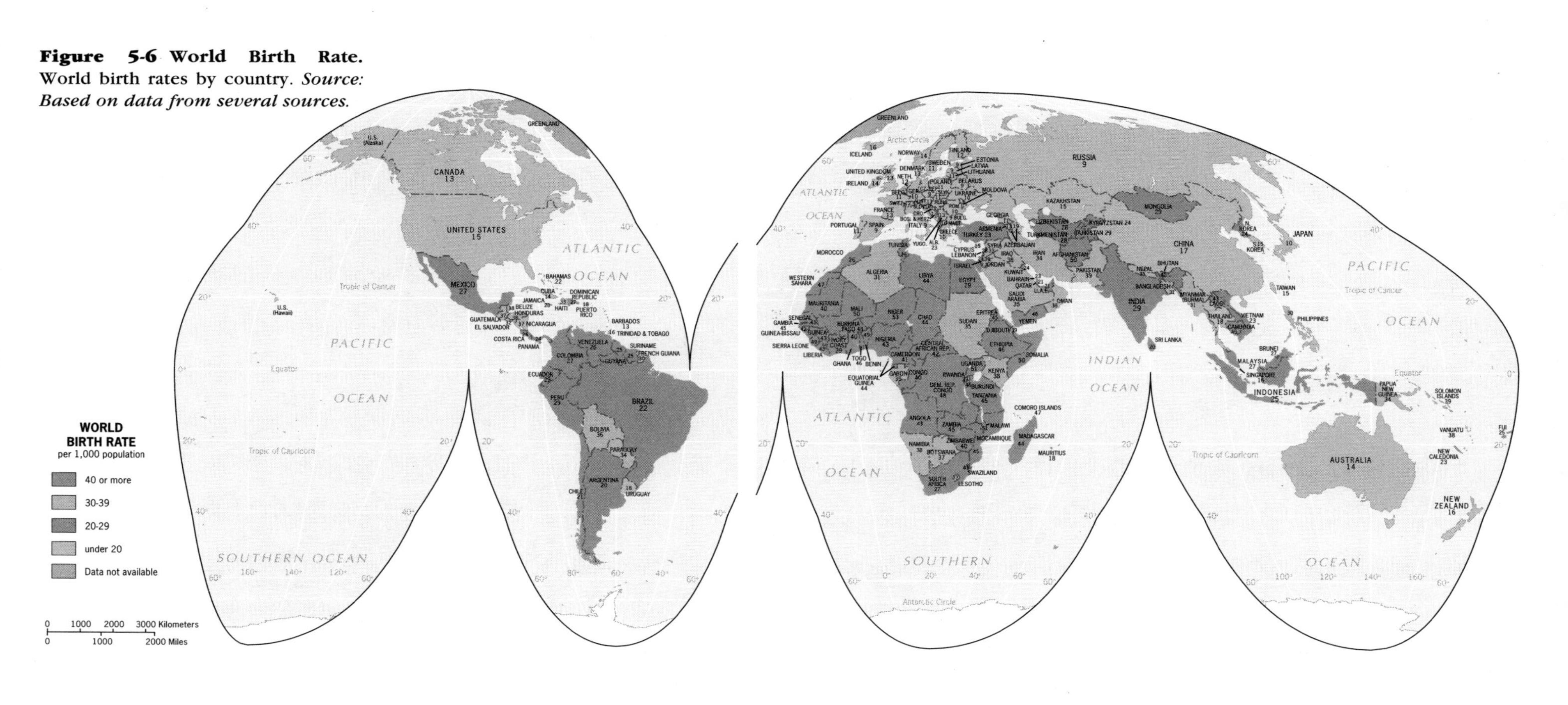

Figure 5-6 World Birth Rate. World birth rates by country. *Source: Based on data from several sources.*

Figure 5-7 World Mortality Rate. World death rates by country. *Source: Based on data from several sources.*

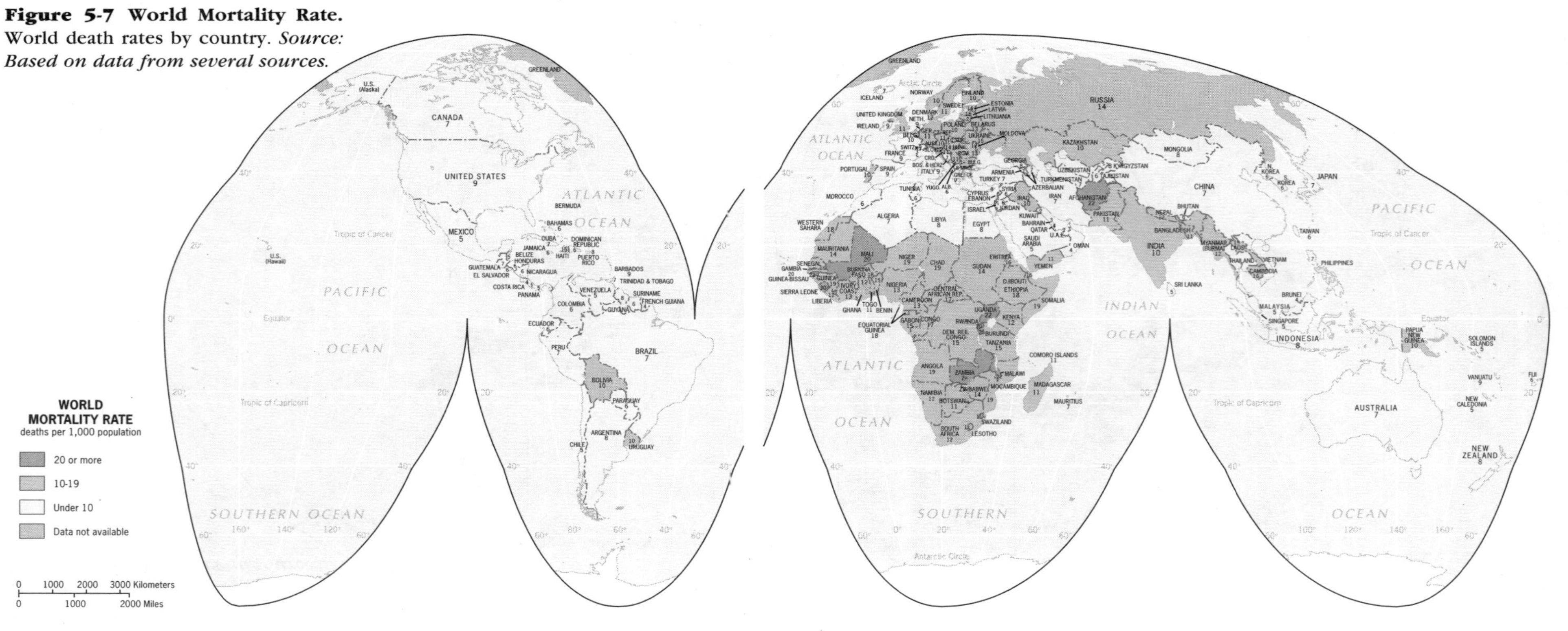

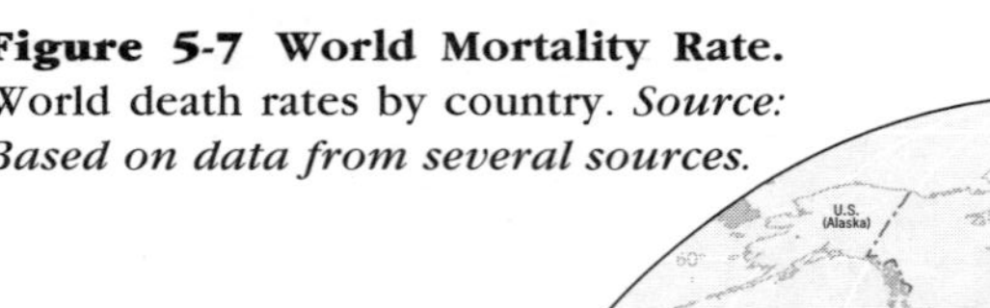

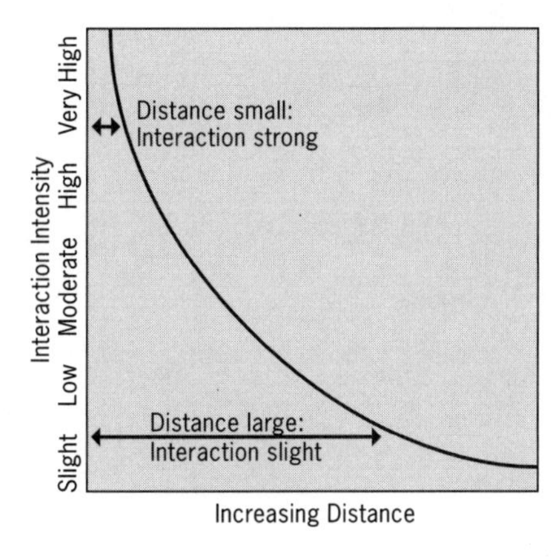

Figure 6-2
Distance Decay.

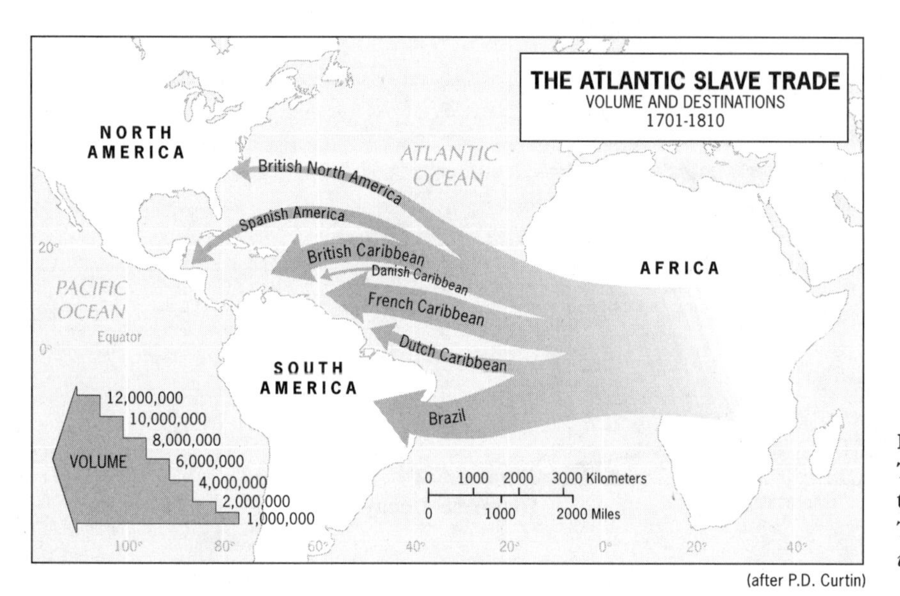

Figure 6-3 The Atlantic Slave Trade. Dimensions of the Atlantic slave trade. *Source: After a map in P. Curtin,* The Atlantic Slave Trade *(Madison: University of Wisconsin Press, 1969), p. 57.*

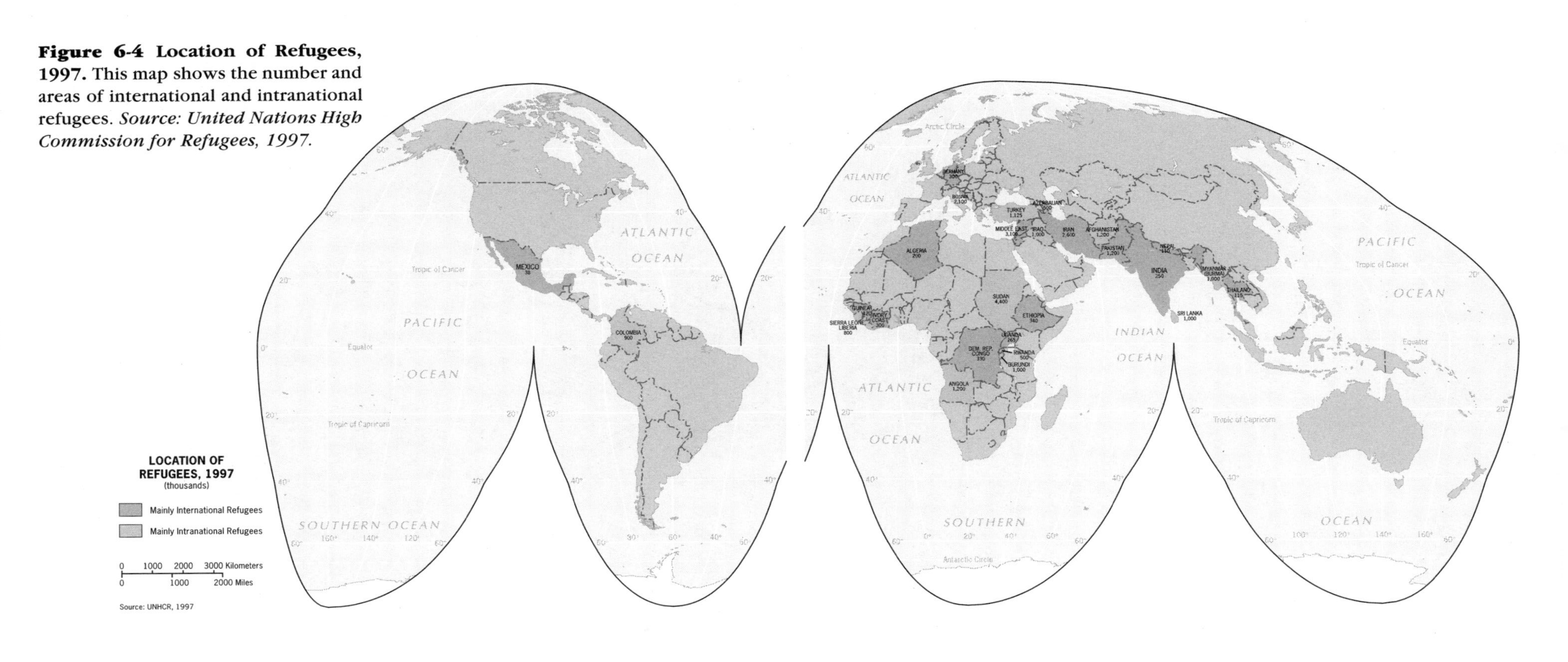

Figure 6-4 Location of Refugees, 1997. This map shows the number and areas of international and intranational refugees. *Source: United Nations High Commission for Refugees, 1997.*

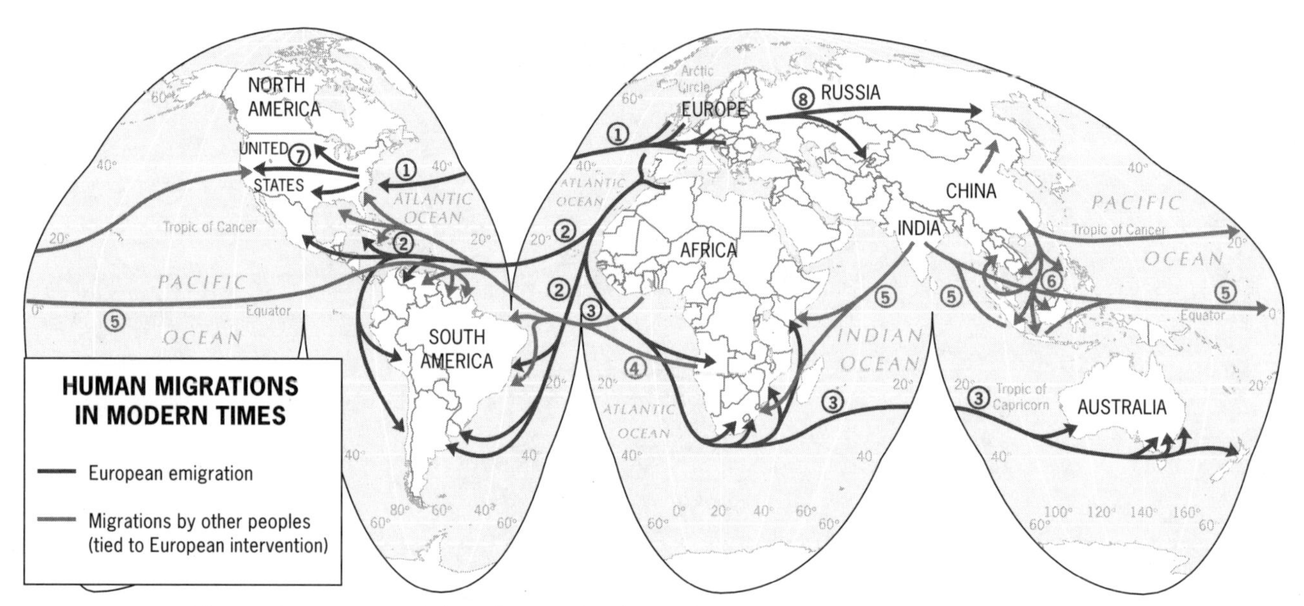

Figure 7-1 Human Migrations in Modern Times. Major routes of migrants.

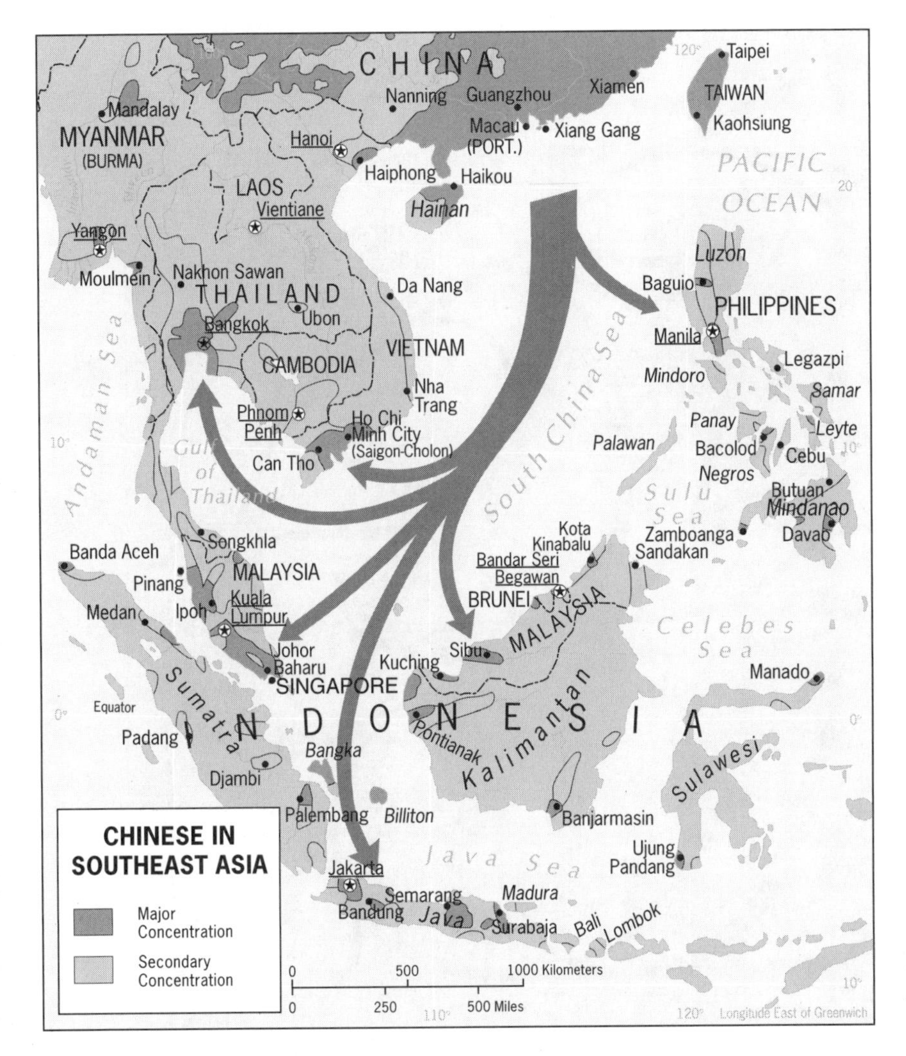

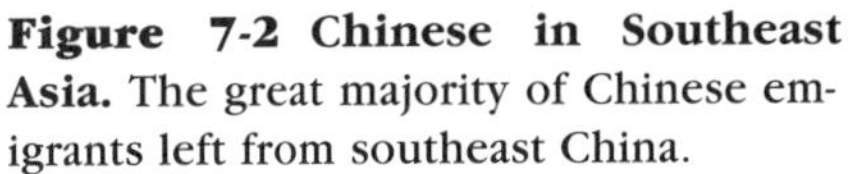
Figure 7-2 Chinese in Southeast Asia. The great majority of Chinese emigrants left from southeast China.

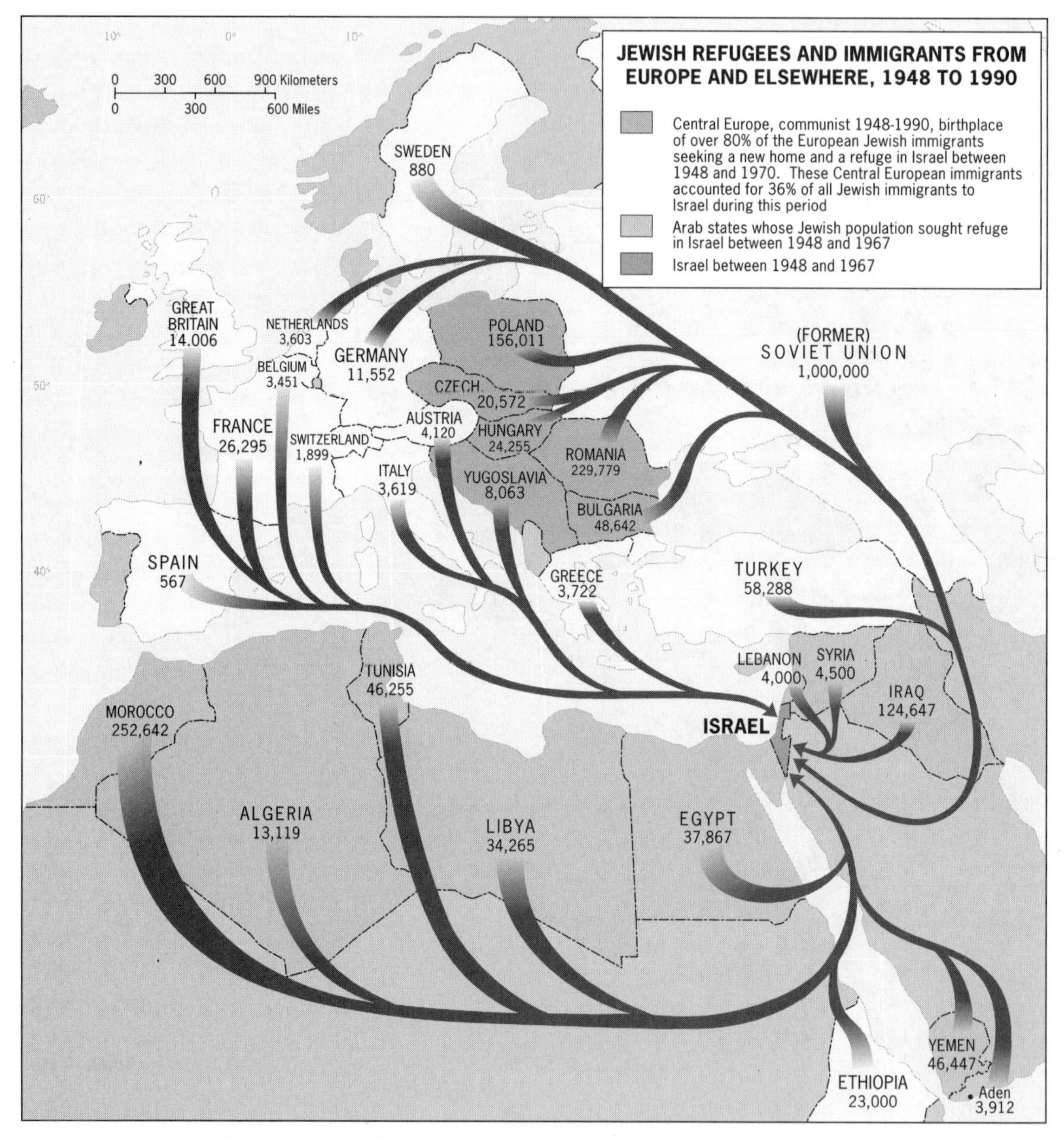

Figure 7-3A Jewish Refugees and Immigrants from Europe and Elsewhere, 1948 to 1990. *Source: From a map in M. Gilbert,* Atlas of the Arab-Israeli Conflict *(New York: Macmillan, 1974), p. 38.*

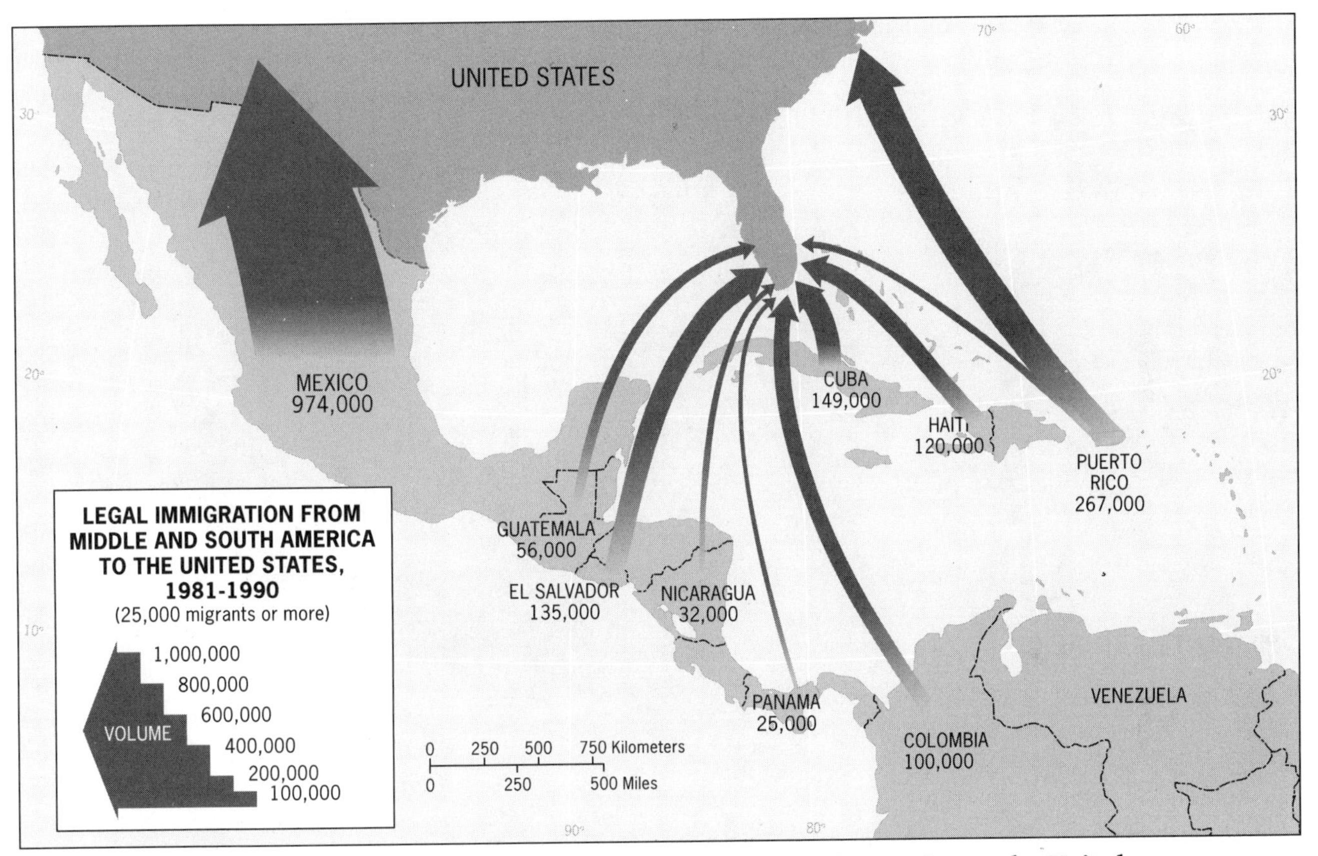

Figure 7-4 Legal Immigration from Middle and South America to the United States, 1981–1990. *Source: Based on data in U.S. Bureau of the Census,* Statistical Abstract of the United States: 1991, *111th ed. (Washington, D.C., 1991), p. 10.*

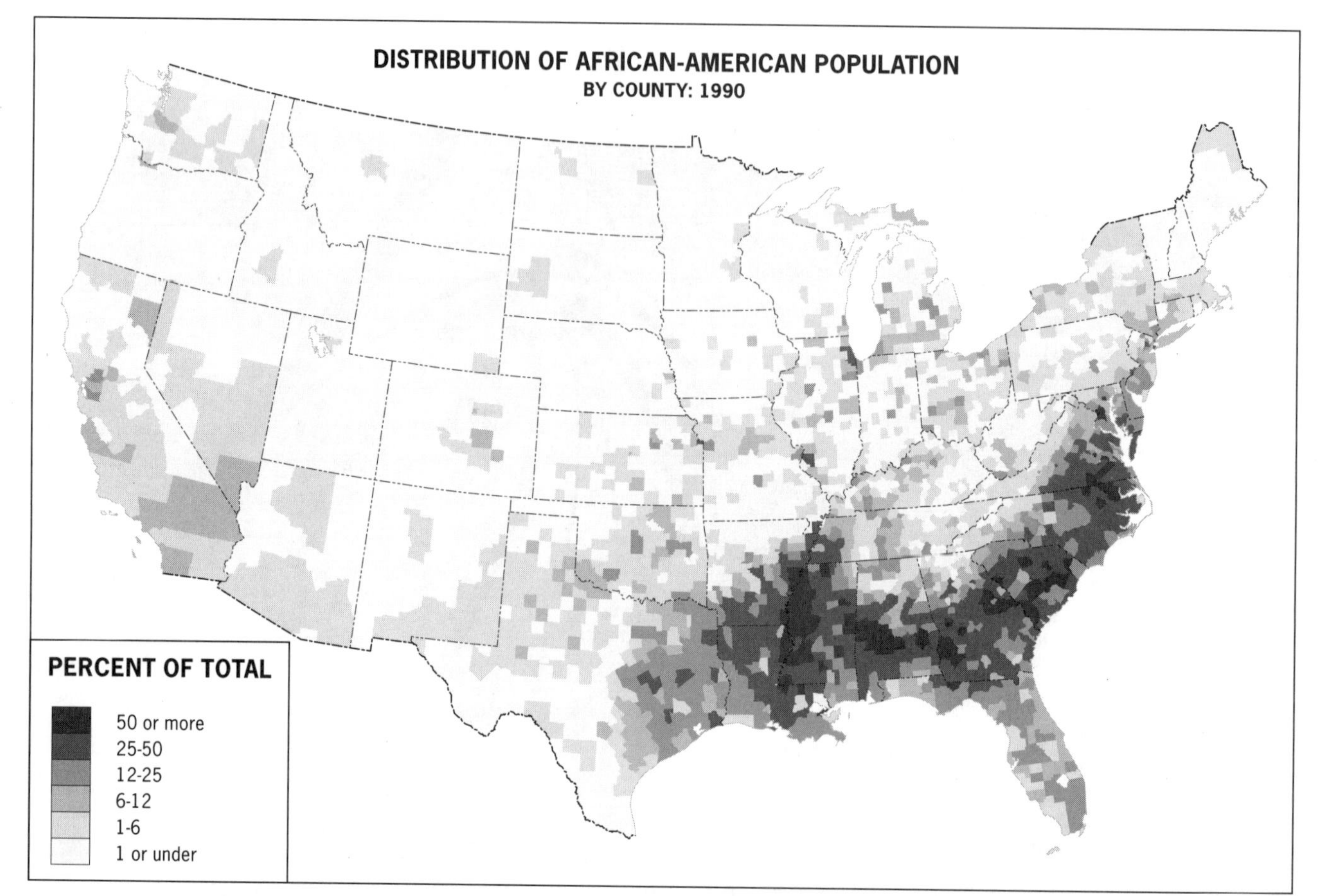

Figure 7-6 Distribution of African-American Population. African-Americans, by count, 1990. *Source: U.S. Department of Commerce, Economics and Statistics Administration, Bureau of the Census.*

Figure 8-2 **Language Families of the World.** Generalized map of the world distribution of language families. *Source: Based on a map prepared by Hammond, Inc., for the first edition, 1977.*

Figure 8-3 Languages of Europe. Generalized map of language-use regions in Europe. *Source: Based on a map in Murphy, A. B. 1998 "European Languages," T. Unwin, ed.,* A European Geography. *London: Longman.*

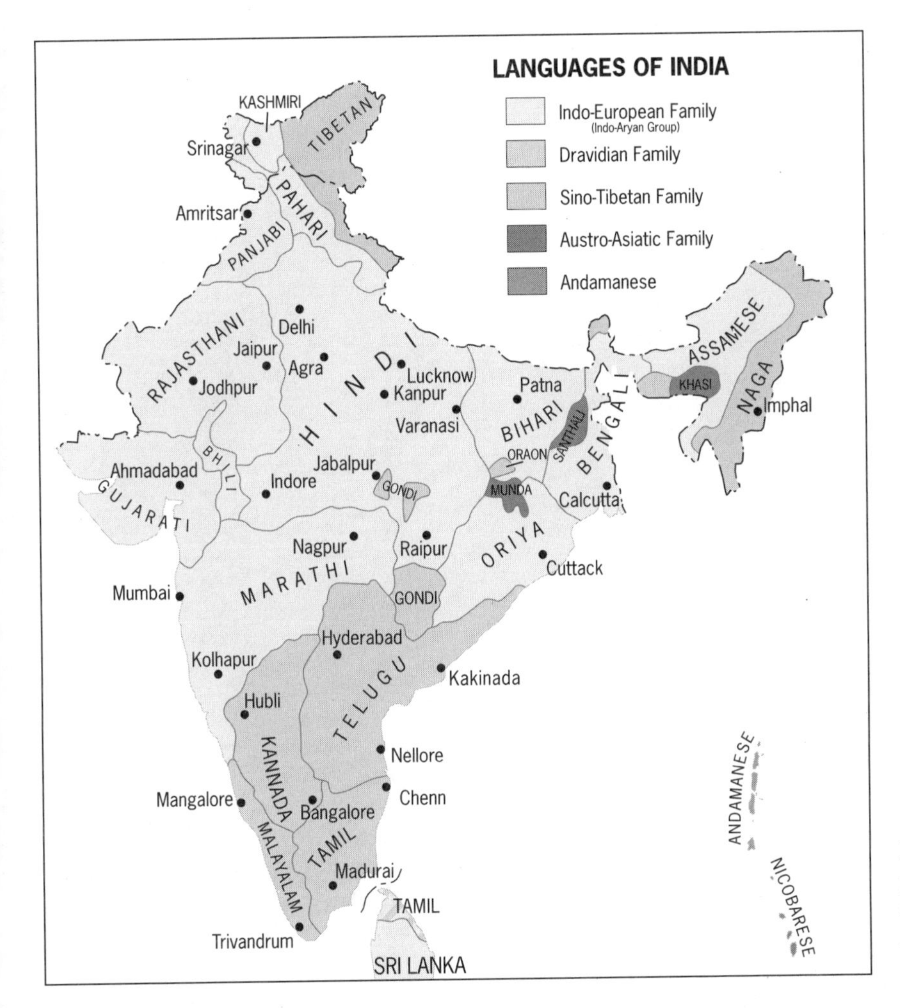

Figure 8-4 Languages of India. Major languages of the Indian subcontinent. *Source: From a map prepared by Hammond, Inc., for the first edition, 1977.*

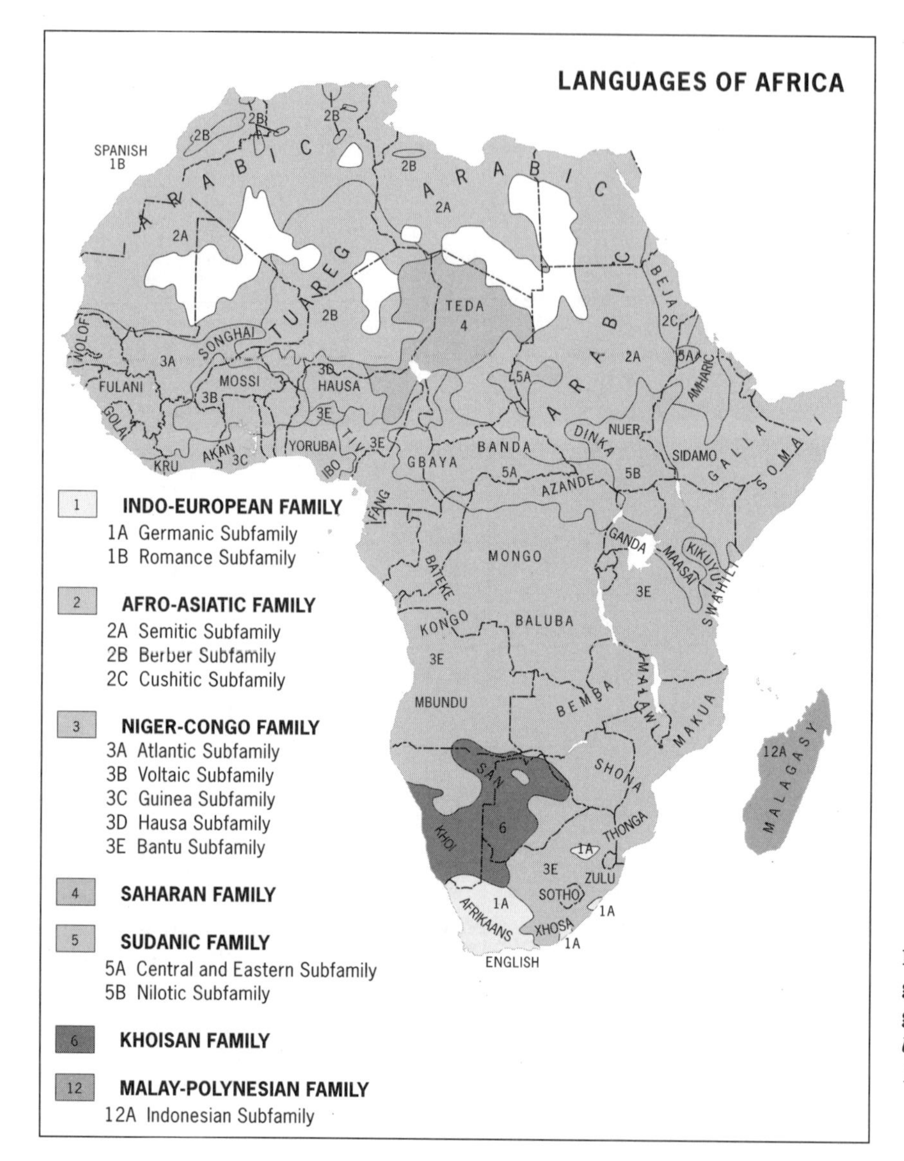

Figure 8-5 Languages of Africa. Regional classification of African languages. *Source: From a map prepared by Hammond, Inc., for the first edition 1977.*

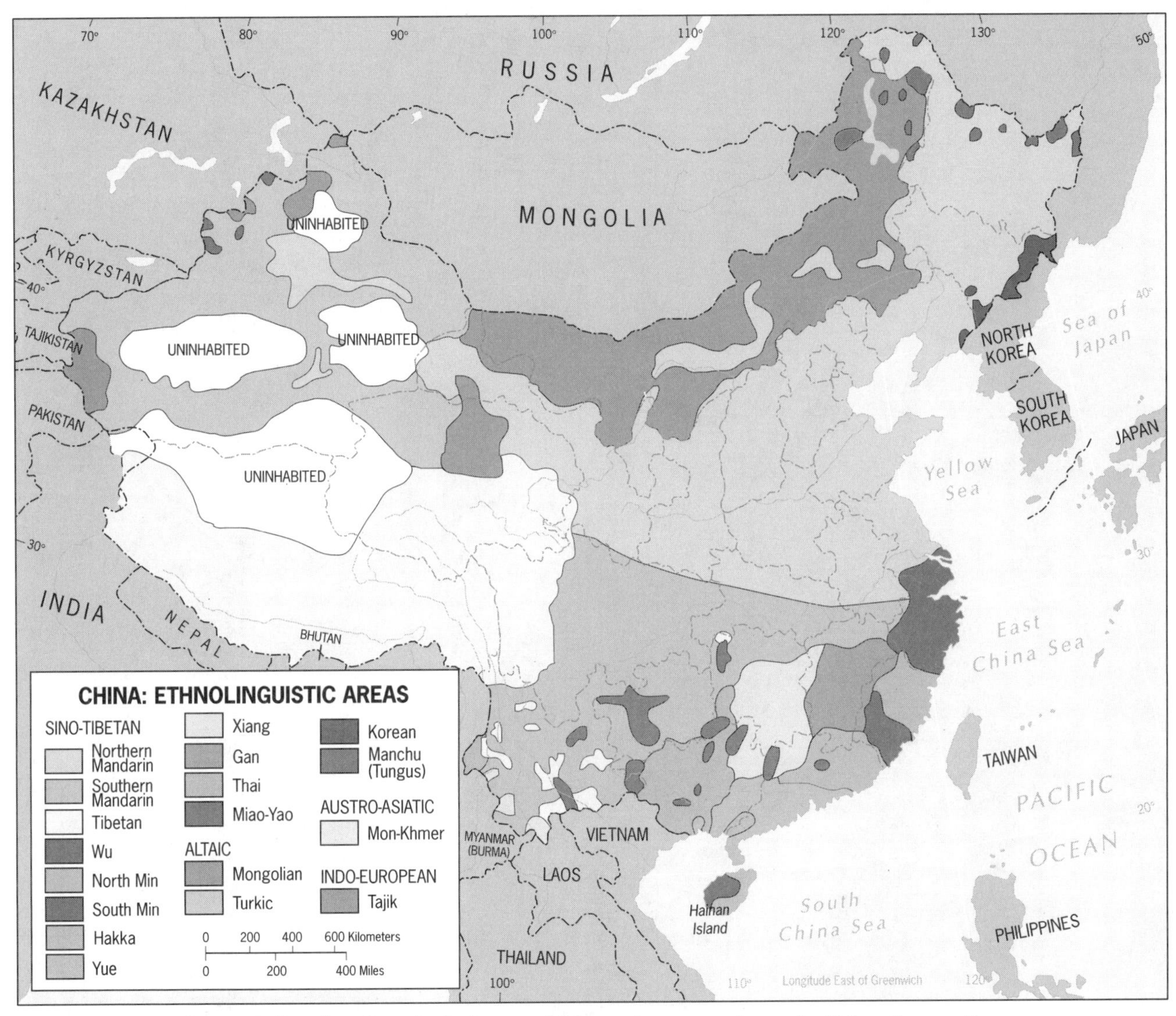

Figure 8-6 Ethnolinguistic Areas of China. Languages in use in China. *Source: From several sources including Academia Sinica, Republic of China Yearbook, and university publications.*

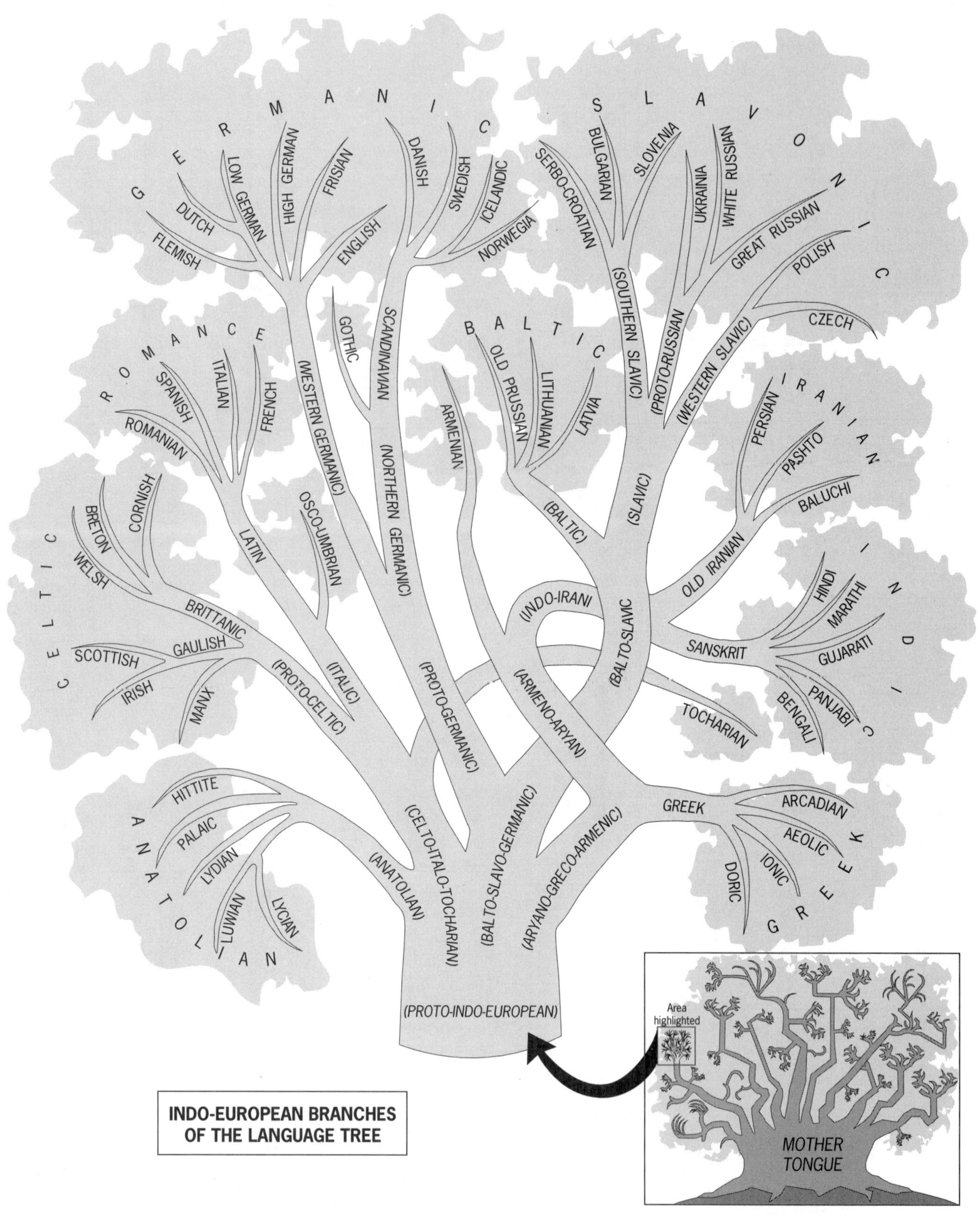

Figure 9-1 Indo-European Branches of the Language Tree. *Source: From T. V. Gamkrelidze and V. V. Ivanov, "The Early History of Indo-European Languages,"* Scientific American, *March 1990, p. 111.*

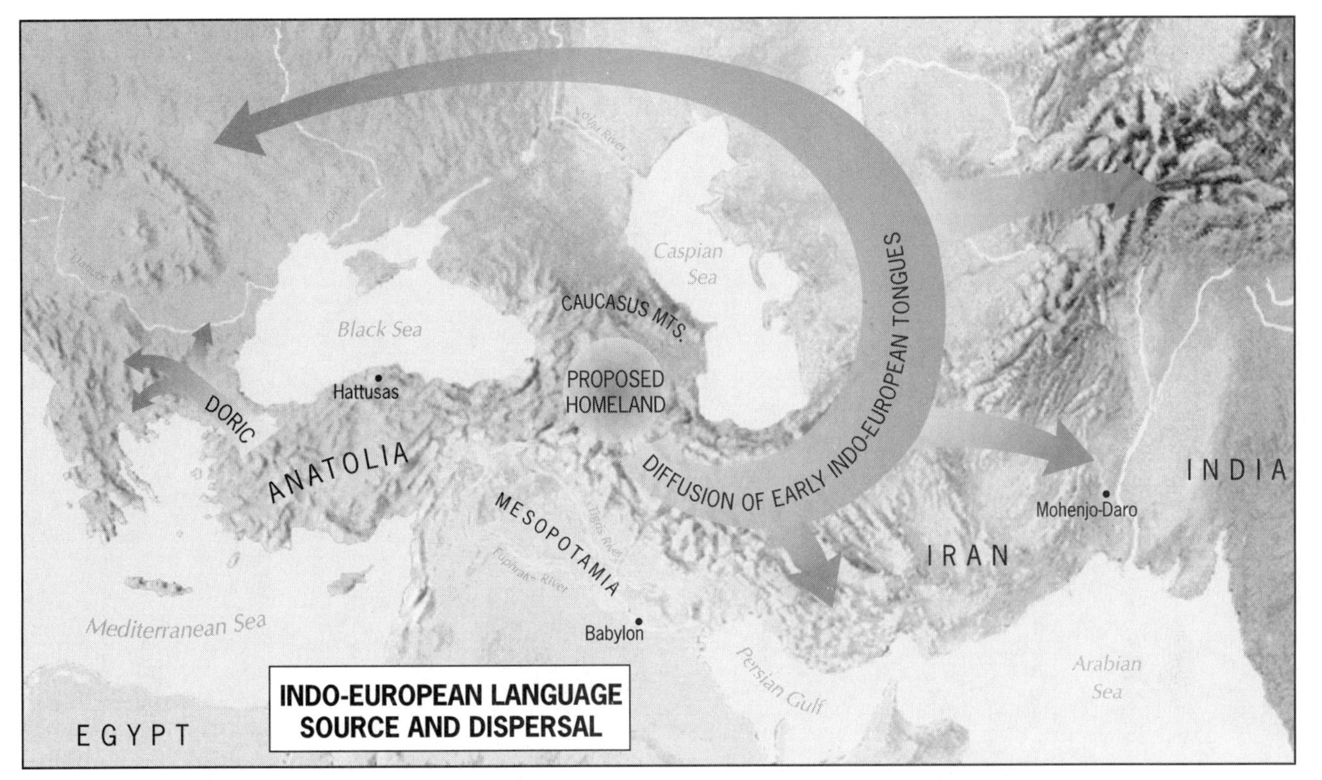

Figure 9-2 Indo-European Language Source and Dispersal. Postulated diffusion of an Indo-European proto-language. *Source: From T. V. Gamkrelidze and V. V. Ivanov,* Scientific American, *March 1990, p. 112.*

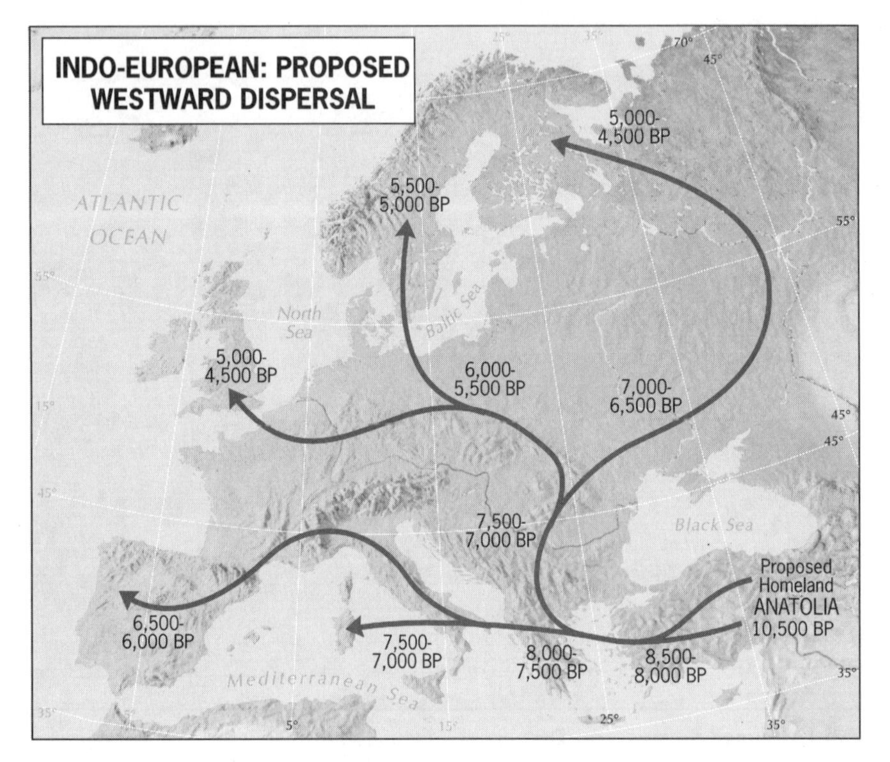

Figure 9-3 Indo-European Proposed Westward Dispersal. The approximate timing of the westward dispersal of the Indo-European languages.

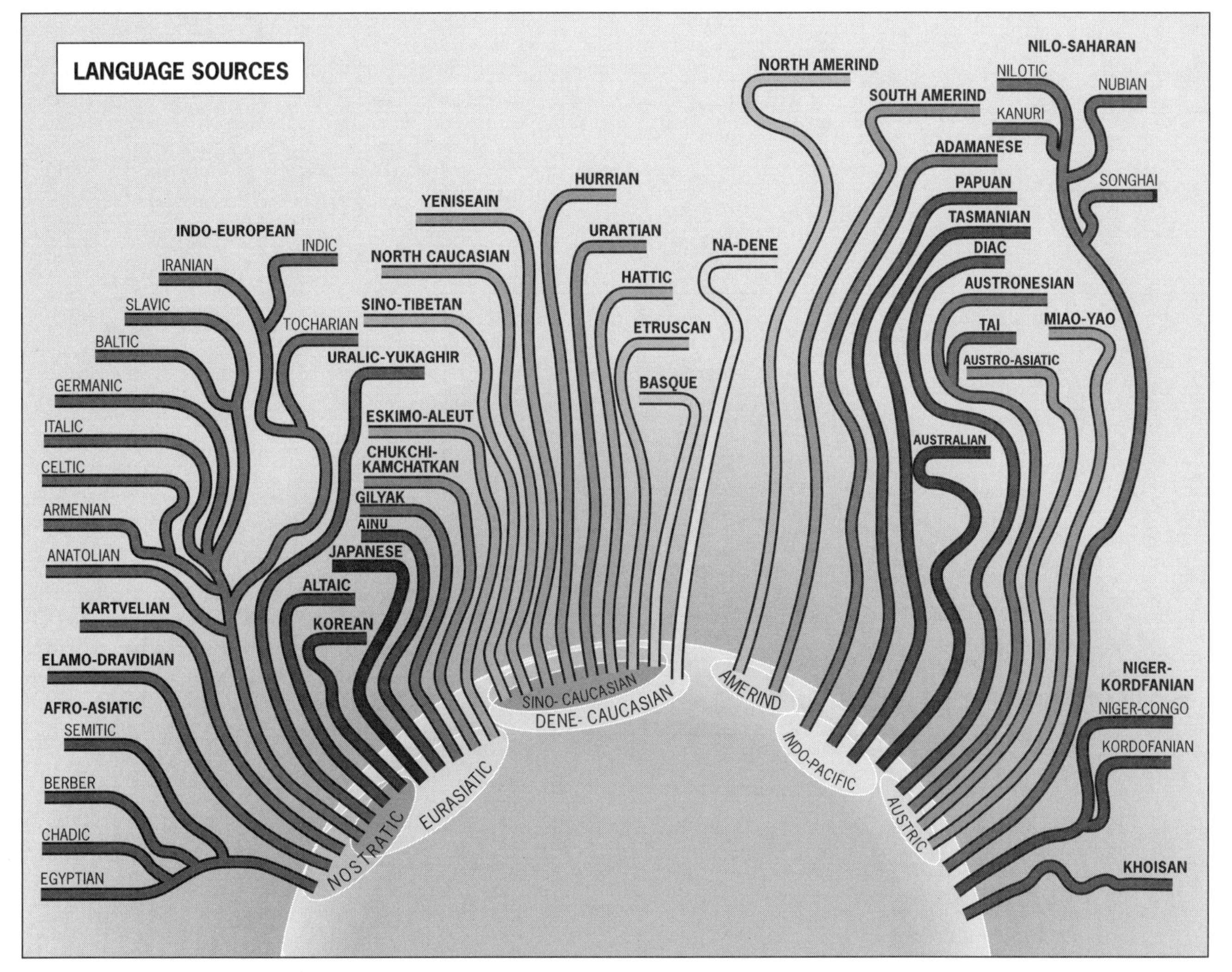

Figure 9-4 Language Sources. *Source: After a diagram in Philip E. Ross, "Hard Words,"* Scientific American, *April 1991, p. 139.*

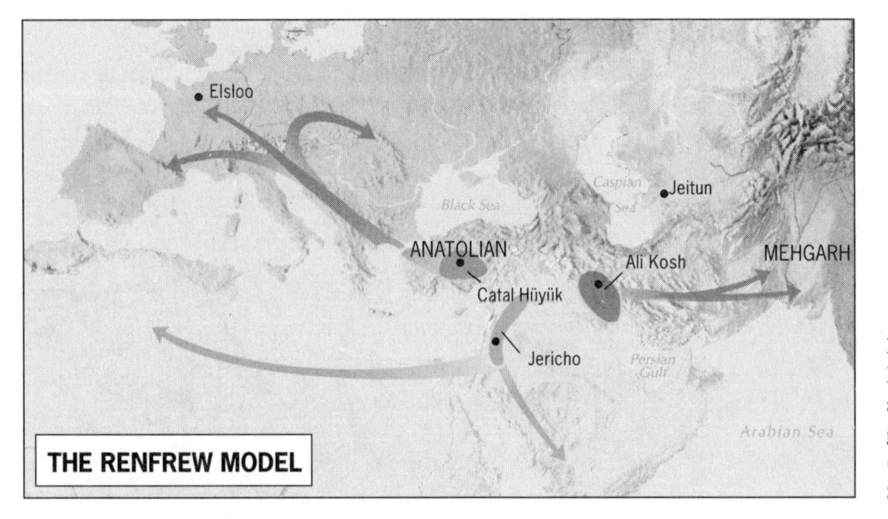

Figure 9-5 The Renfrew Model. The Renfrew Model poses that three source areas of agriculture each gave rise to a great language family. *Source: From "The Origins of Indo-European Languages,"* Scientific American, *1989, p. 114.*

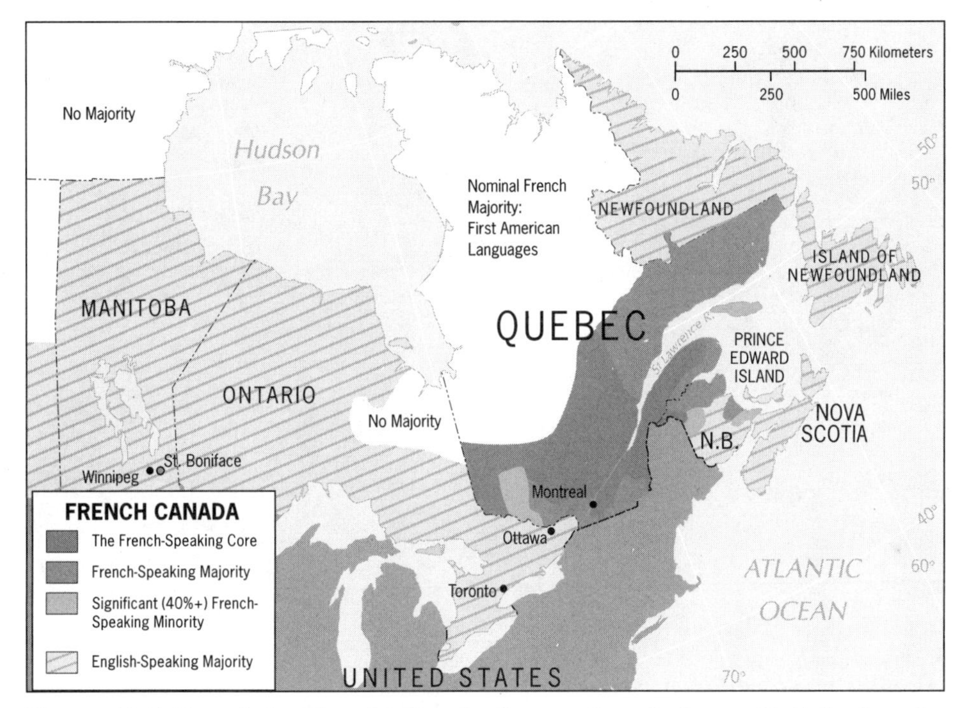

Figure 10-5 French Speakers in Canada. *Sources: Canada Census, Statistics Canada,* The National Atlas of Canada *(1985), and* The Canada Year Book.

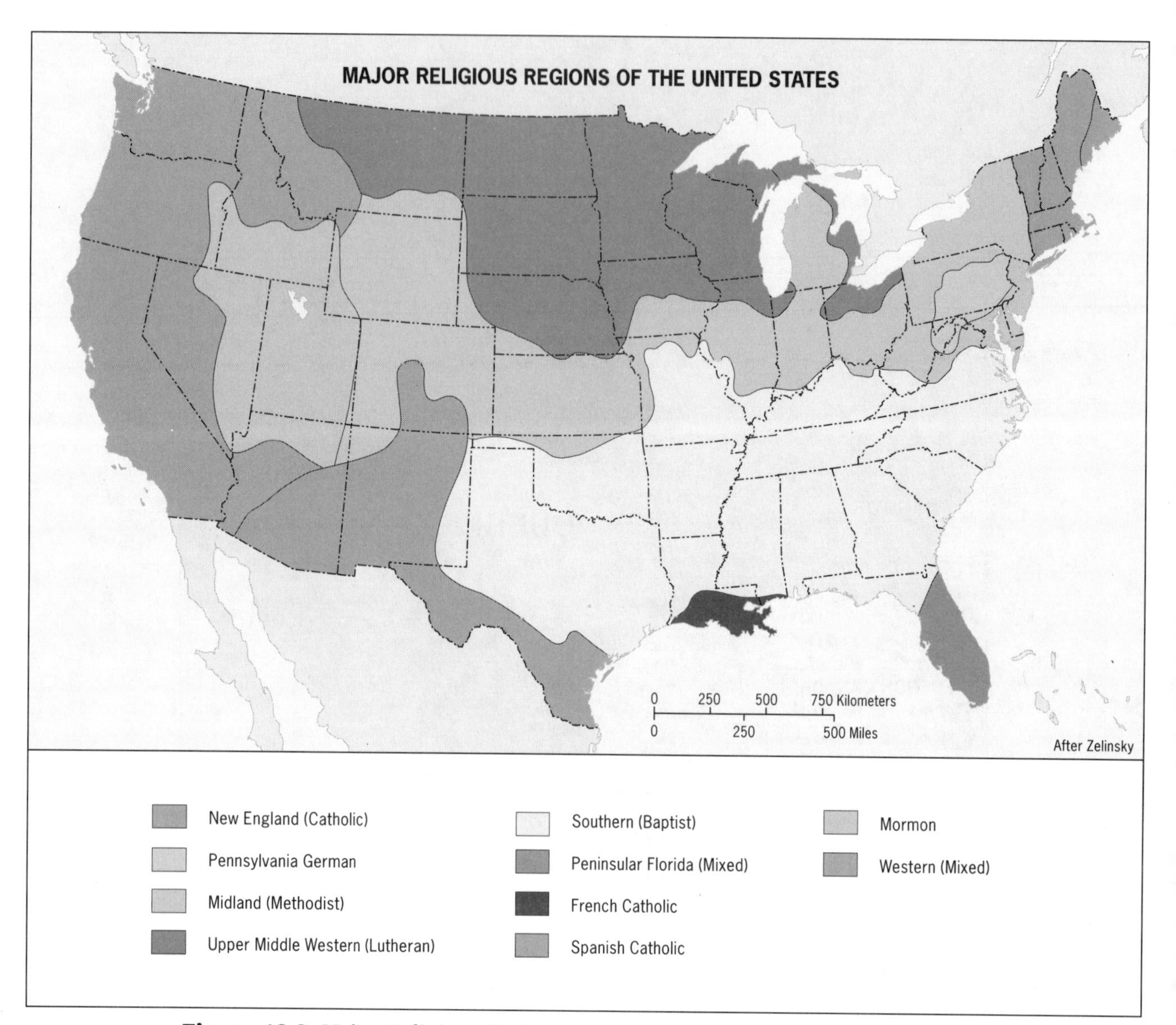

Figure 12-2 Major Religious Regions of the United States. A generalized map of religious regions in the United States shows concentrations of the major religions. *Source: Modified from W. Zelinksy, "An Approach to the Religious Geography of the United States,"* Annals of the AAG *51, 1961, p. 139.*

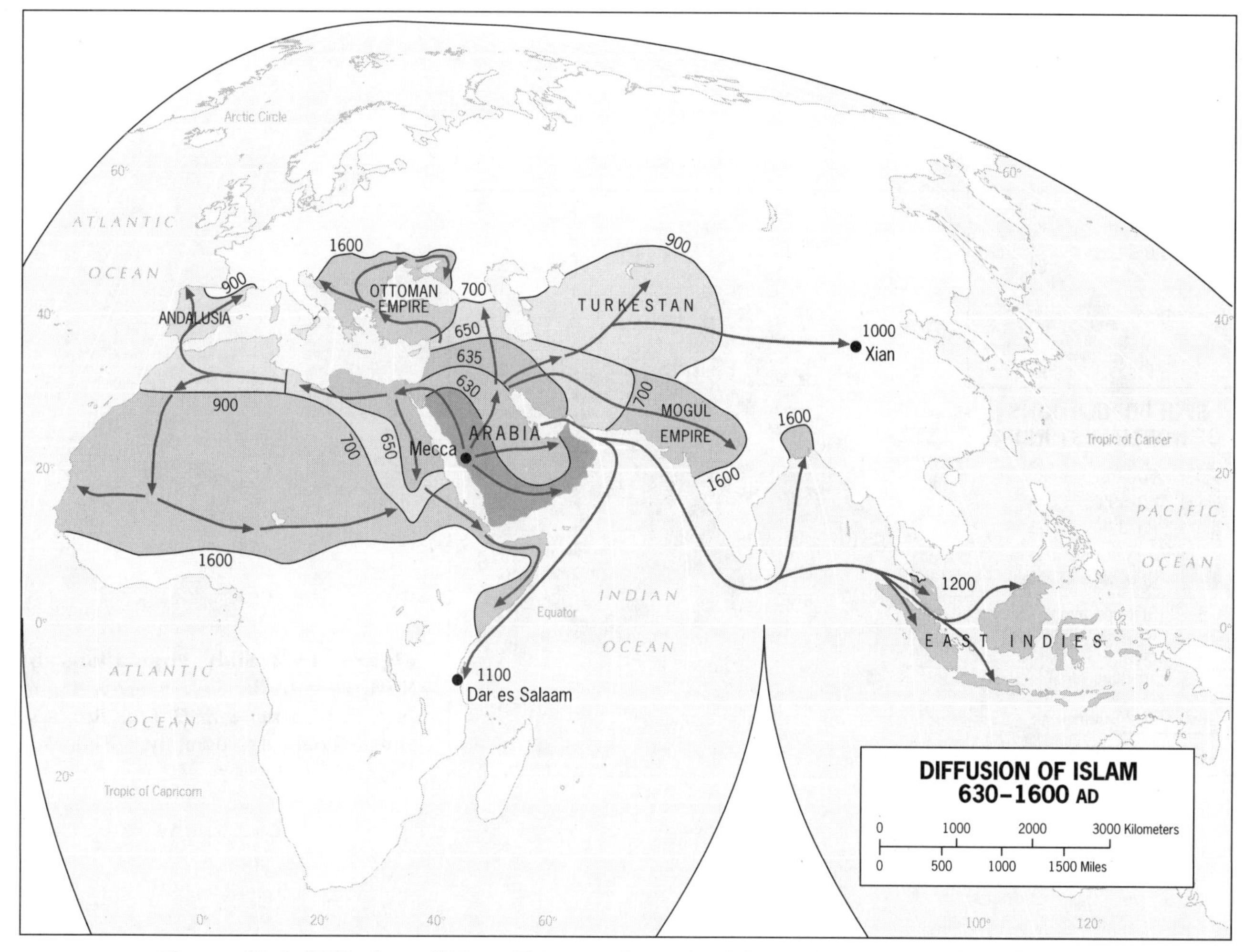

Figure 12-4 Diffusion of Islam. This map shows the diffusion of Islam from 630–1600 A.D.

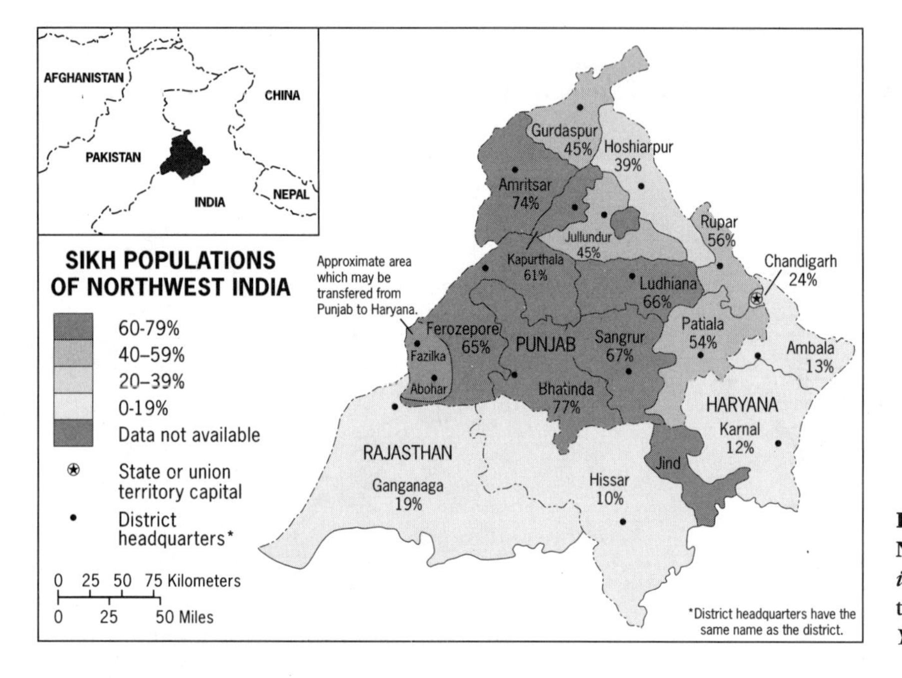

Figure 13-2 Sikh Populations of Northwest India. *Source: From a map in M. I. Glassner and H. J. de Blij*, Systematic Political Geography, 4th ed. *New York: Wiley, 1989, p. 402.*

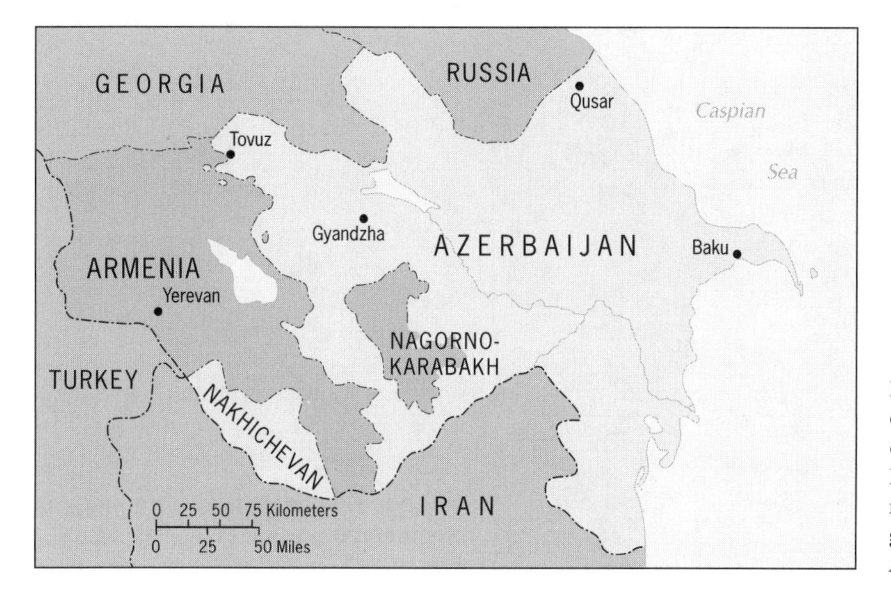

Figure 13-3 Two Exclaves in Transcaucasia. This map shows two Transcaucasian exclaves: Muslim-Azerbaijan Nakhichevan, cut off by Christian Armenia, and Christian-Armenian Nagorno-Karabakh, surrounded by Muslim Azerbaijan.

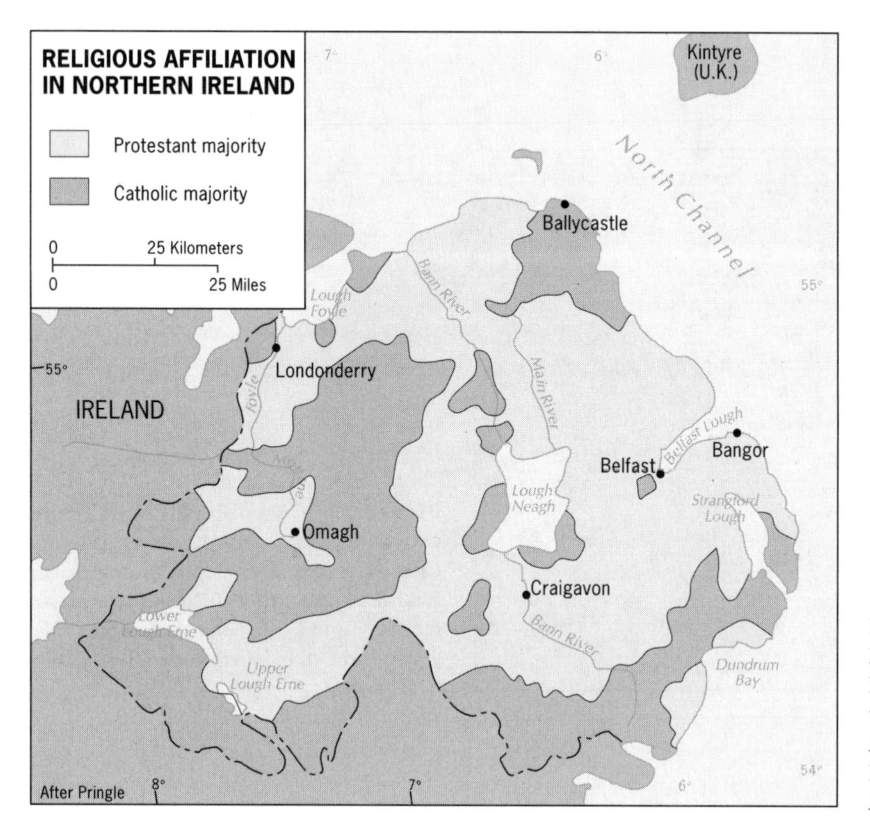

Figure 13-5 Religious Affiliation in Northern Ireland. Areas of Catholic and Protestant majorities are scattered throughout Northern Ireland. *Source: From D. G. Pringle,* One Island, Two Nations? *Letchworth: Research Studies Press/Wiley, 1985, p. 21.*

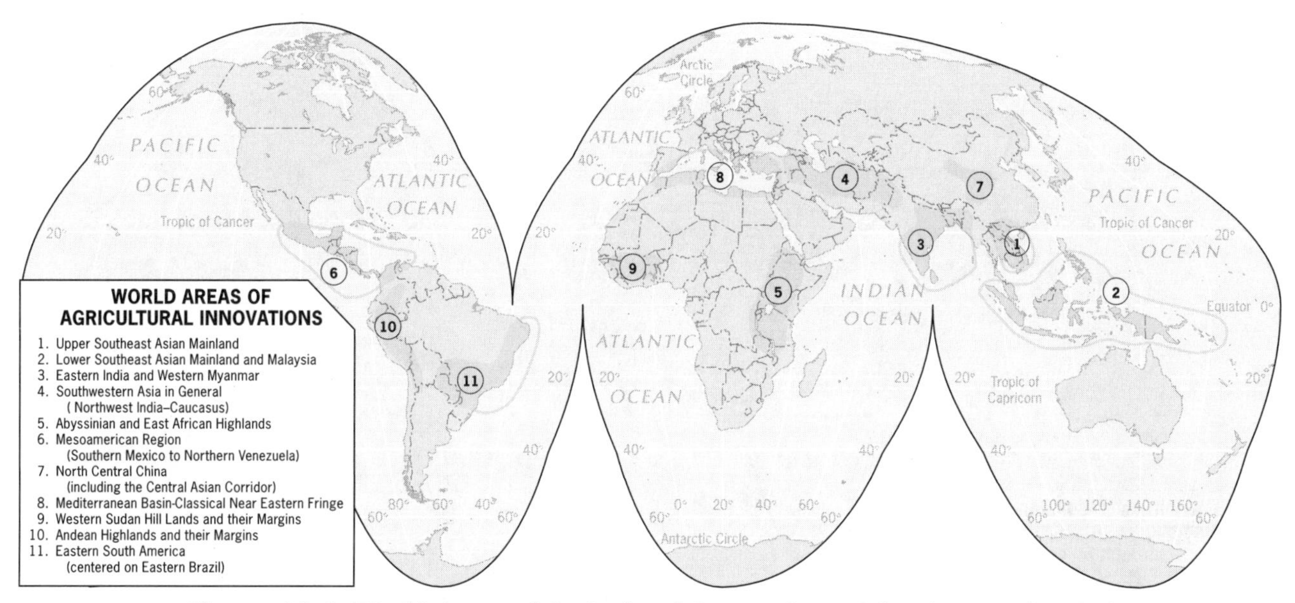

Figure 14-2 World Areas of Agricultural Innovations. Cultural geographer Carl Sauer identified 11 areas where agricultural innovations occurred. *Source: From C. O. Sauer,* Agricultural Origins and Dispersals. *New York: American Geographical Society, 1952, p. 24.*

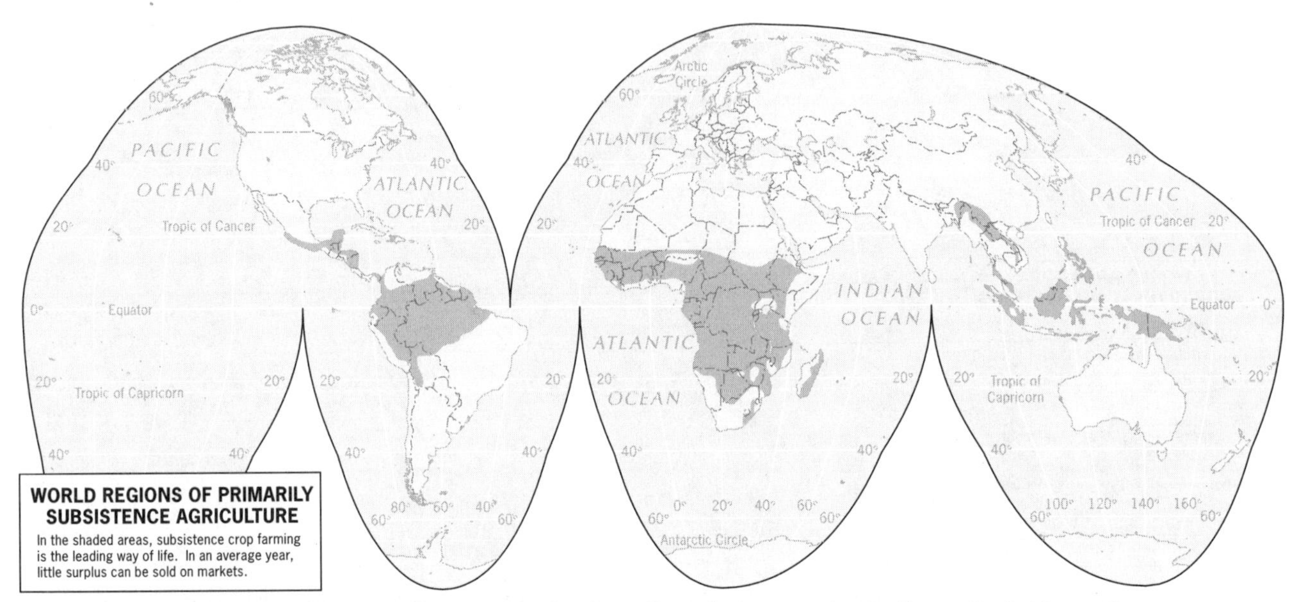

Figure 14-3 World Regions of Primarily Subsistence Agriculture. Definitions of subsistence farming vary. India and China are not shaded because farmers sell some produce on markets; in equatorial Africa and South America, subsistence allows little of this.

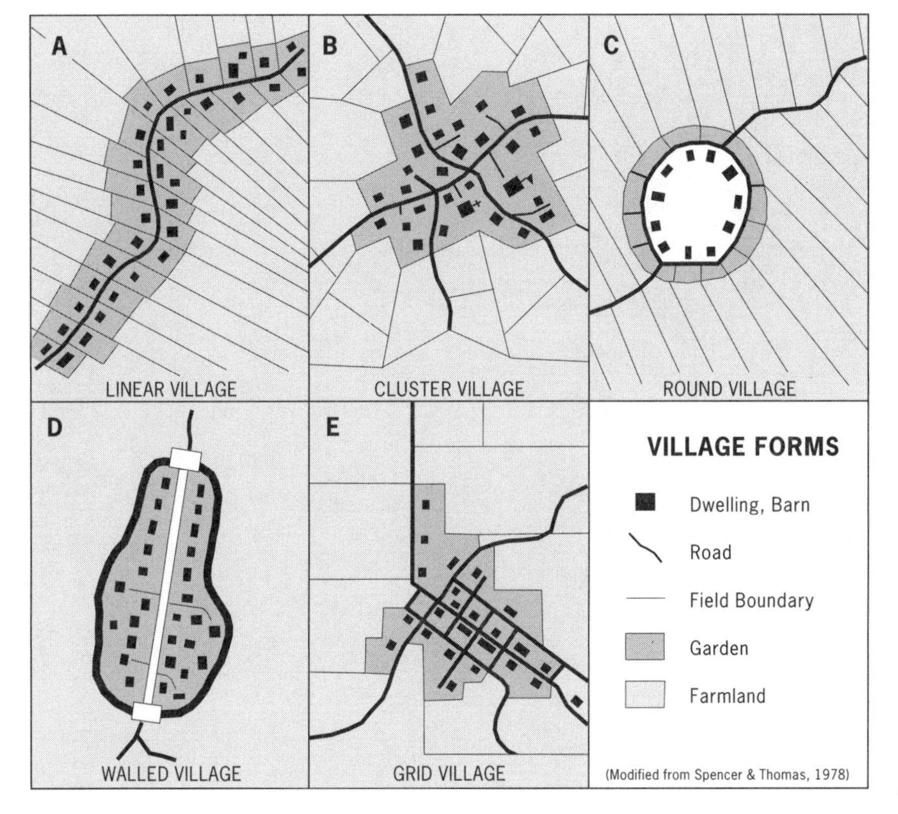

Figure 15-3 Village Forms. Five different representative village layouts are shown here. *Source: From J. E. Spencer and W. H. Thomas,* Introducing Cultural Geography. *New York: Wiley, 1978, p. 154.*

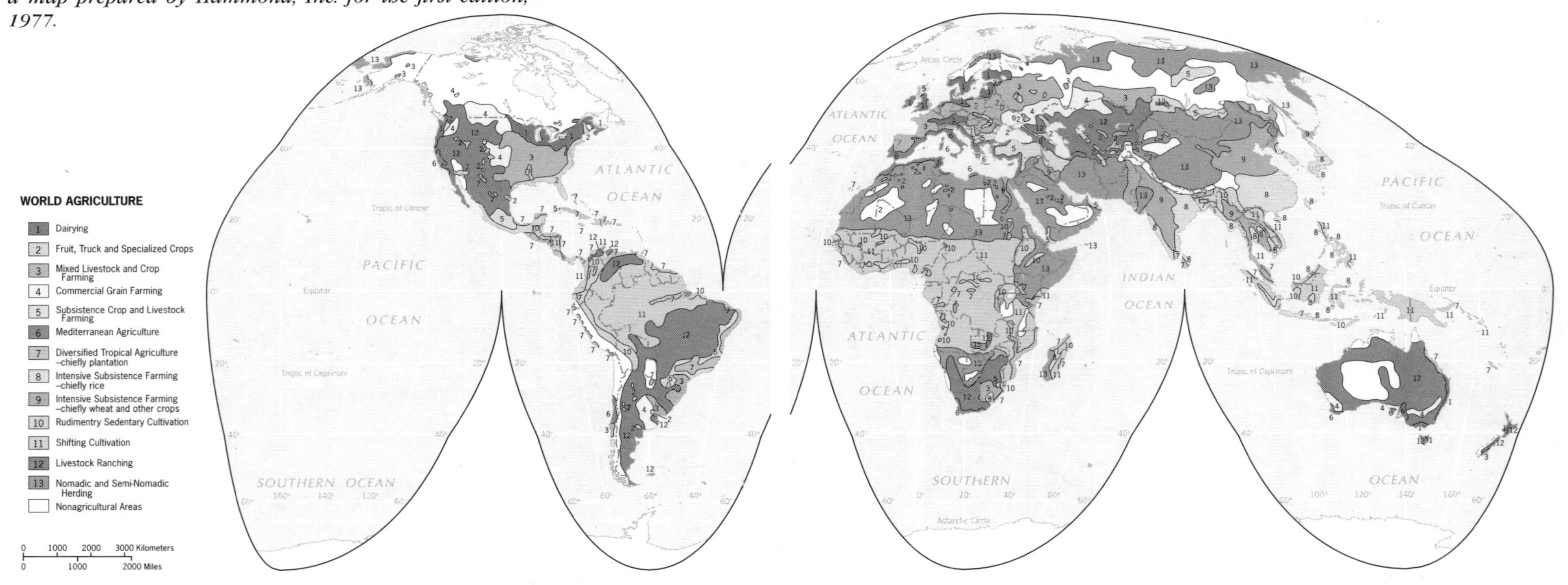

Figure 16-1 World Agriculture. Different kinds of agricultural areas are shown through the world. *Source: From a map prepared by Hammond, Inc. for the first edition, 1977.*

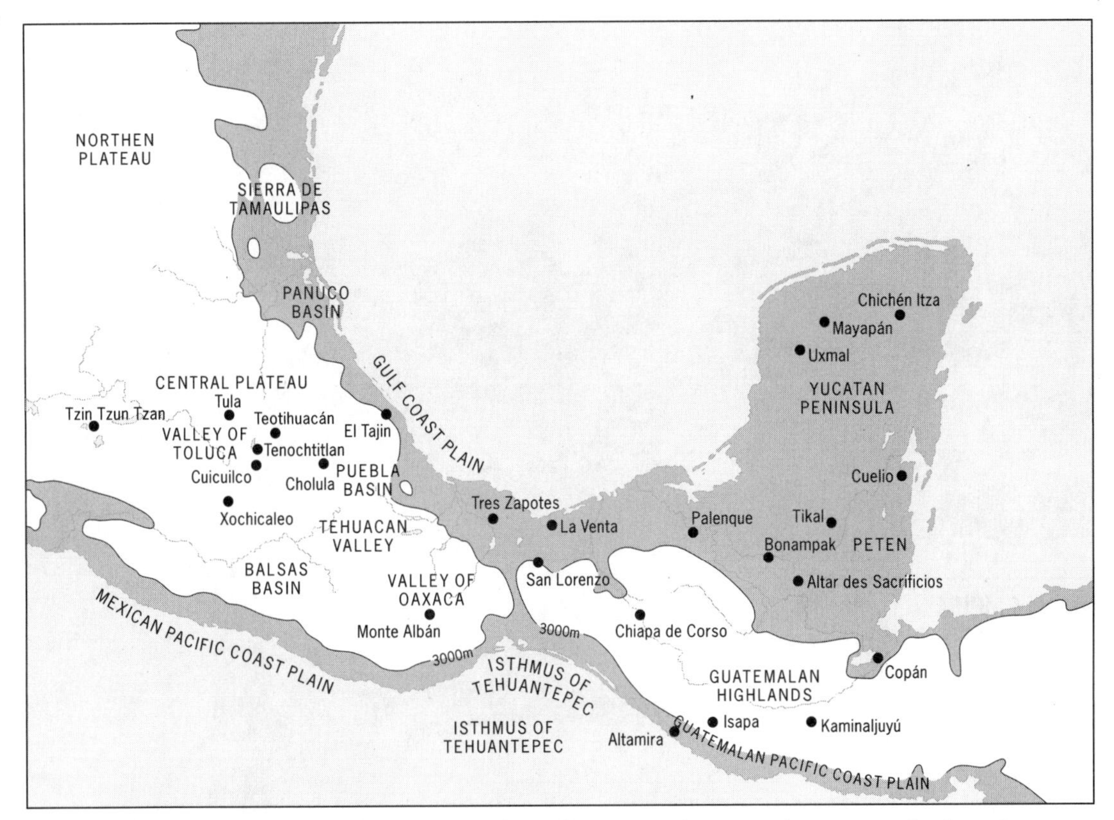

Figure 17-2 Maya and Aztec America. This map indicates early centers of culture in Maya and Aztec America.

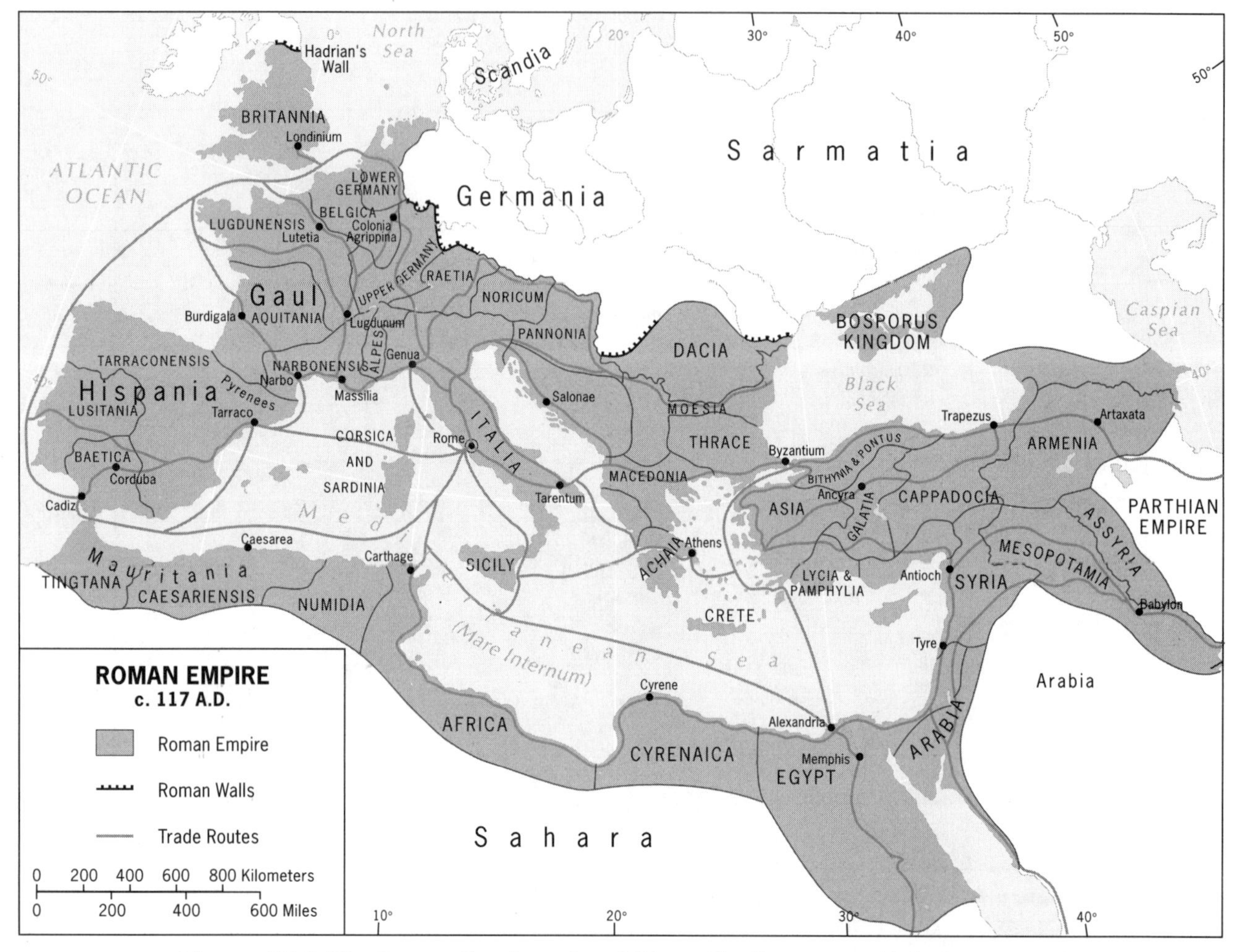

Figure 17-4 The Roman Empire, circa 117 A.D. The Romans established a system of cities linked by a network of land and sea routes. Many of the Roman cities have grown into modern metropolises.

Figure 18-2 Xianggang–Shenzhen. Shenzhen, China's most successful Special Economic Zone, lies adjacent to Xianggang (Hong Kong), one of the economic "tigers" of the Pacific Rim. This proximity has propelled Shenzhen's SEZ ahead of all others. *Source: From a map in H. J. de Blij and P. O. Muller,* Geography: Realms, Regions, and Concepts, *8th ed. New York: Wiley, 1997).*

Figure 18-6 Urban Population as a Percentage of the Total Population. *Source: Data from Population Reference Bureau,* World Population Data Sheet 1998. *Washington, D.C., 1998.*

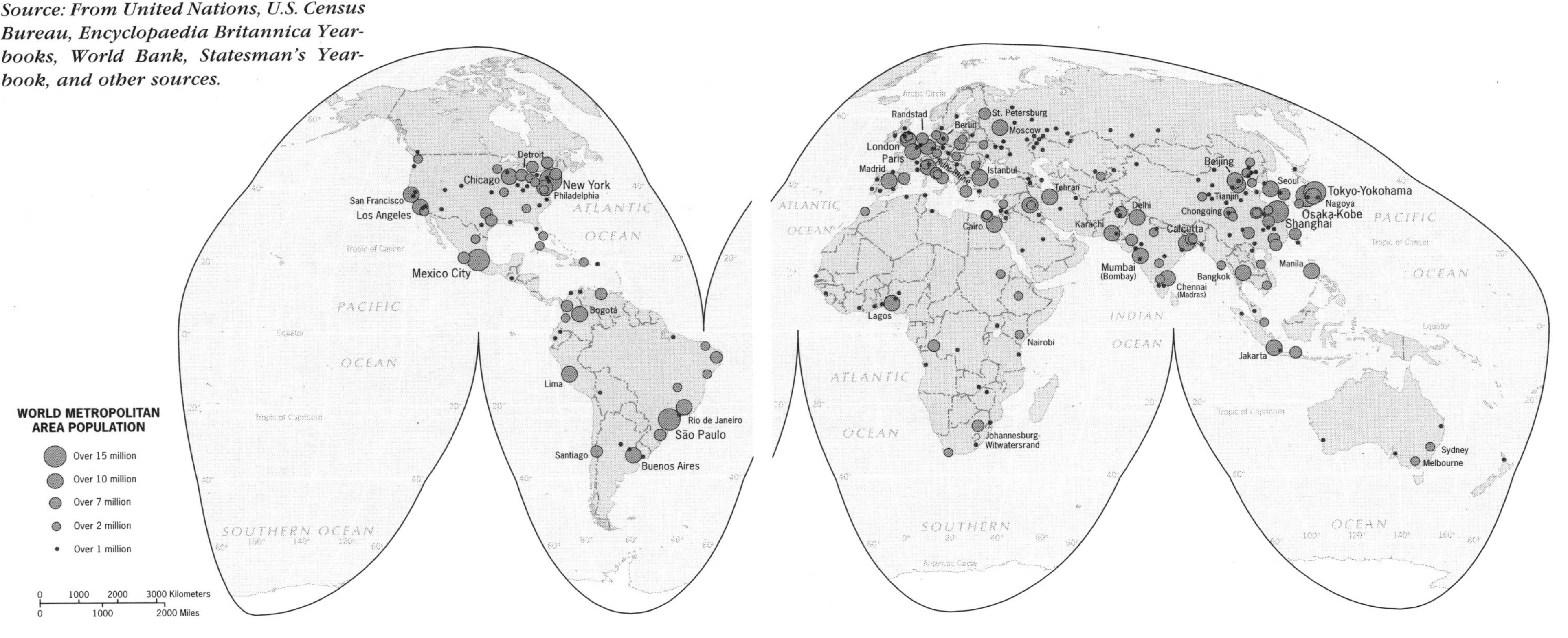

Figure 18-7 World Metropolitan Area Population. Based on data from numerous, often contradictory, sources, data on urban centers often are inconsistent. *Source: From United Nations, U.S. Census Bureau, Encyclopaedia Britannica Yearbooks, World Bank, Statesman's Yearbook, and other sources.*

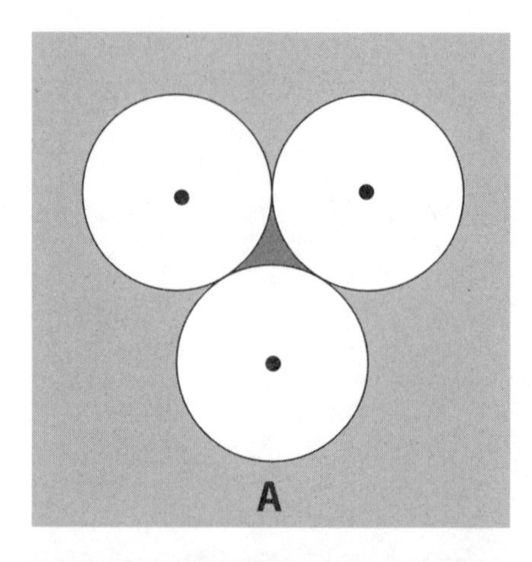

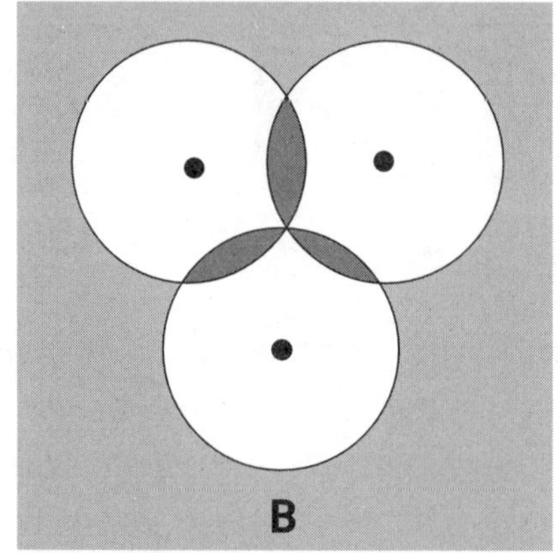

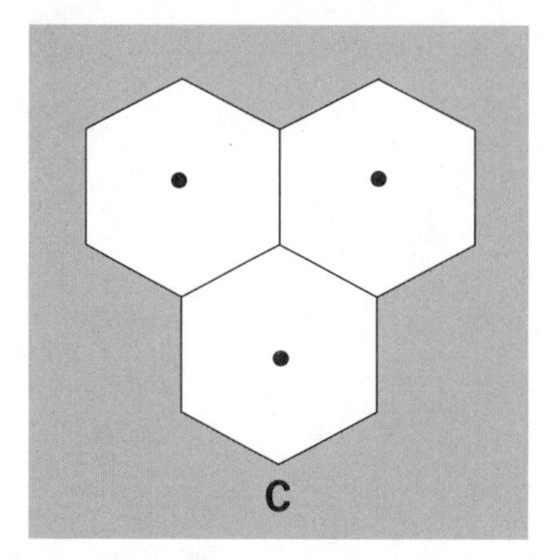

Figure 19-2 Christaller's Hexagonal Trade Areas Surrounding Urban Centers. Constructing Christaller's hexagonal trade areas surrounding urban centers involves: (A) unserved areas shown in purple; (B) purple areas indicate places where the conditions of monopoly would not be fulfilled; and (C) hexagons completely fill an area without overlap.

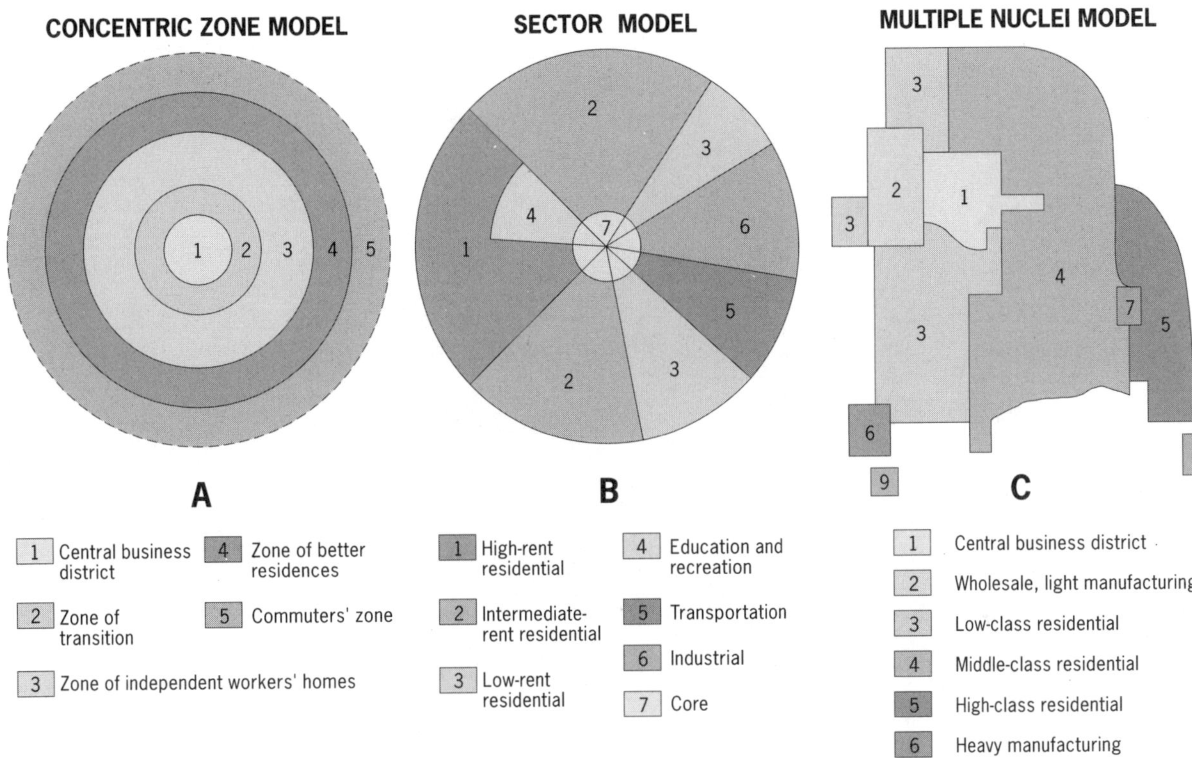

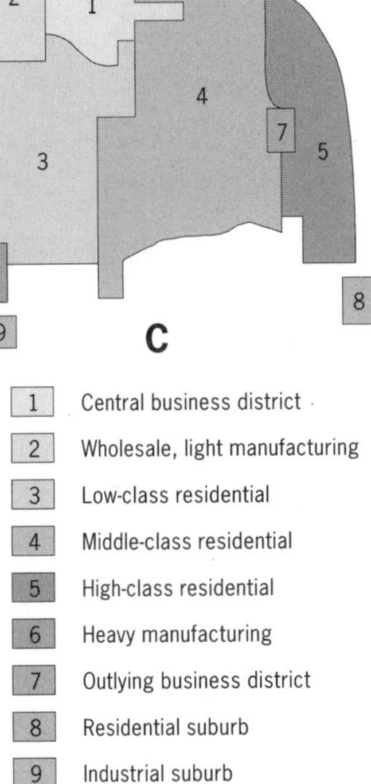

Figure 19-4 Three Classical Models of Urban Structure. The three classical models of urban structure are concentric zone model, sector model, and multiple nuclei model.

URBAN REALMS MODEL

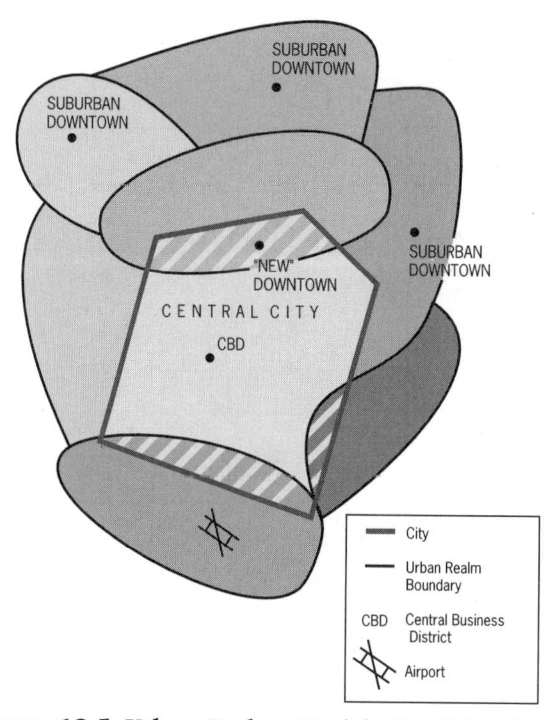

Figure 19-5 Urban Realms Model. The Urban Realms Model includes central business district, central city, new downtown, and suburban downtown. *Source: From T. Hartshorn and P. O. Muller, "Suburban Downtowns and the Transformation of Metropolitan Atlanta's Business Landscape,"* Urban Geography 10 (1989), p. 375. *Reproduced by permission of* Urban Geography.

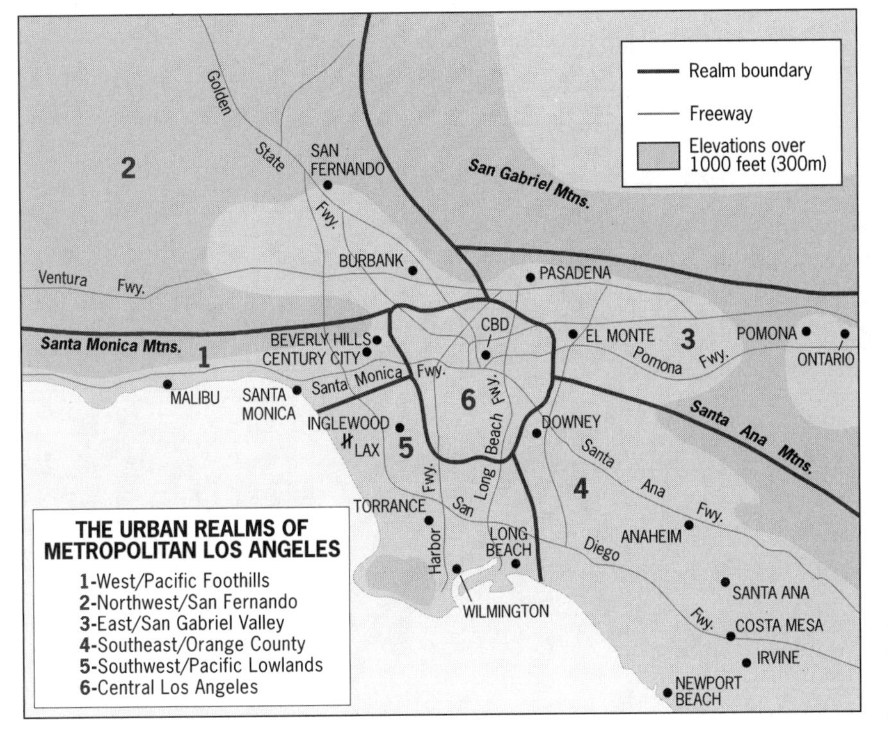

Figure 19-6 The Urban Realms of Metropolitan Los Angeles. *Source: From a map in H. J. de Blij and P. O. Muller,* Geography: Regions and Concepts, *5th ed. New York: Wiley, 1988, p. 220, designed by P. O. Muller.*

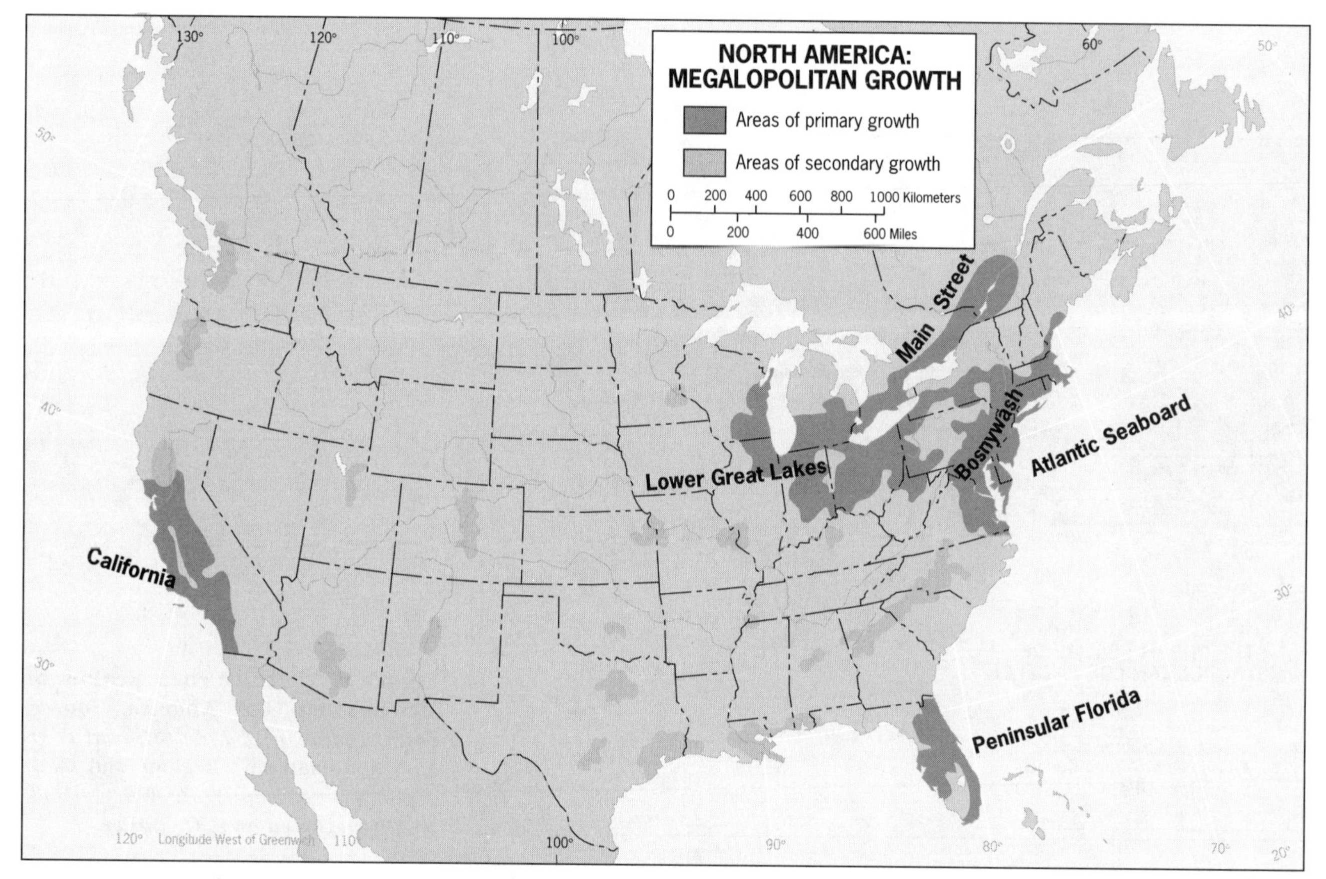

Figure 20-1 North American Megalopolitan Growth. This map shows evolving megalopolises in North America. *Source: From a map in H. J. de Blij and P. O. Muller,* Geography: Realms, Regions, and Concepts, *7th ed. New York: Wiley, 1994.*

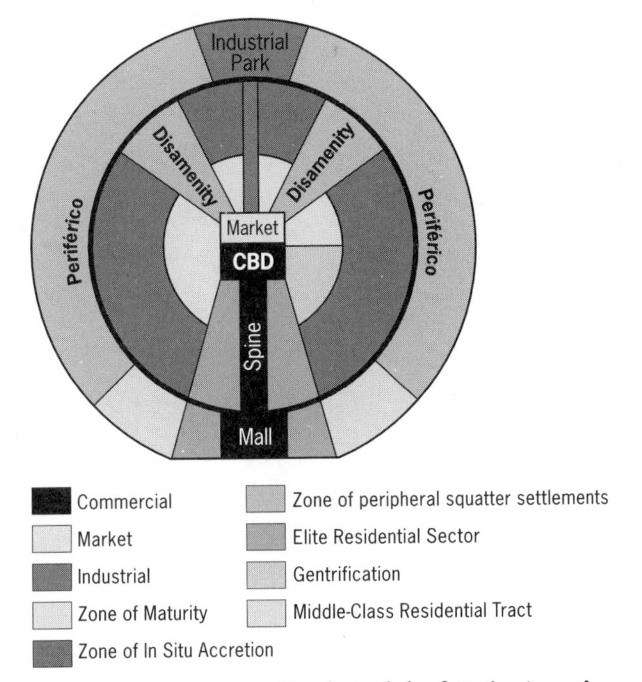

Figure 20-3 A Generalized Model of Latin American City Structure. This model includes commercial/industrial zones, elite residential sector, zone of maturity, zone of *in situ* accretion, and zone of peripheral squatter settlements. *Source: From E. Griffin and L. Ford, "A Model of Latin American City Structure,"* The Geographical Review *70 (1980), p. 406.*

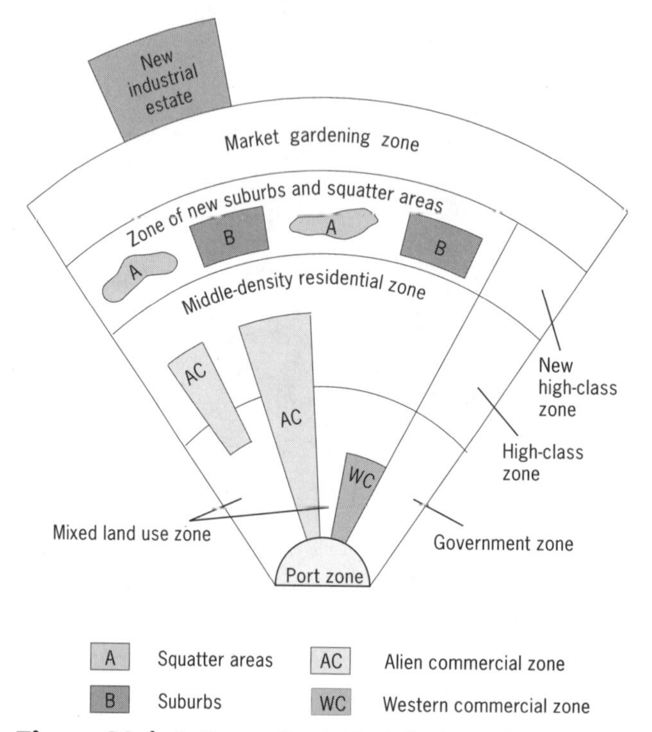

Figure 20-4 A Generalized Model of Land Use Areas in the Large Southeast Asian City. A model of land use in the large Southeast Asian city includes port zone, government zone, mixed land use zone, high-class zone, new high-class zone, middle-density residential zone, zone of new suburbs and squatter areas, market gardening zone, and new industrial zone. *Source: From T. G. McGee,* The Southeast Asian City, *London: Bell, 1967, p. 128. Reprinted by permission of the publisher.*

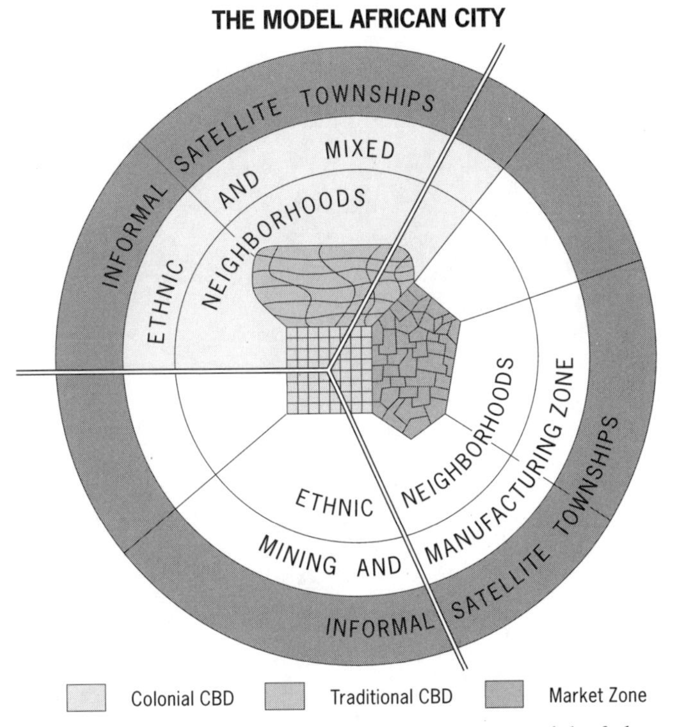

Figure 20-5 A Model African City. One model of the African city includes colonial CBD, traditional CBD, and market zone.

Figure 21-1 World Economies. *Source: Based on data from the World Bank,* World Development Report 1993. *Oxford: Oxford University Press, 1994, pp. 238–239.*

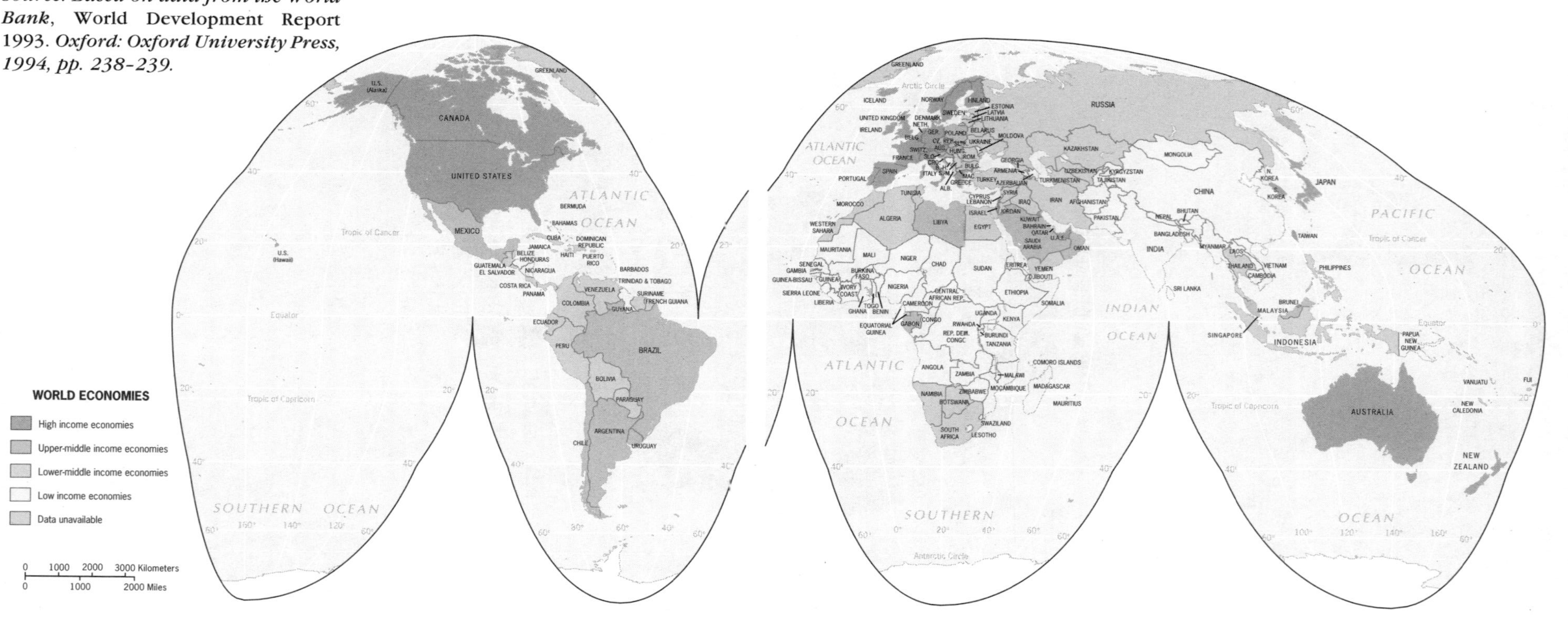

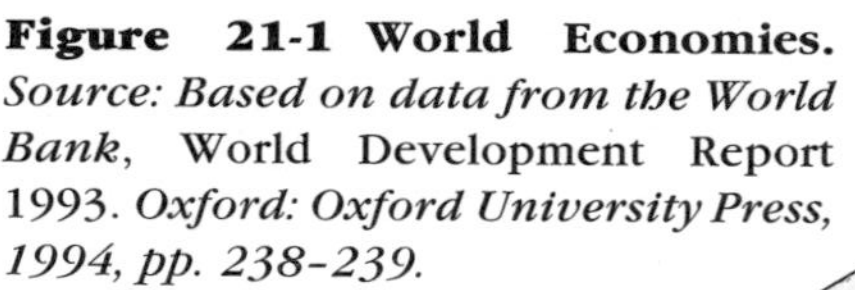

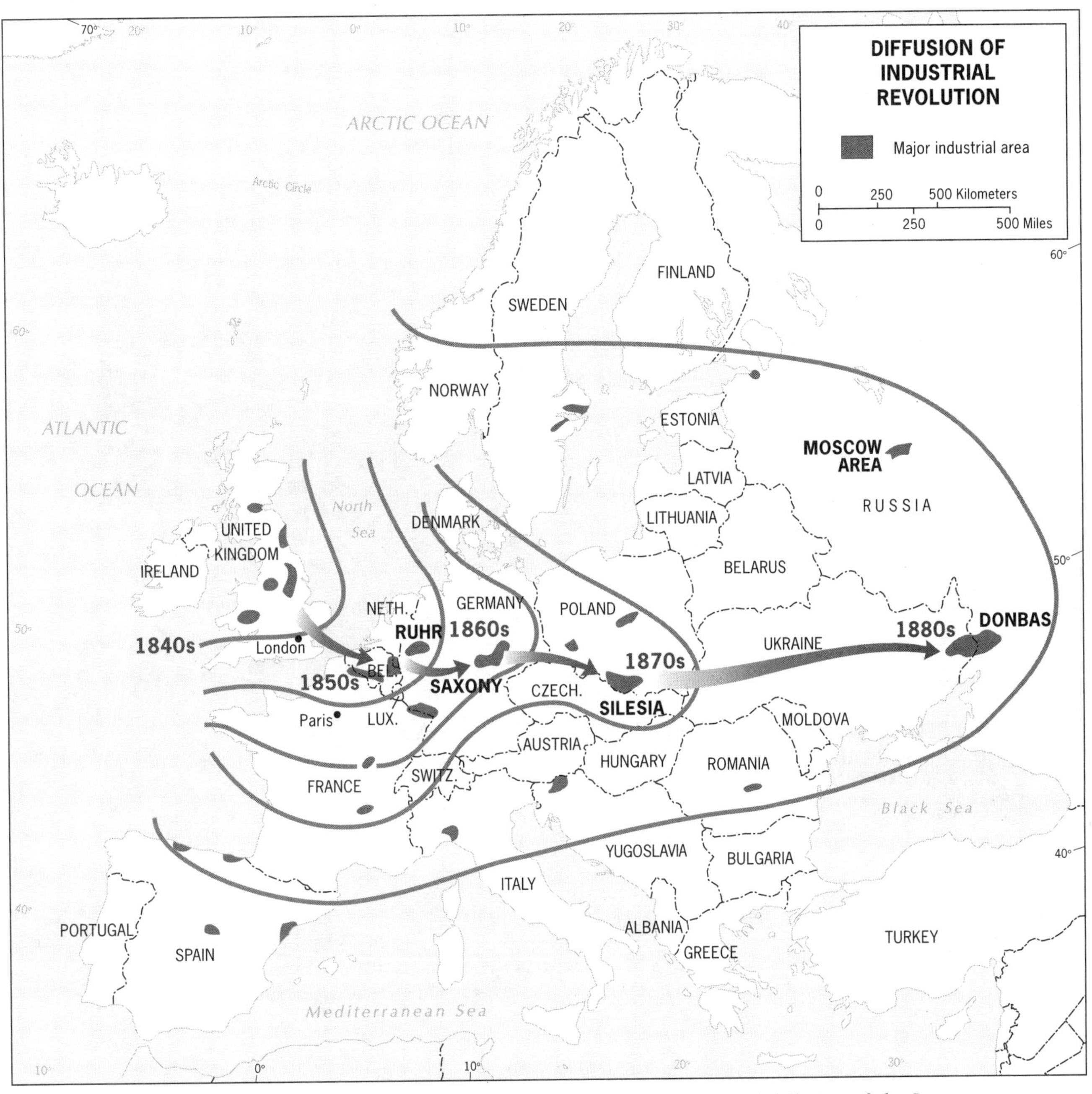

Figure 22-1 Diffusion of Industrial Revolution. The eastward diffusion of the Industrial Revolution during the second half of the nineteenth century is depicted on this map.

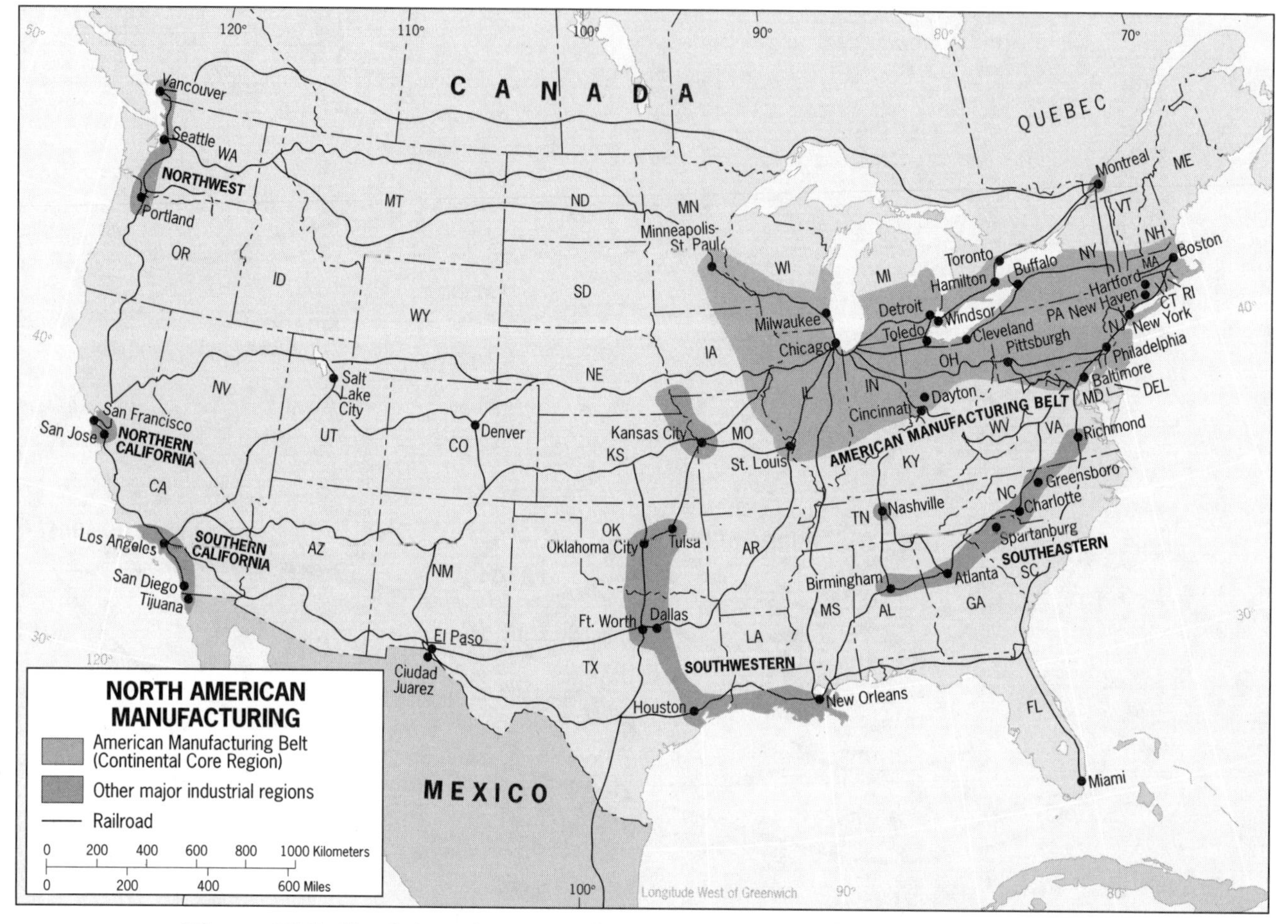

Figure 23-3 North America's Manufacturing Regions. North American manufacturing has dispersed westward and southward, but the eastern core area remains dominant.

Figure 23-5 East Asia's Manufacturing Regions. For decades, the Northeast was China's most rapidly growing industrial area. Now the Chang District is taking the lead.

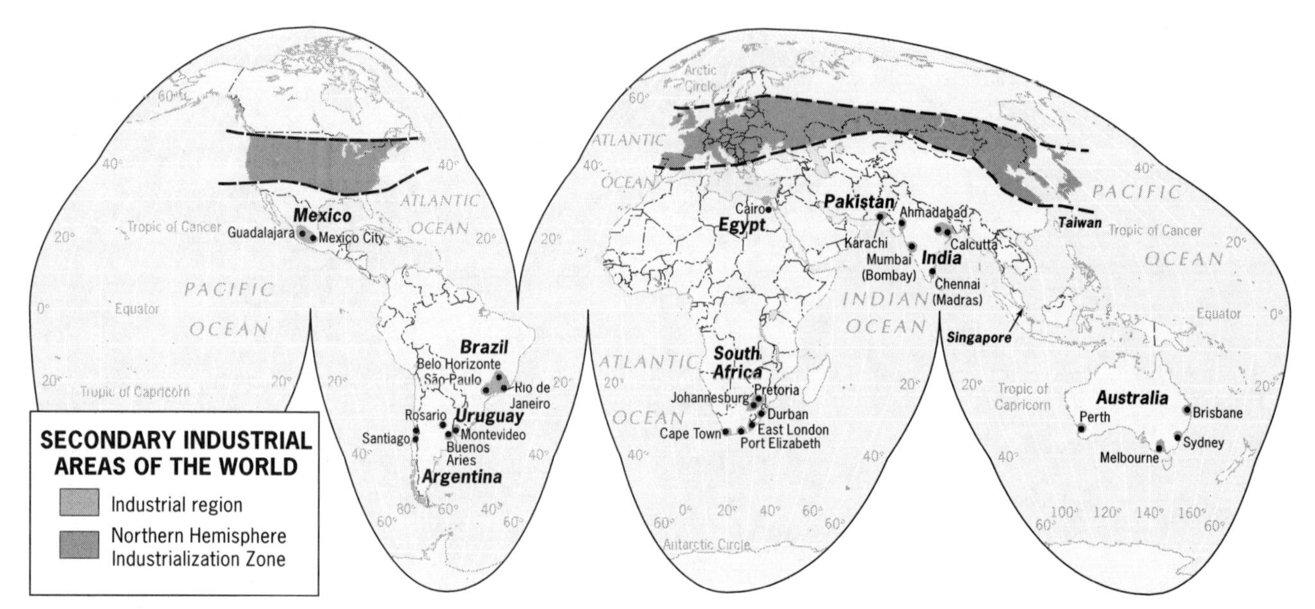

Figure 23-6 Secondary Industrial Areas of the World.

Figure 24-1 Increases in Value of Manufacturing Exports to OECD Countries. This map shows the percentage of increases in value of manufacturing exports to OECD countries from major low- and middle-income trading partners, 1970–1992. *Source: The World Bank* World Development Report 1994. Infrastructure for Development, *Oxford: Oxford University Press*.

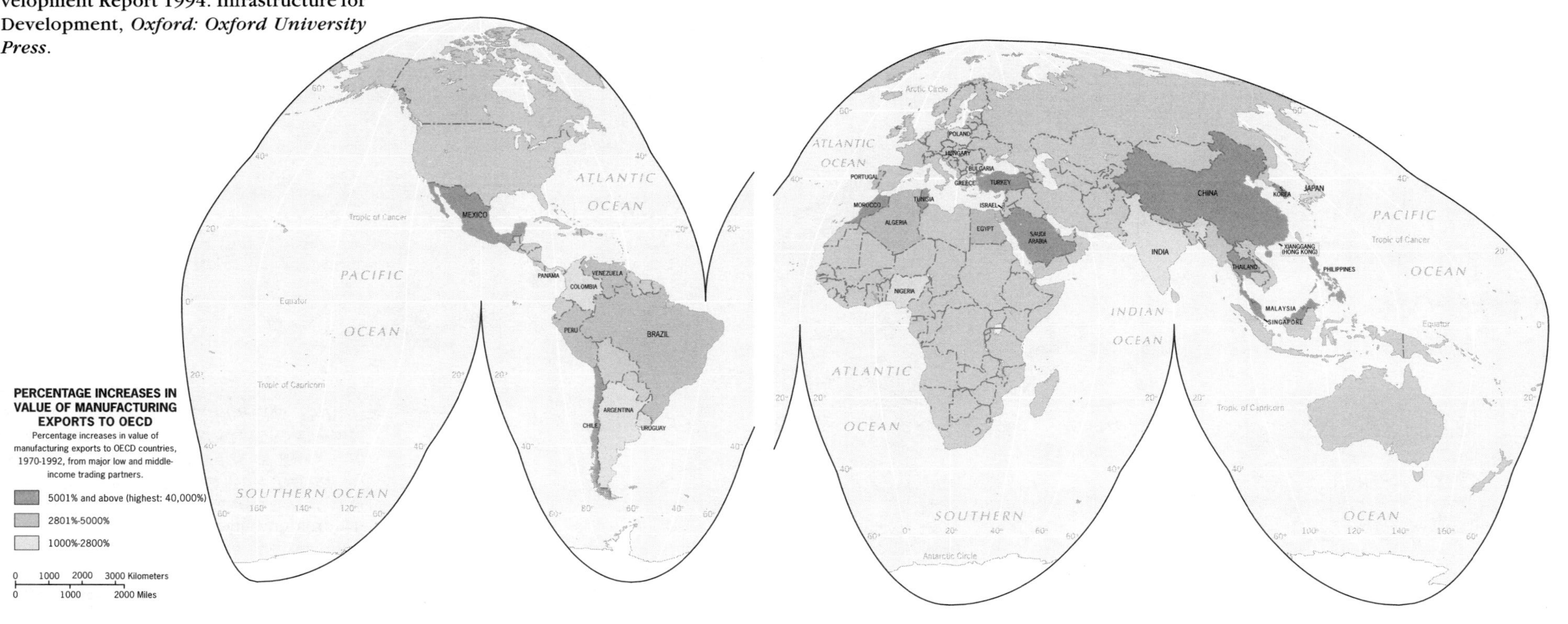

Figure 24-3 Major World Cities. In 1995 John Friedman delineated the major world cities according to global financial, multinational, national, subnational/regional articulations. *Source: J. Friedman, "Where We Stand in a Decade of World City Research," in P. C. Knox and P. J. Taylor, eds.,* World Cities in a World System. *Cambridge: Cambridge University Press, pp. 21–47.*

Figure 24-4 Access to the Internet. This map depicts Internet connected computers per 1000 population as of January 1997. *Source: "Access to the Internet,"* Scientific American *277(1): July 1997, p. 26.*

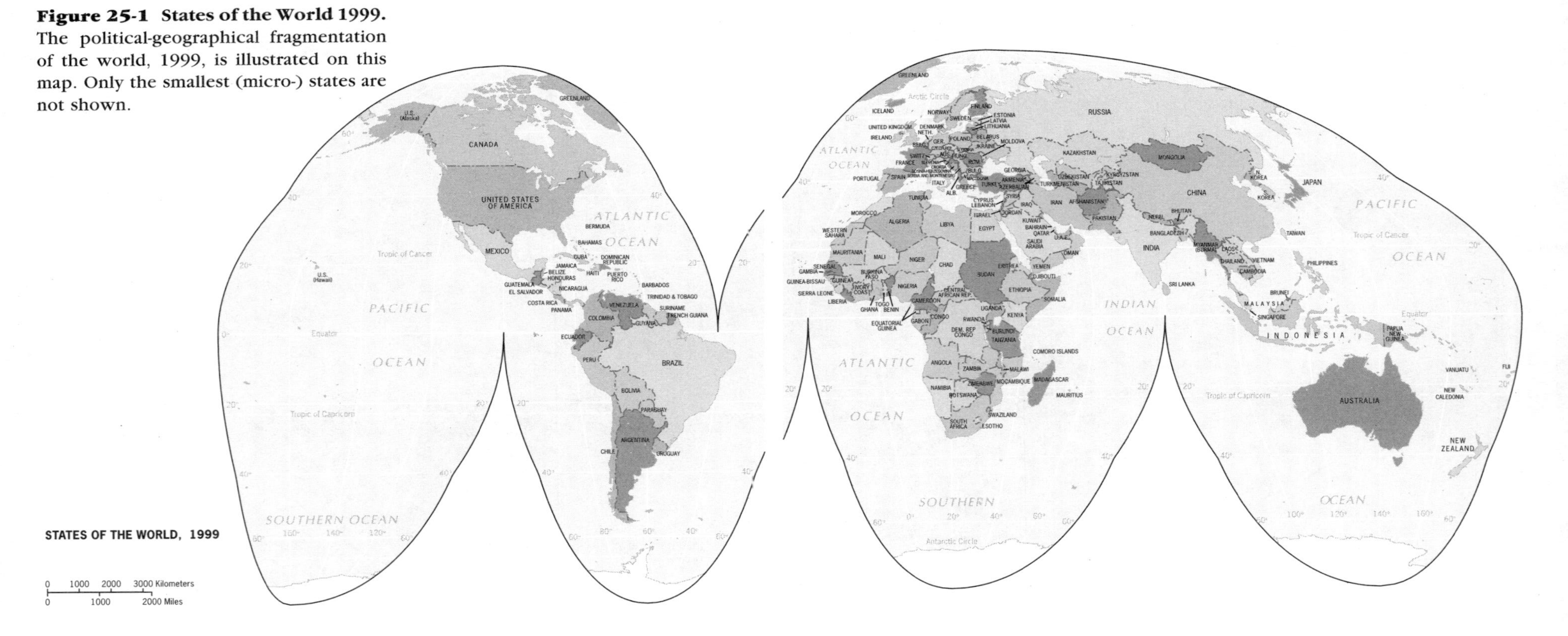

Figure 25-1 States of the World 1999. The political-geographical fragmentation of the world, 1999, is illustrated on this map. Only the smallest (micro-) states are not shown.

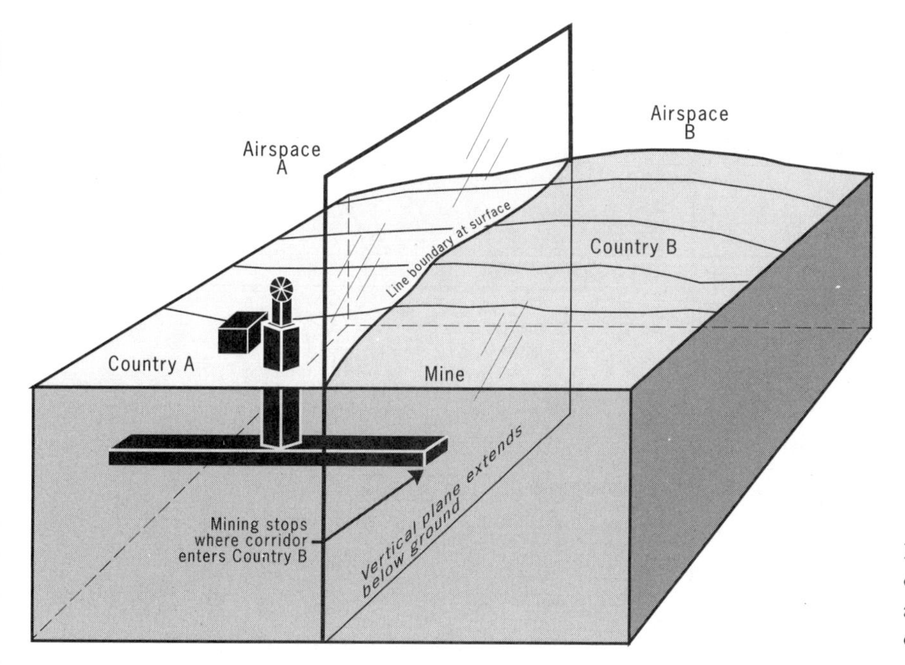

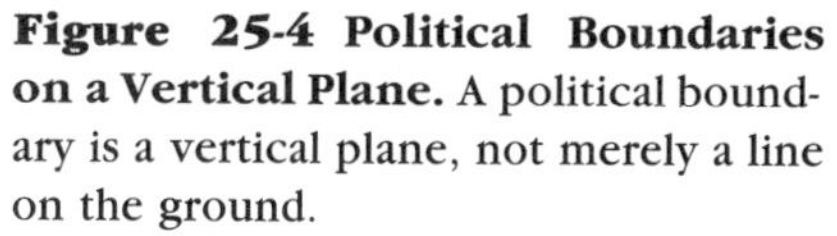

Figure 25-4 Political Boundaries on a Vertical Plane. A political boundary is a vertical plane, not merely a line on the ground.

GENETIC POLITICAL BOUNDARY TYPES

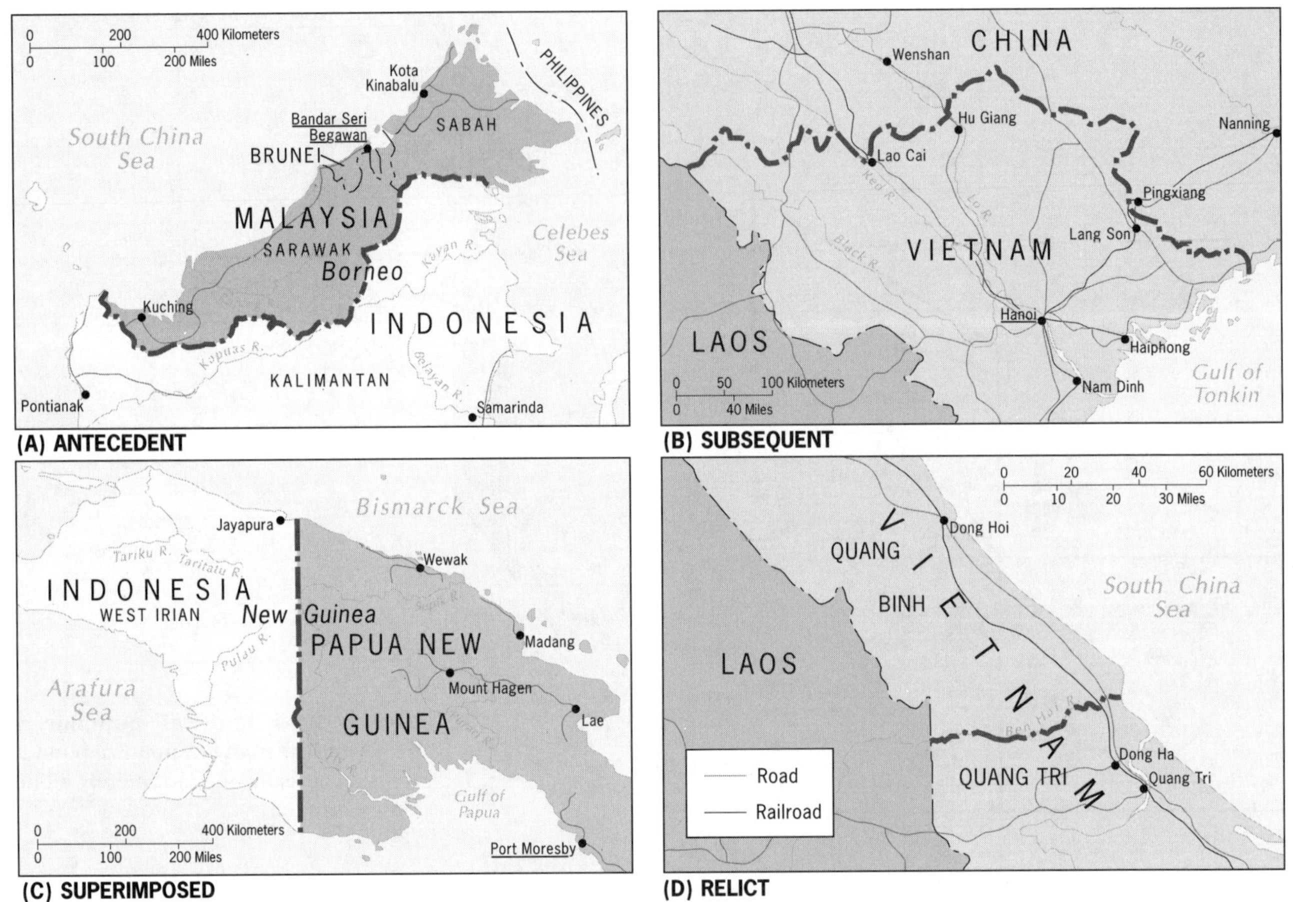

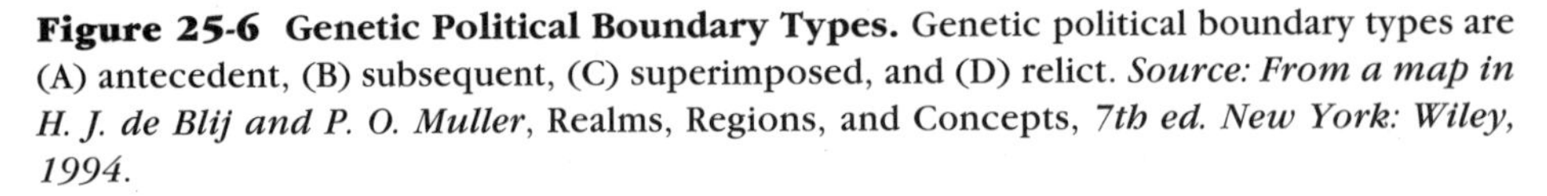

Figure 25-6 Genetic Political Boundary Types. Genetic political boundary types are (A) antecedent, (B) subsequent, (C) superimposed, and (D) relict. *Source: From a map in H. J. de Blij and P. O. Muller,* Realms, Regions, and Concepts, *7th ed. New York: Wiley, 1994.*

Figure 25-7 The Former Yugoslavia. The ethnic mosaic of the former Yugoslavia is illustrated on this map. *Source: Based on maps drawn in the Office of the Geographer of the U.S. Department of State, Washington, D.C., 1991.*

Figure 27-4 European Supranationalism. This map shows how the European states have aligned with supranationalist organizations.

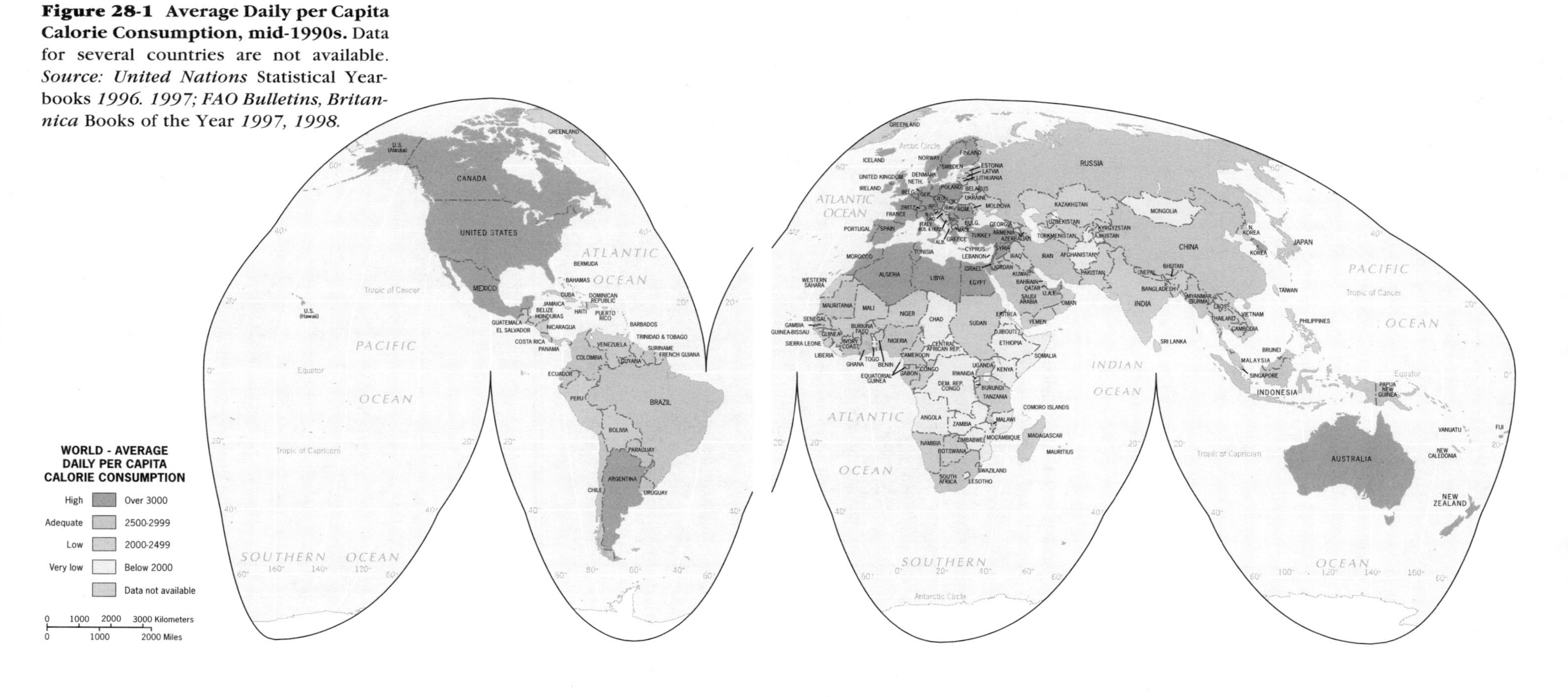

Figure 28-1 Average Daily per Capita Calorie Consumption, mid-1990s. Data for several countries are not available. *Source: United Nations* Statistical Yearbooks *1996. 1997; FAO Bulletins, Britannica* Books of the Year *1997, 1998.*

Table 28-1 Daily Calorie Supply per Capita in Selected Countries mid-1990s

Large Supply		Low Supply	
Denmark	3704	Pakistan	2475
United States	3603	Nicaragua	2311
France	3588	Peru	2277
Italy	3458	Laos	2117
New Zealand	3379	Malawi	2038
Syria	3296		
Mexico	3136	**Very Low Supply**	
Canada	3093		
		Kenya	1991
Adequate Supply		Mongolia	1897
		Haiti	1706
Latvia	2967	Liberia	1640
Malaysia	2807	Afghanistan	1523
Colombia	2758	Tajikistan	1400
Jamaica	2647		
Moldova	2525		

Source: United Nations, *Statistical Yearbooks* 1996, 1997, FAO Bulletins, Britannica *Books of the Year* 1997, 1998.

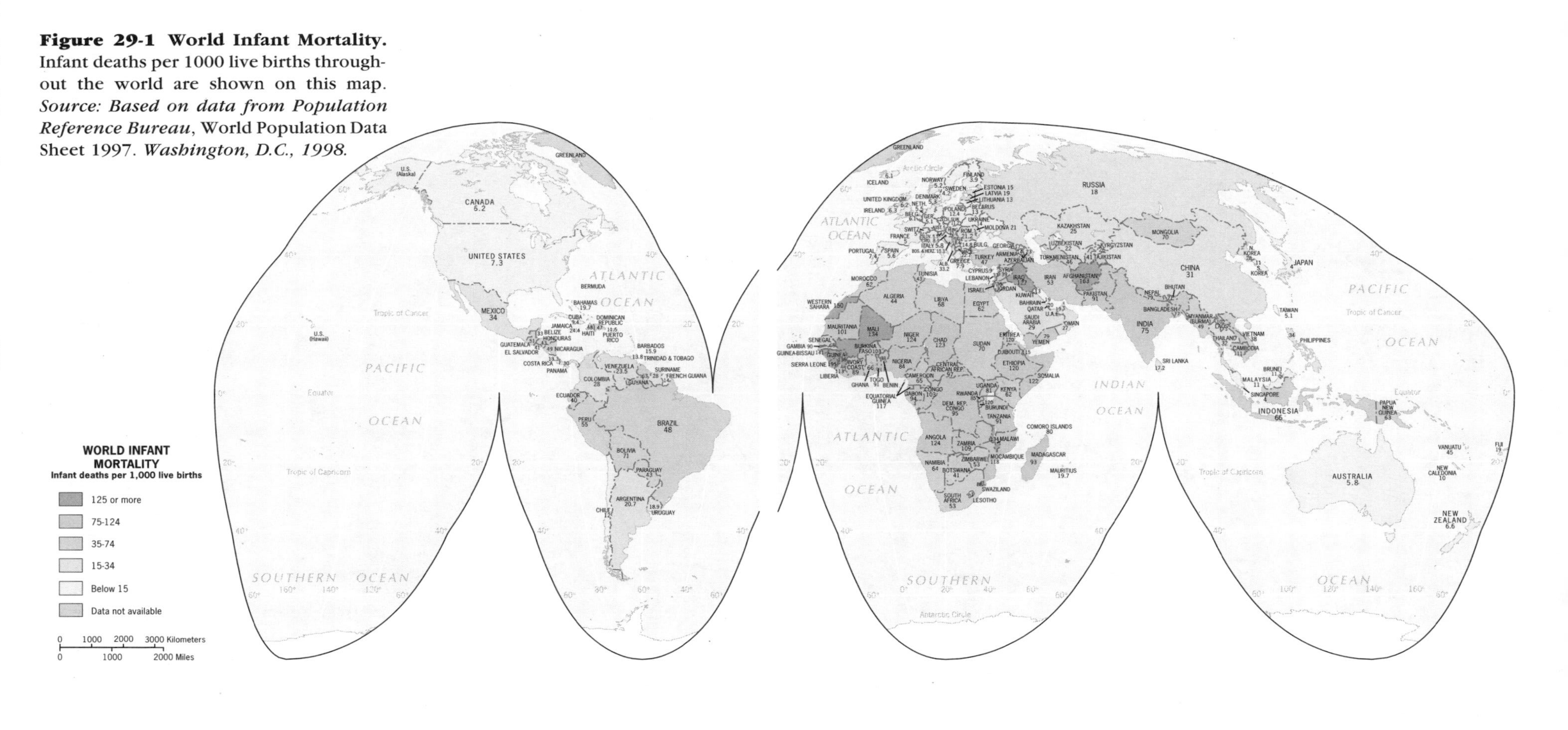

Figure 29-1 World Infant Mortality. Infant deaths per 1000 live births throughout the world are shown on this map. *Source: Based on data from Population Reference Bureau*, World Population Data Sheet 1997. *Washington, D.C., 1998.*

Figure 29-2 Life Expectancy at Birth.

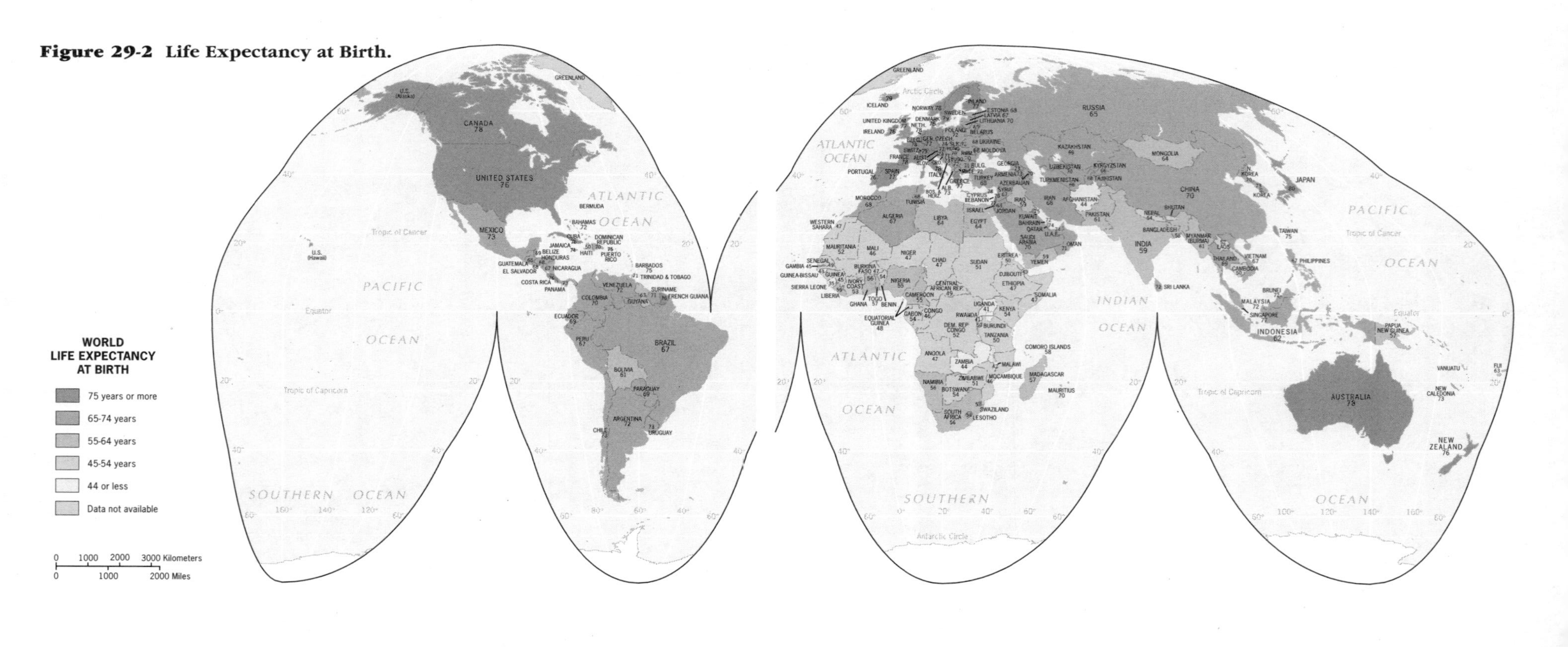

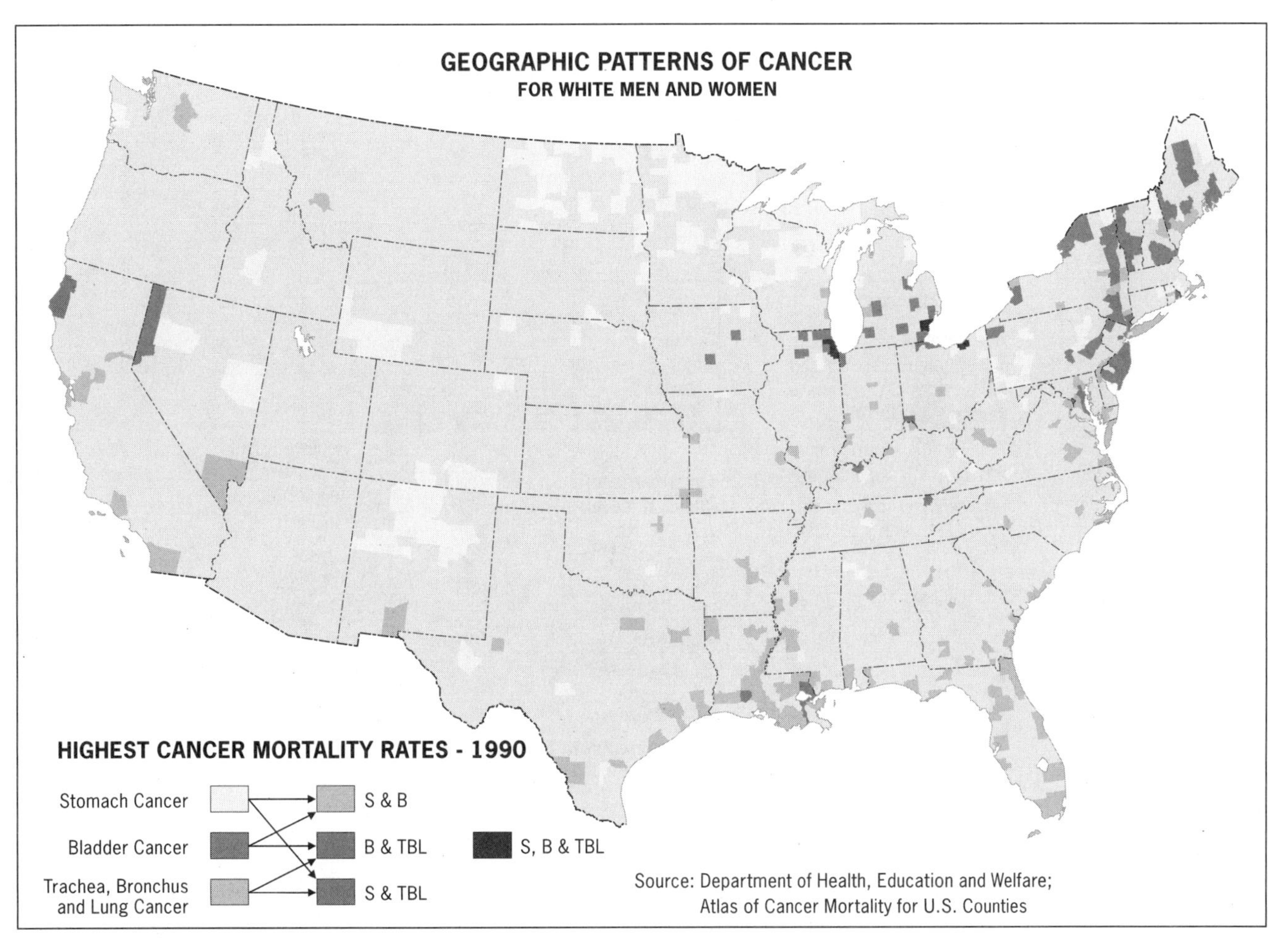

Figure 29-14 Highest Cancer Mortality Rates, 1990. The regional aspects of cancer incidence in the United States as of 1990 are illustrated in this map. *Source: Department of Health, Education and Welfare;* Atlas of Cancer Mortality for U.S. Counties.

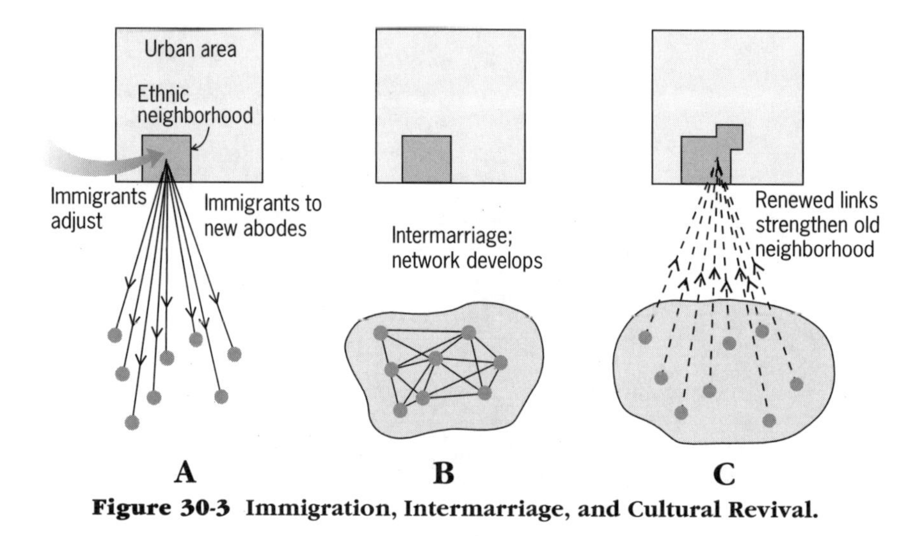

Figure 30-3 Immigration, Intermarriage, and Cultural Revival.

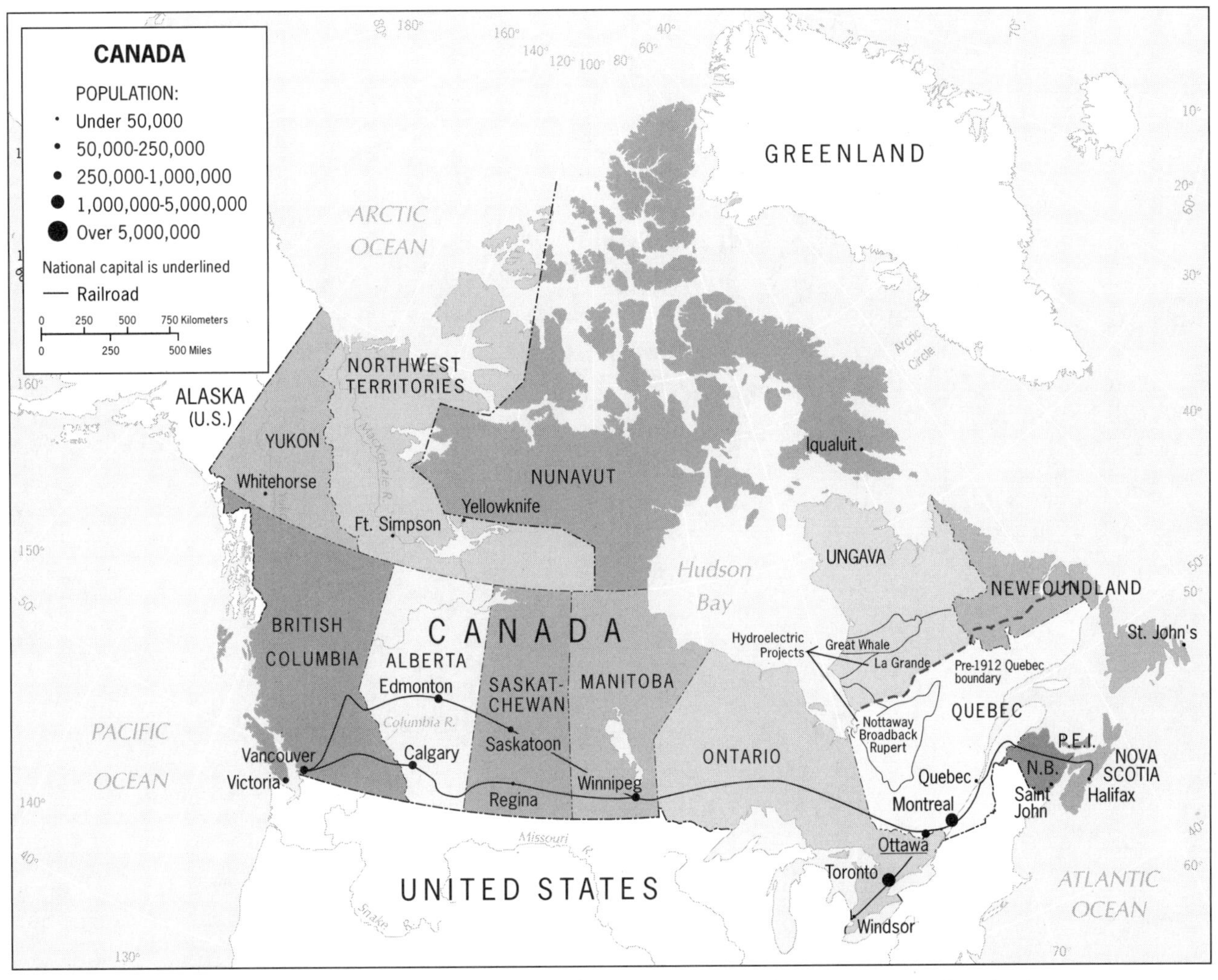

Figure 30-4 Canada's Provinces and Territories. Canada's provinces and territories and their capitals are illustrated here. The entity entitled Nunavut was proposed in 1992 to recognize the territorial rights of indigenous peoples in this area; it formally comes into being in 1999.

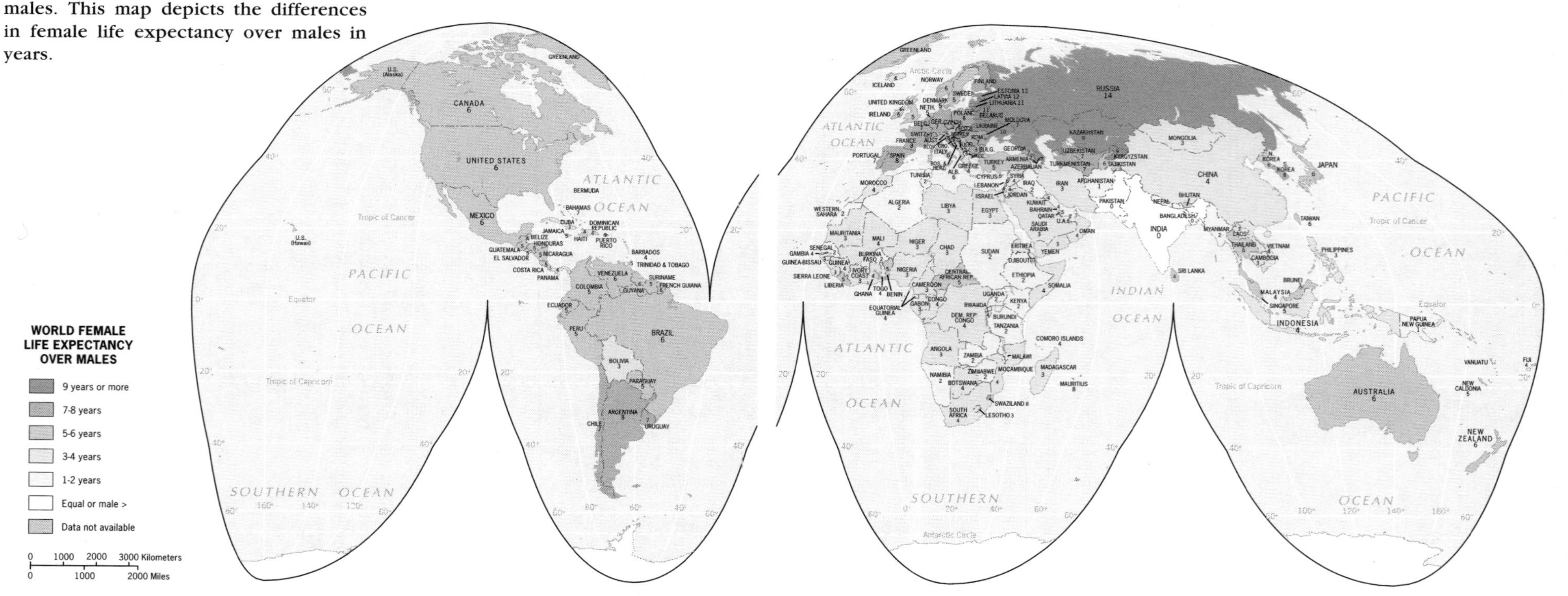

Figure 31-1 World Female Life Expectancy over Males. Generally female life expectancy is higher than that of males. This map depicts the differences in female life expectancy over males in years.

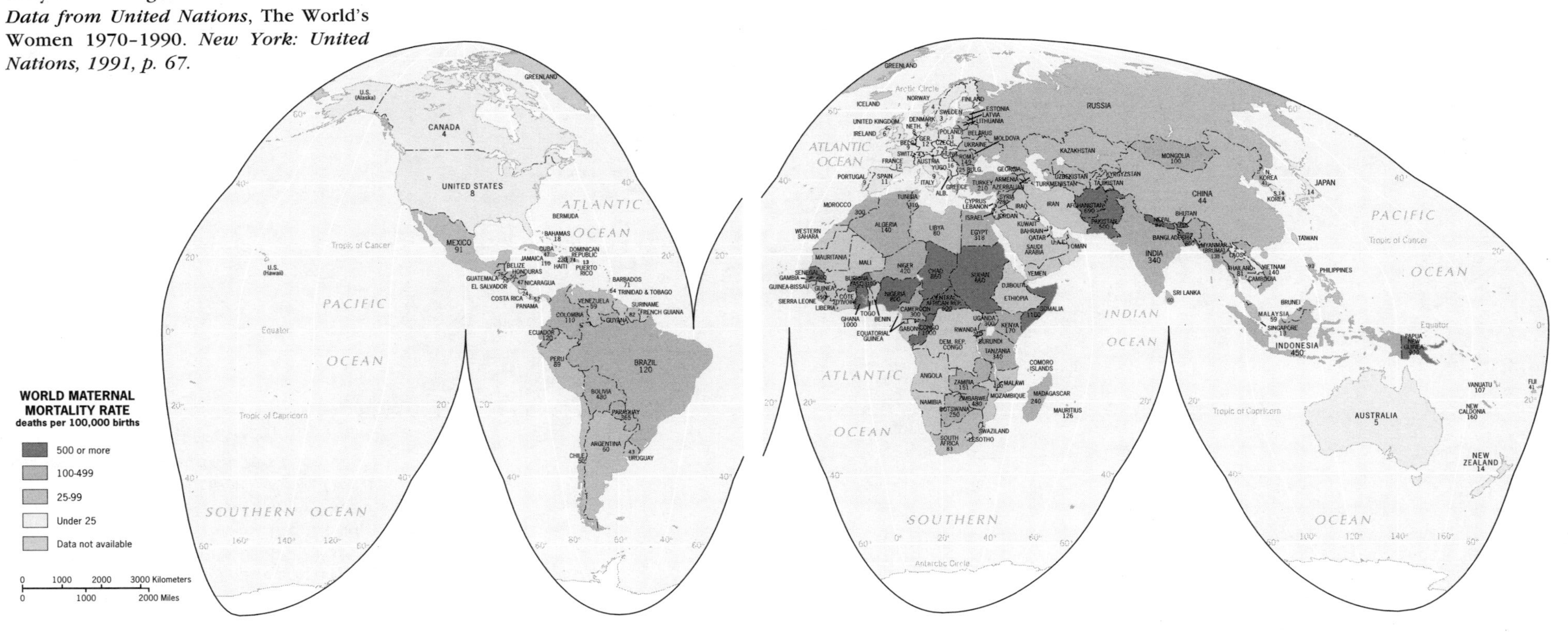

Figure 31-2 World Maternal Mortality Rate. Maternal mortality rate reflects the number of deaths per 100,000 live births. This map shows the maternal mortality rate throughout the world. *Source: Data from United Nations*, The World's Women 1970–1990. *New York: United Nations, 1991, p. 67.*

Figure 31-3 Women's Education as a Ratio of Men's. This map represents the average of data for all three levels of education during 1985–1987. *Source: Data from United Nations*. The World's Women 1970–1990. *New York: United Nations, 1991, p. 50. Later informal data suggest that the situation has been deteriorating since the late 1980s.*

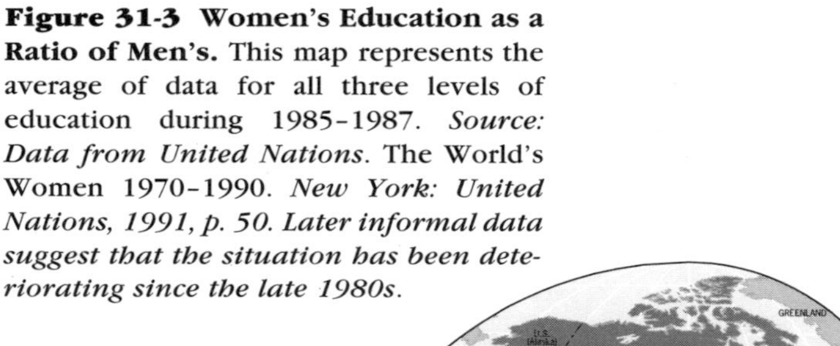

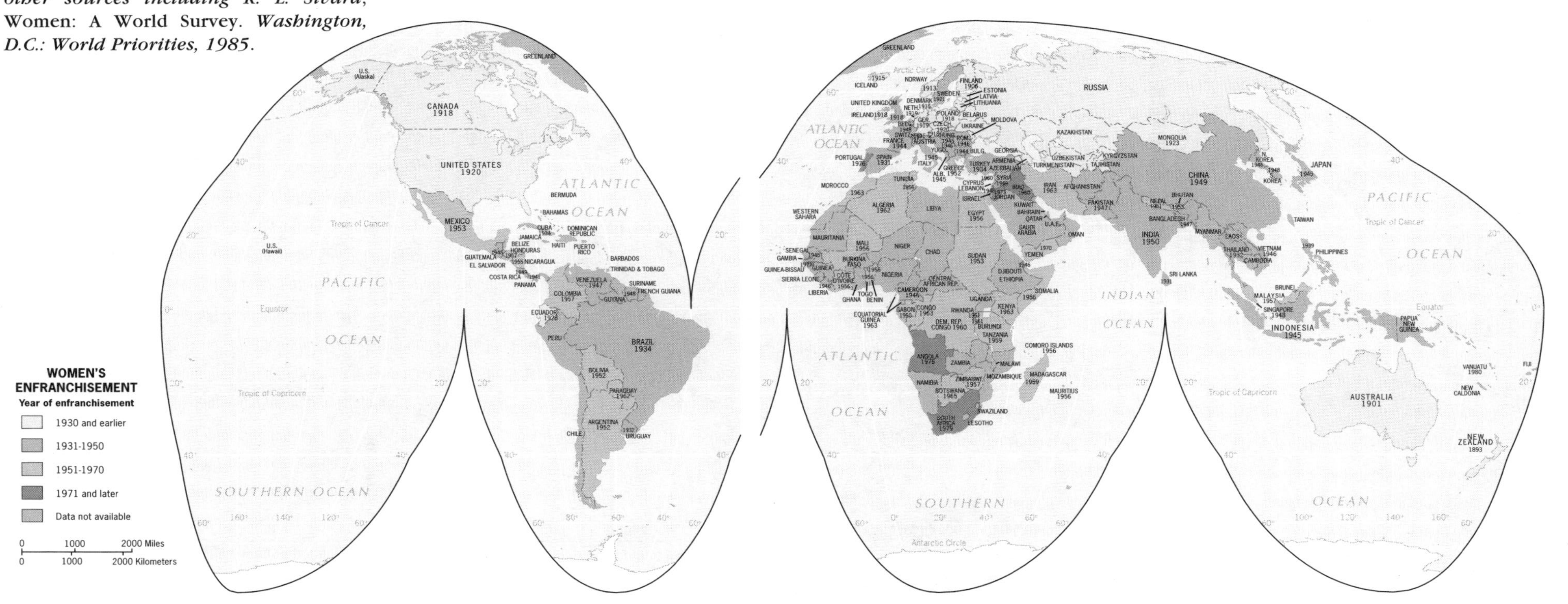

Figure 31-4 Women's Enfranchisement. The years that women were enfranchised are shown on this world map. *Source: Data from United Nations,* The World's Women 1970–1990. *New York: United Nations, 1991, p. 39 and from other sources including R. L. Sivard,* Women: A World Survey. *Washington, D.C.: World Priorities, 1985.*

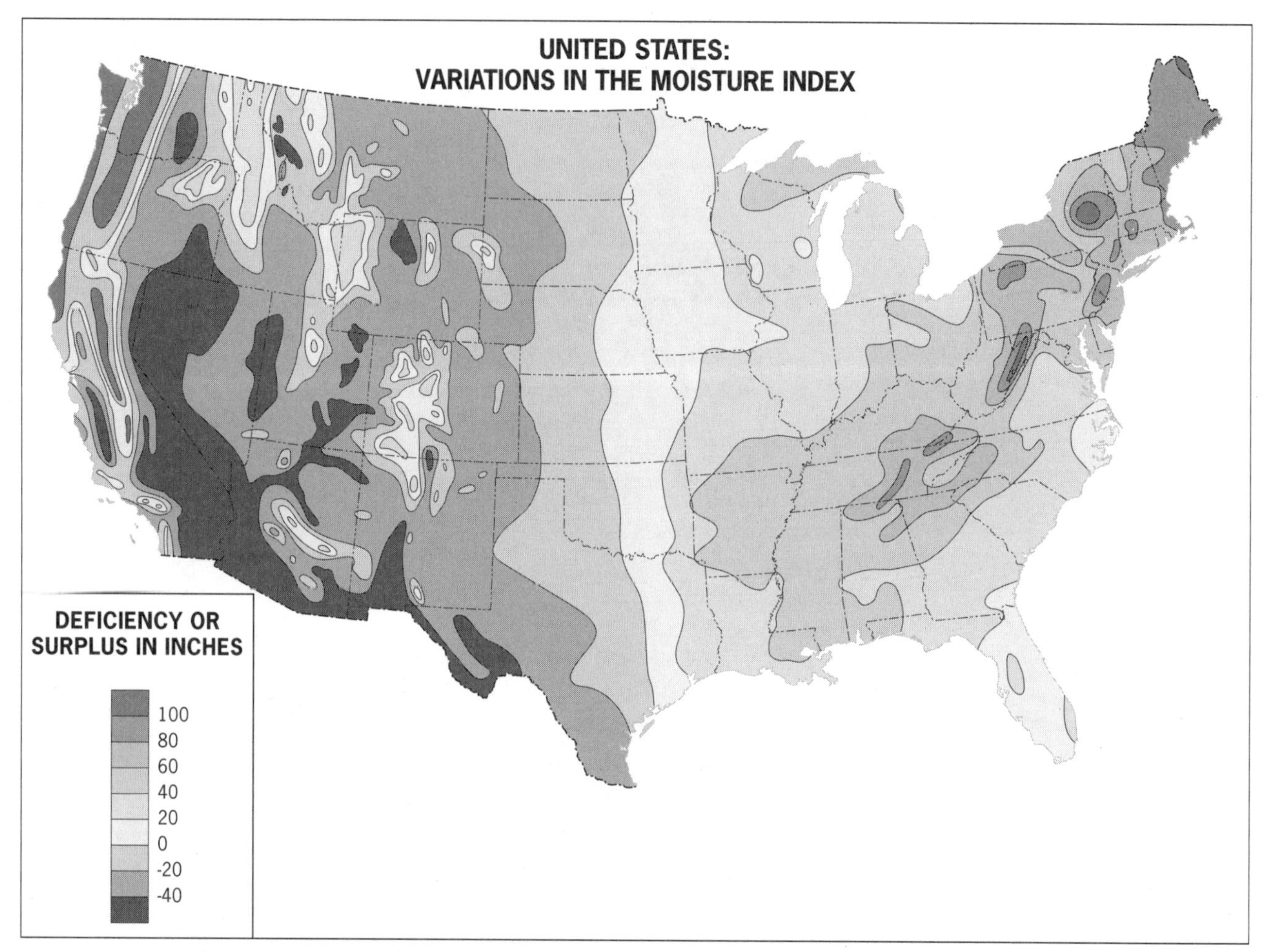

Figure 32-2 Variations in the Moisture Index in the United States. This map shows the variation in moisture surplus and deficiency in the United States. *Source: From a map in E. A. Fernald and D. J. Patton, editors,* Water Resources Atlas of Florida *(Tallahassee: Florida State University, 1984) p. 6.*

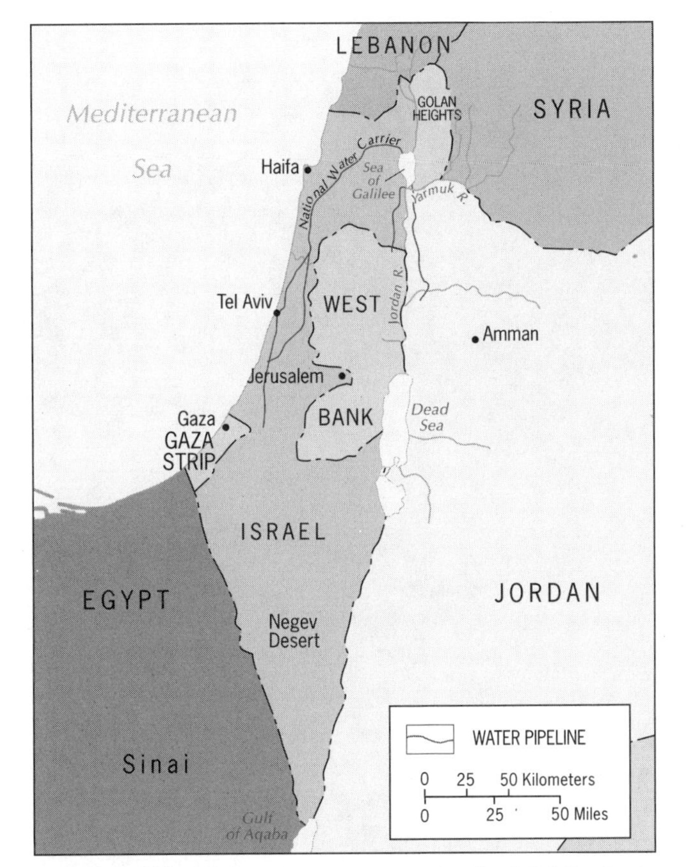

Figure 32-4 Key Water Resources in the Middle East.

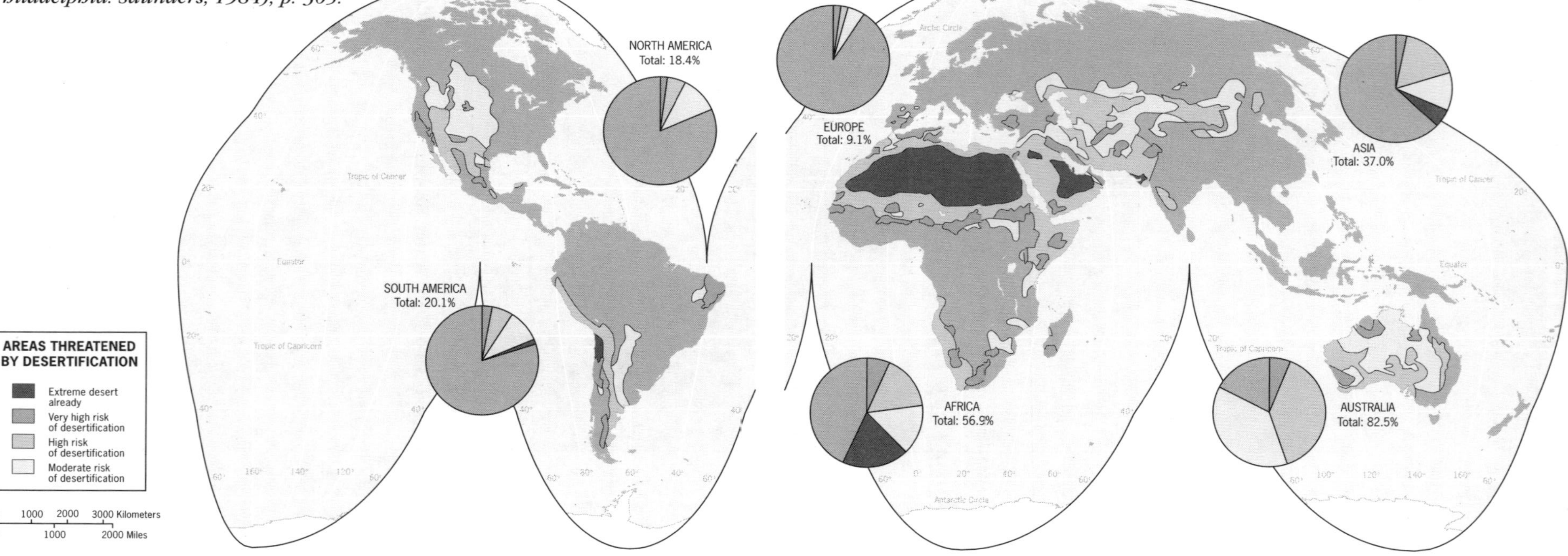

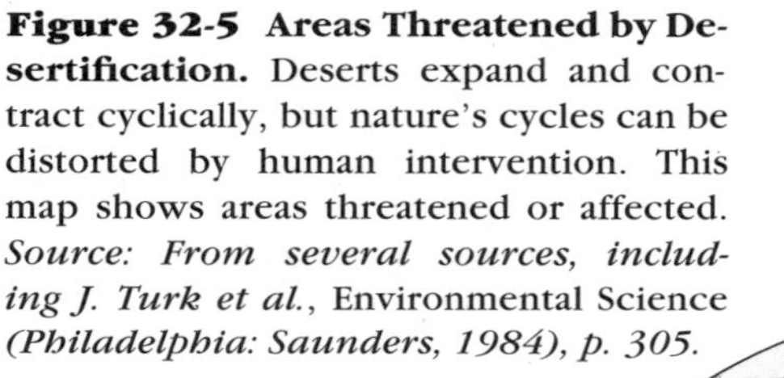

Figure 32-5 Areas Threatened by Desertification. Deserts expand and contract cyclically, but nature's cycles can be distorted by human intervention. This map shows areas threatened or affected. *Source: From several sources, including J. Turk et al.,* Environmental Science *(Philadelphia: Saunders, 1984), p. 305.*

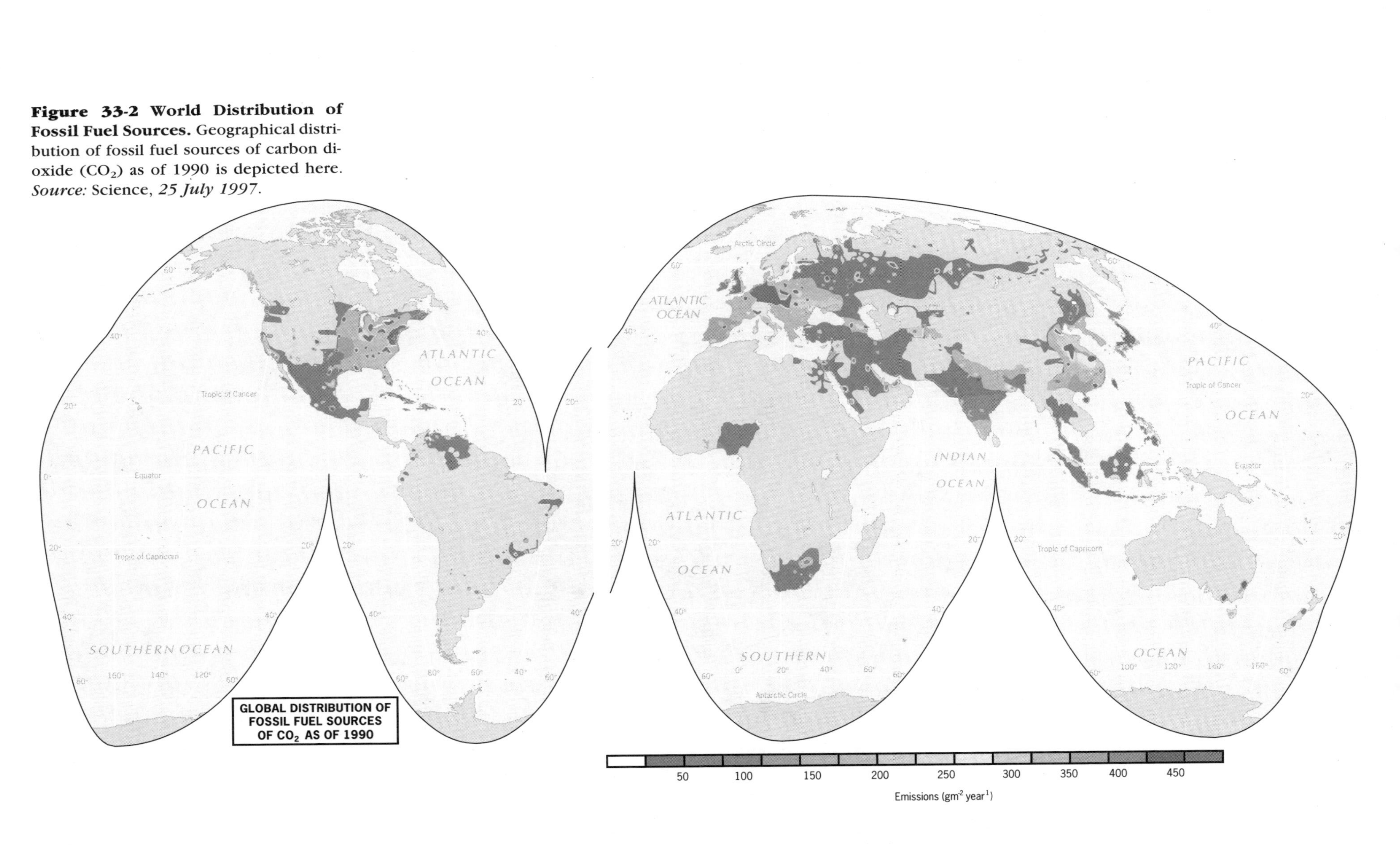

Figure 33-2 World Distribution of Fossil Fuel Sources. Geographical distribution of fossil fuel sources of carbon dioxide (CO_2) as of 1990 is depicted here. *Source:* Science, *25 July 1997*.

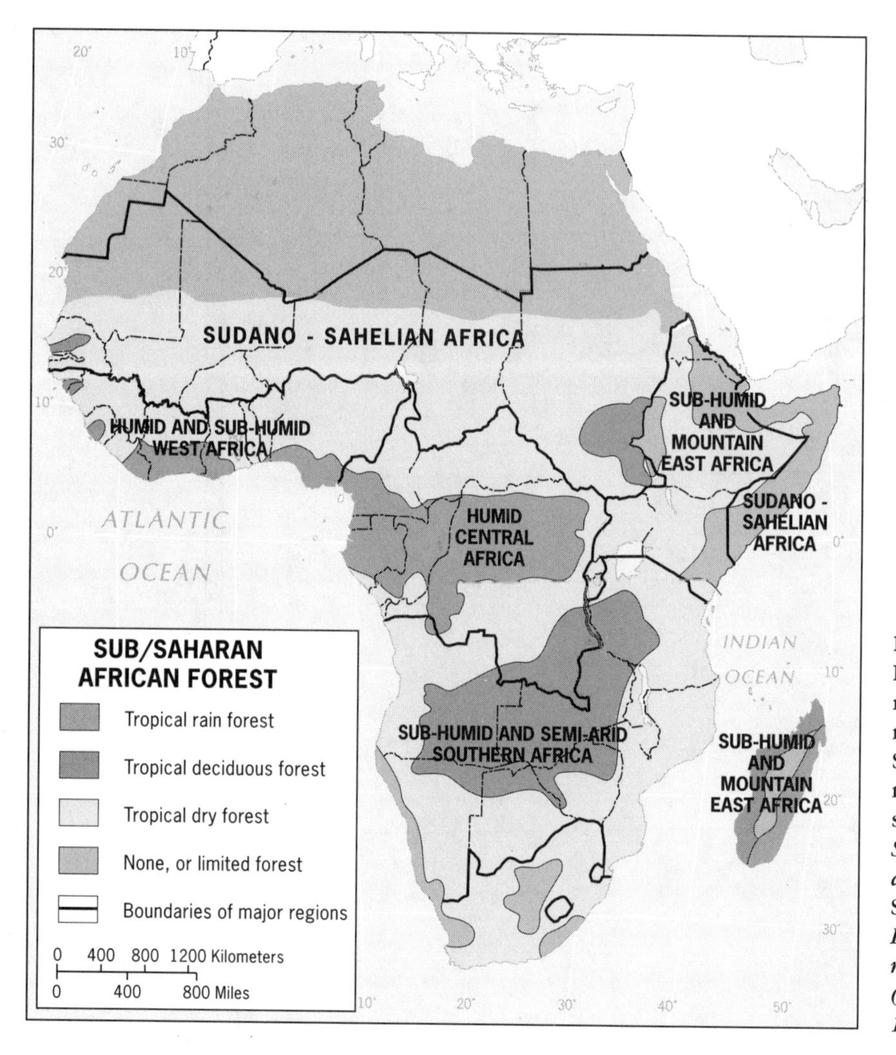

Figure 33-4 Major Regions and Forest Zones in Subsaharan Africa. This map in a World Bank technical paper on the forest sector in Subsaharan Africa shows major regions of deforestation, following state boundaries. *Source: N. P. Sharma, S. Rietbergen, C. R. Heimo, and J. Patel,* A Strategy for the Forest Sector in Sub-Saharan Africa, *World Bank Technical Paper No., 251, Africa Technical Department Series (Washington, D.C.: The World Bank, 1994).*

Figure 35-1 Devolutionary Pressures in Europe. Centrifugal forces have resulted in devolutionary pressures in various places in Europe. *Source: From a map in H. J. de Blij and P. O. Muller*, Geography: Realms, Regions, and Concepts, 8th ed. *(New York: Wiley, 1997).*

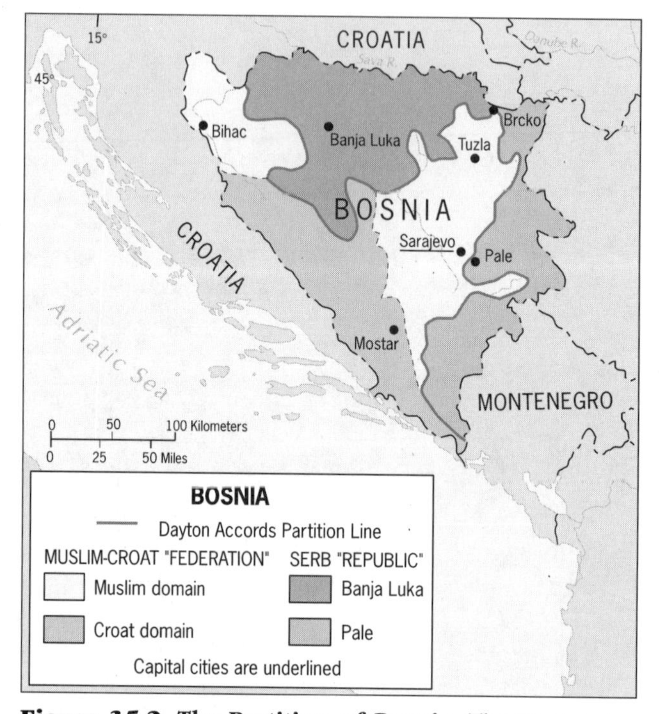

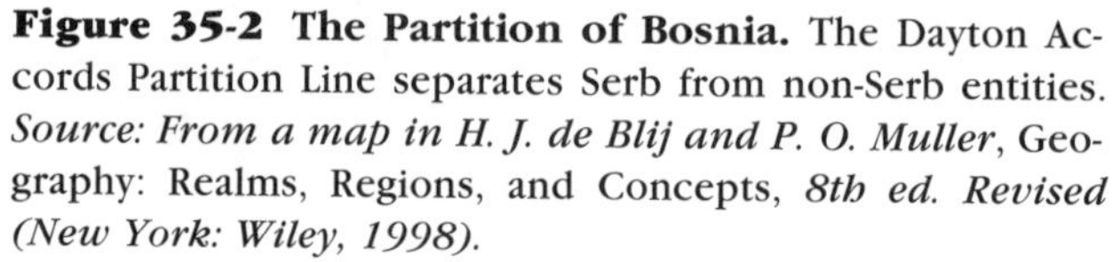

Figure 35-2 The Partition of Bosnia. The Dayton Accords Partition Line separates Serb from non-Serb entities. *Source: From a map in H. J. de Blij and P. O. Muller,* Geography: Realms, Regions, and Concepts, *8th ed. Revised (New York: Wiley, 1998).*

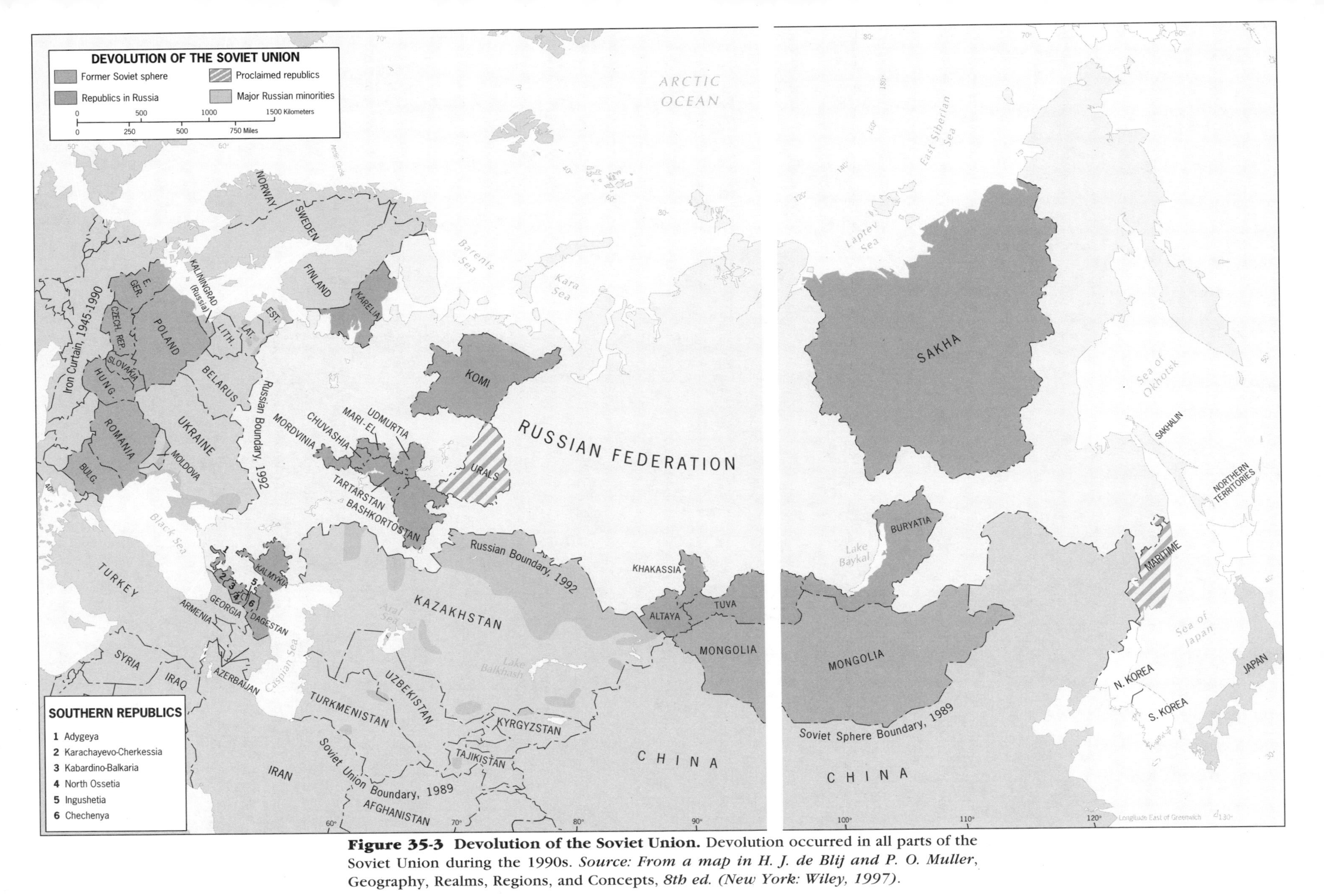

Figure 35-3 Devolution of the Soviet Union. Devolution occurred in all parts of the Soviet Union during the 1990s. *Source: From a map in H. J. de Blij and P. O. Muller,* Geography, Realms, Regions, and Concepts, *8th ed. (New York: Wiley, 1997).*

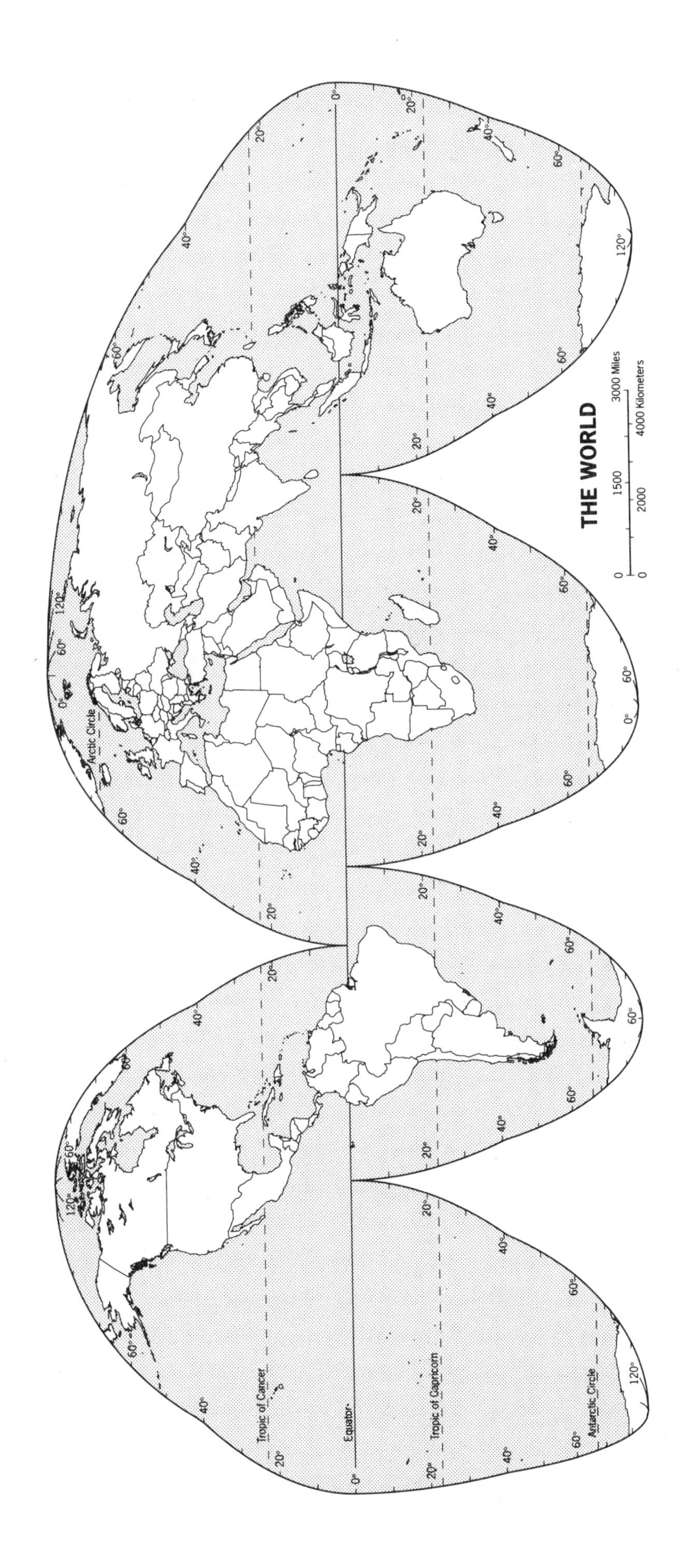
THE WORLD
0 1500 3000 Miles
0 2000 4000 Kilometers
Arctic Circle
Tropic of Cancer
Equator
Tropic of Capricorn
Antarctic Circle

EUROPE
0 200 400 600 Kilometers
0 100 200 300 Miles
Arctic Circle
30°
70°
20°
10°
0°
10°
20°
30°
40°
40°
10°
60°
60°
50°
50°
40°
40°
30°
30°
0°
10°
20°
30°

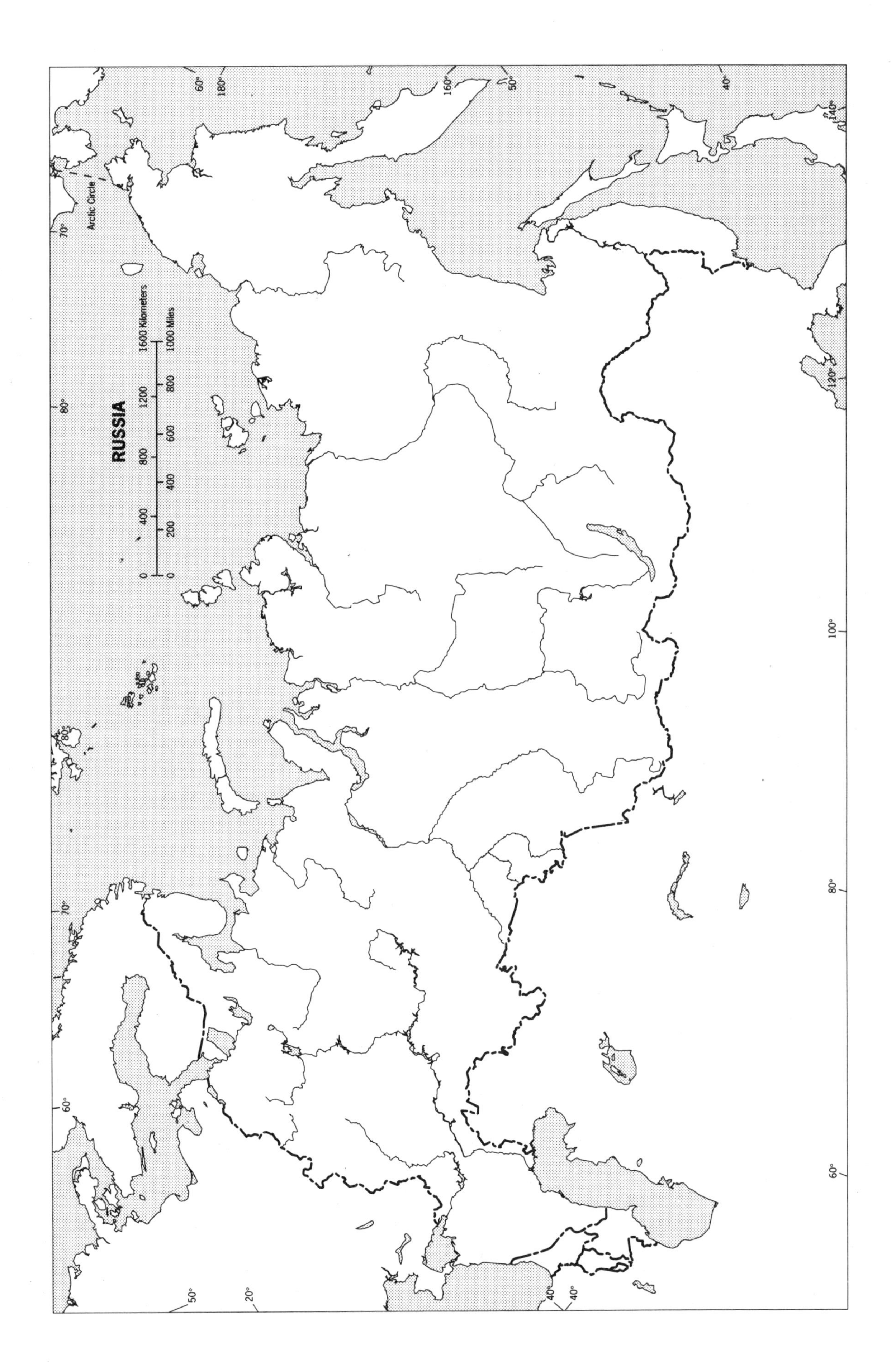
RUSSIA
Arctic Circle
0 400 800 1200 1600 Kilometers
0 200 400 600 800 1000 Miles
180°
160°
140°
120°
100°
80°
60°
40°
20°
50°
70°

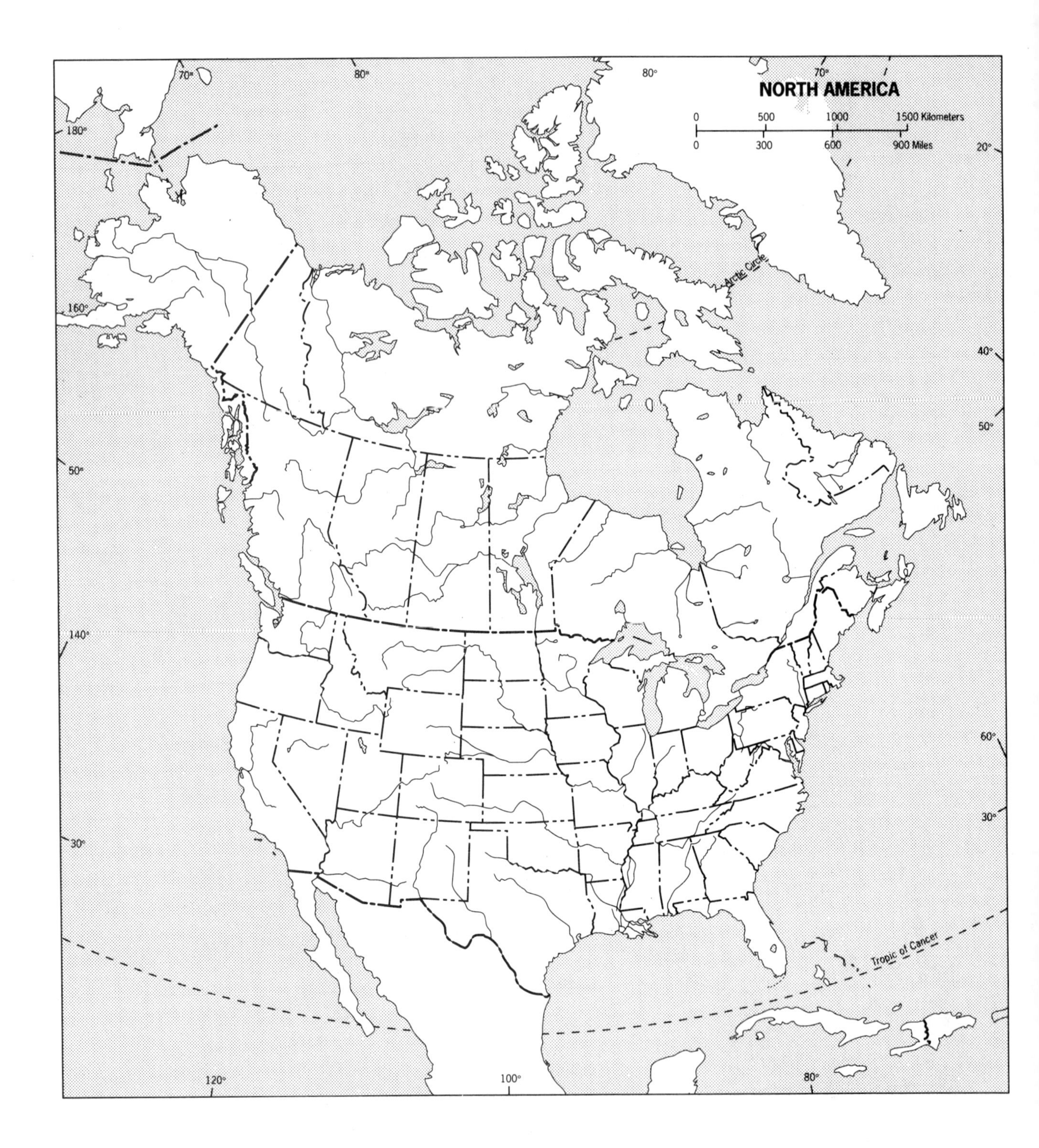
NORTH AMERICA
0
500
1000
1500 Kilometers
0
300
600
900 Miles
Arctic Circle
Tropic of Cancer
180°
160°
140°
120°
100°
80°
70°
80°
70°
20°
40°
50°
50°
60°
30°
30°

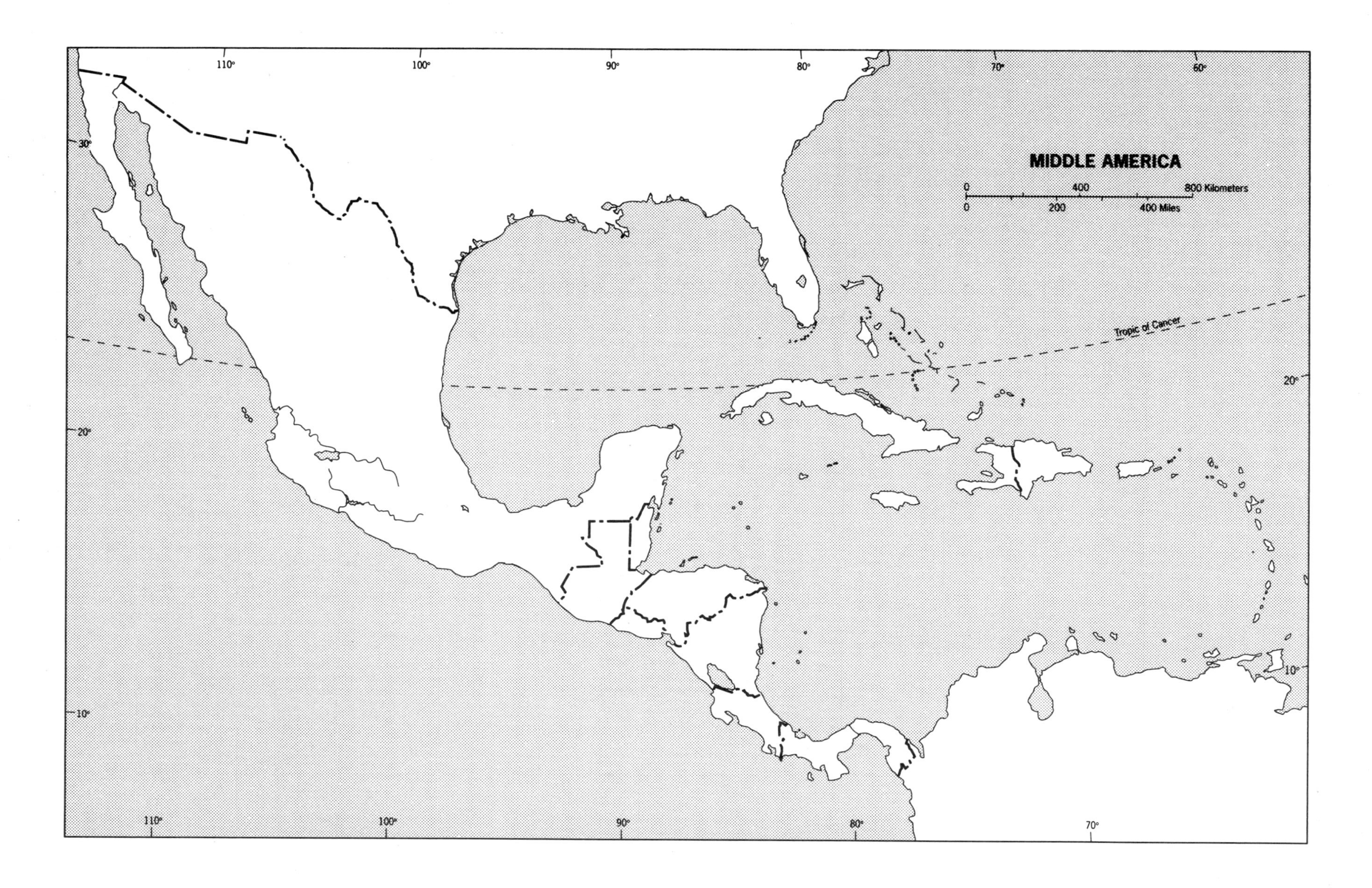
MIDDLE AMERICA
0 400 800 Kilometers
0 200 400 Miles
Tropic of Cancer
110°
100°
90°
80°
70°
60°
30°
20°
10°

SOUTH AMERICA
0
400
800
1200
1600 Kilometers
0
200
400
600
800
1000 Miles
80°
60°
40°
Equator
0°
20°
Tropic of Capricorn
40°
100°
80°
60°
40°
20°

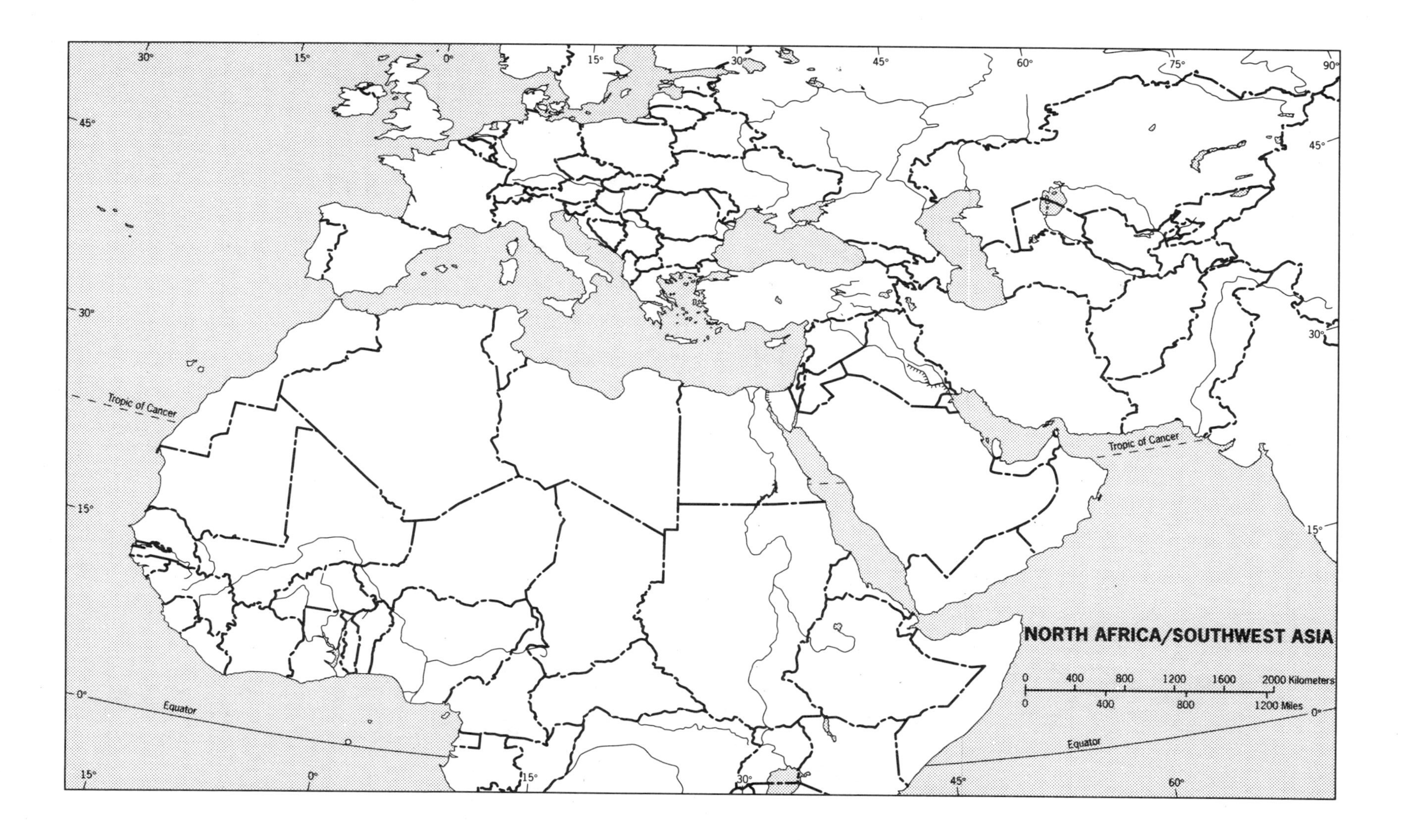

NORTH AFRICA/SOUTHWEST ASIA
0 400 800 1200 1600 2000 Kilometers
0 400 800 1200 Miles
Tropic of Cancer
Tropic of Cancer
Equator
Equator

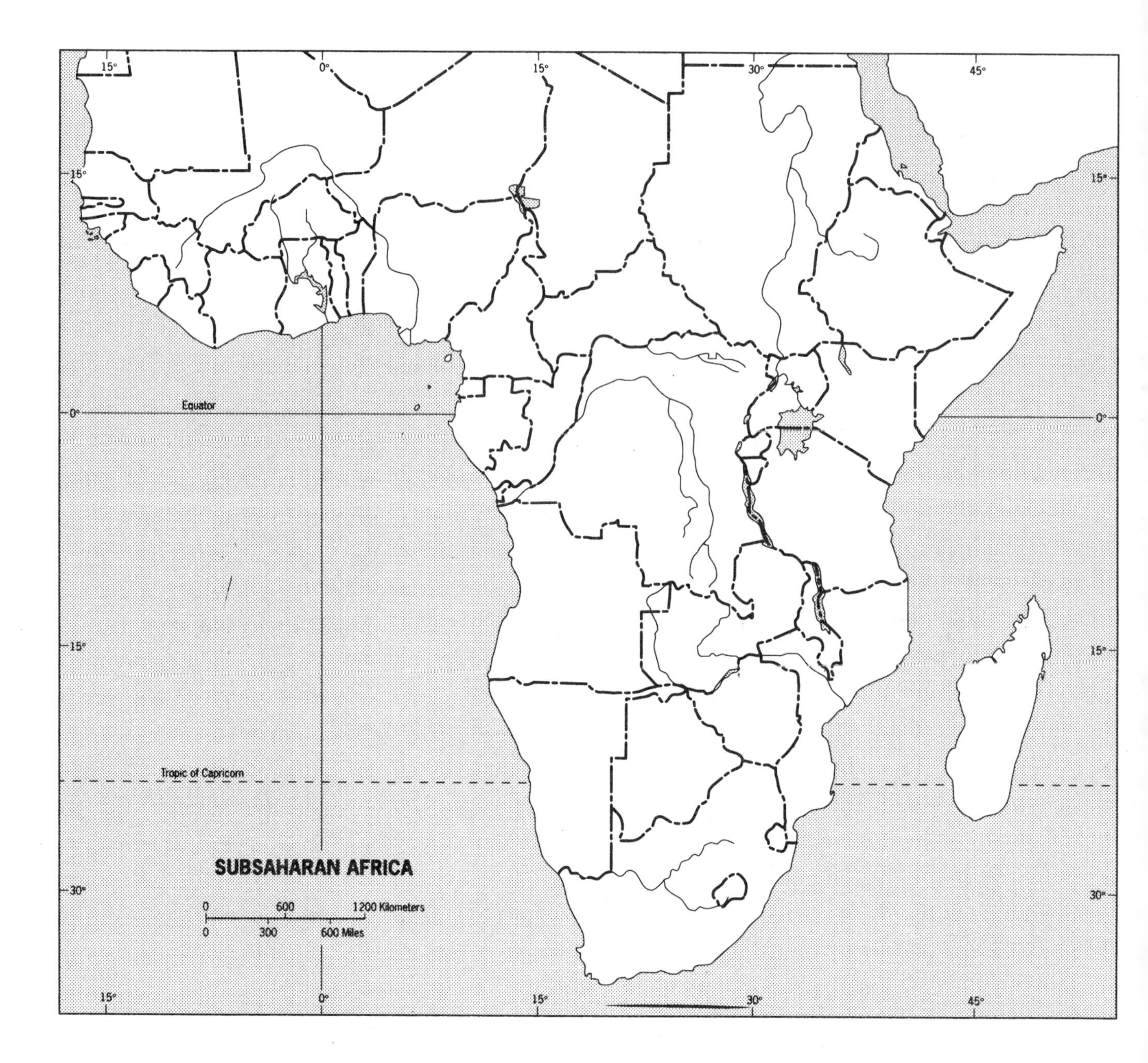
SUBSAHARAN AFRICA
Equator
Tropic of Capricorn
0 600 1200 Kilometers
0 300 600 Miles
15°
0°
15°
30°
45°
15°
0°
15°
30°

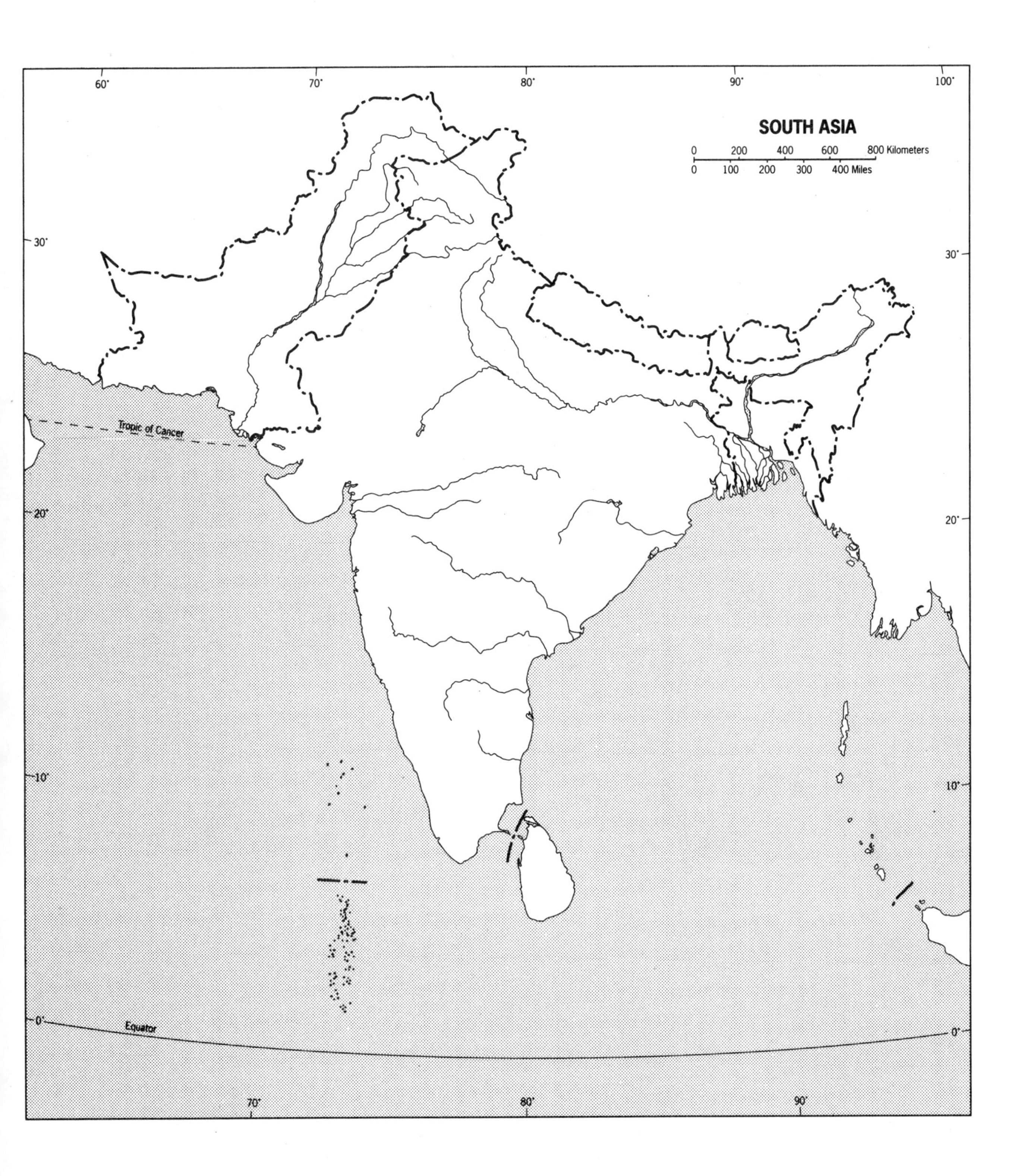
SOUTH ASIA
0 200 400 600 800 Kilometers
0 100 200 300 400 Miles
60°
70°
80°
90°
100°
30°
20°
10°
0°
Tropic of Cancer
Equator

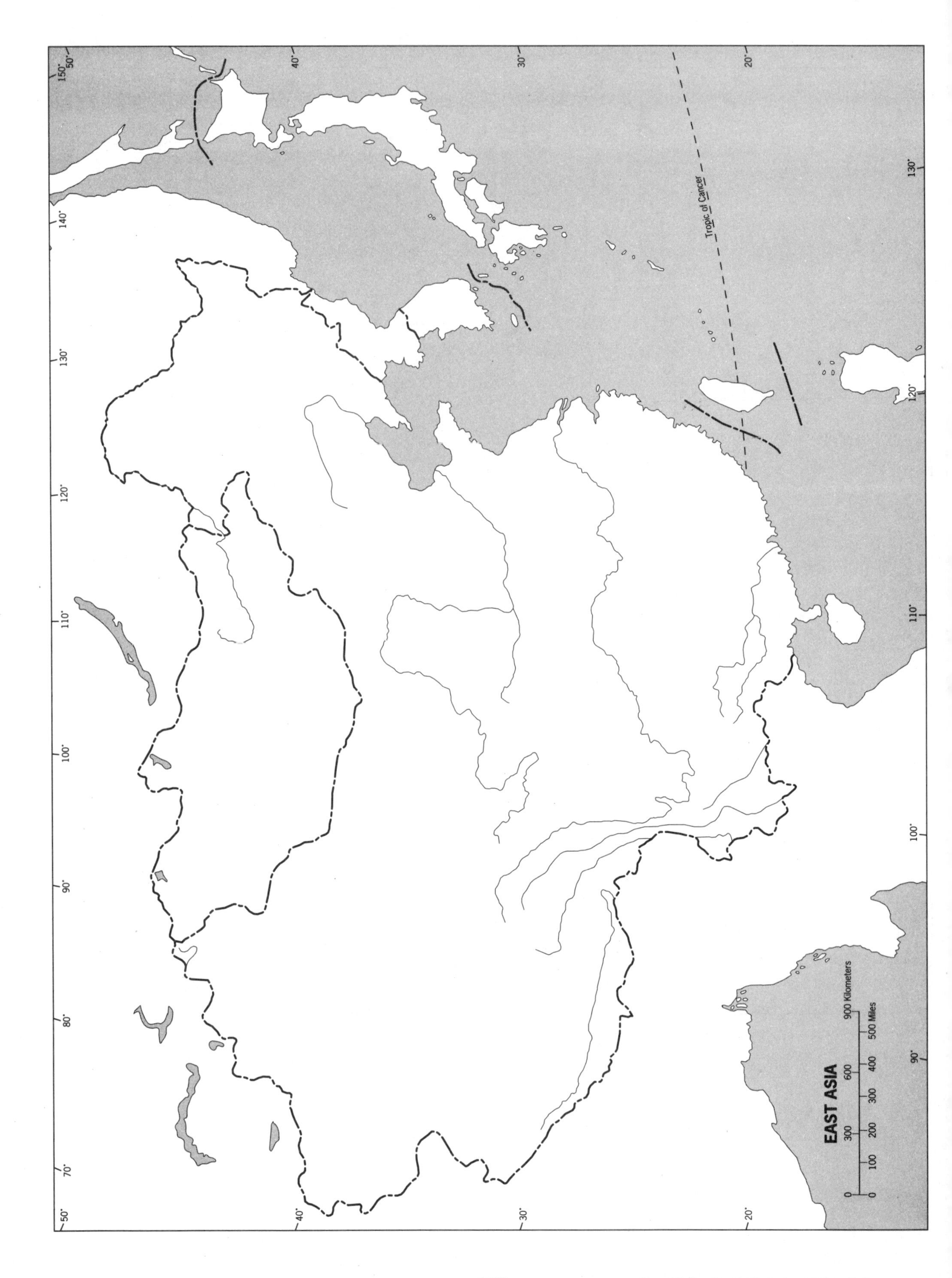
EAST ASIA
Tropic of Cancer
0
300
600
900 Kilometers
0
100
200
300
400
500 Miles
150°
140°
130°
120°
110°
100°
90°
80°
70°
50°
40°
30°
20°

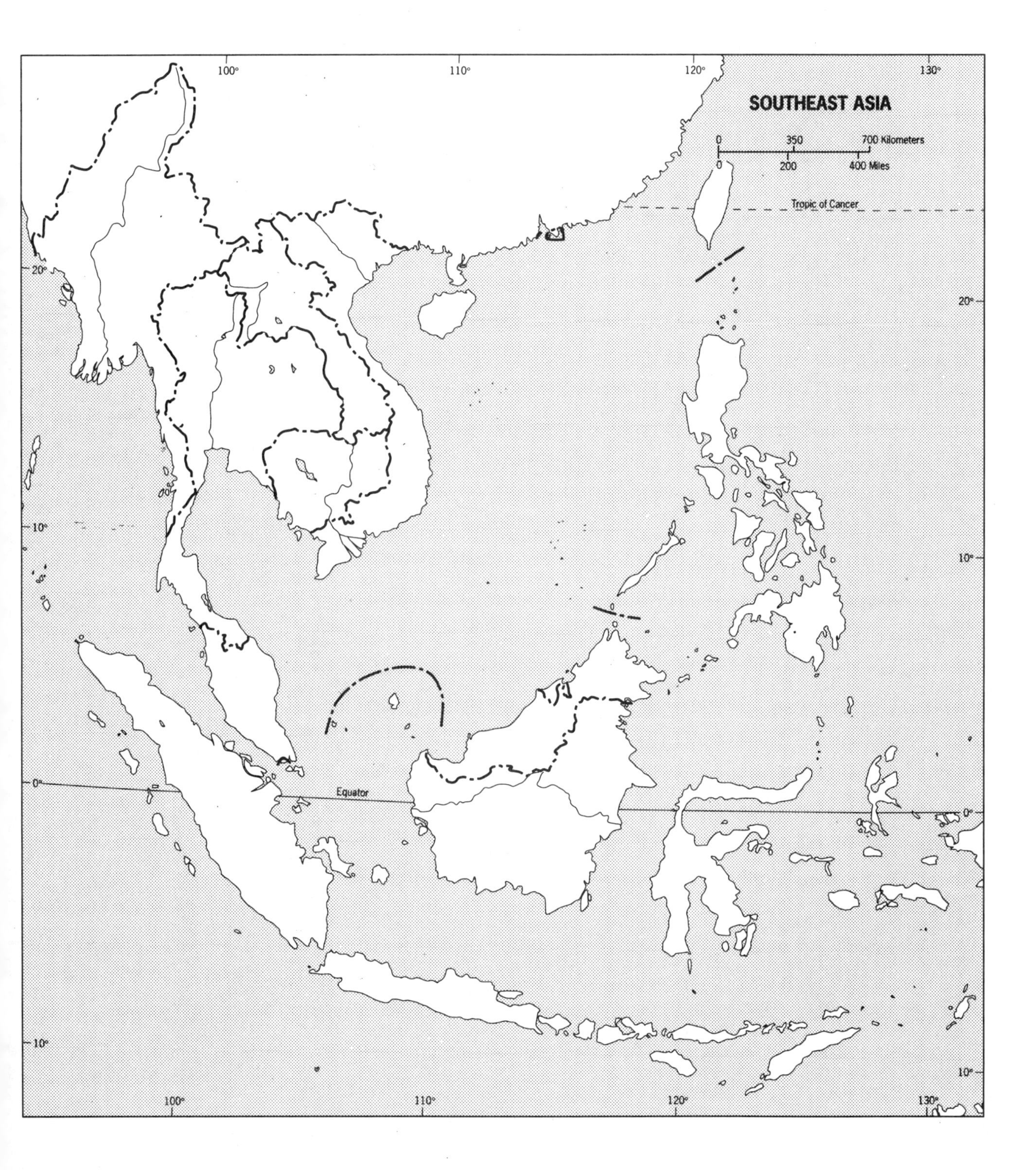
SOUTHEAST ASIA
0
350
700 Kilometers
0
200
400 Miles
Tropic of Cancer
Equator
100°
110°
120°
130°
20°
10°
0°
10°

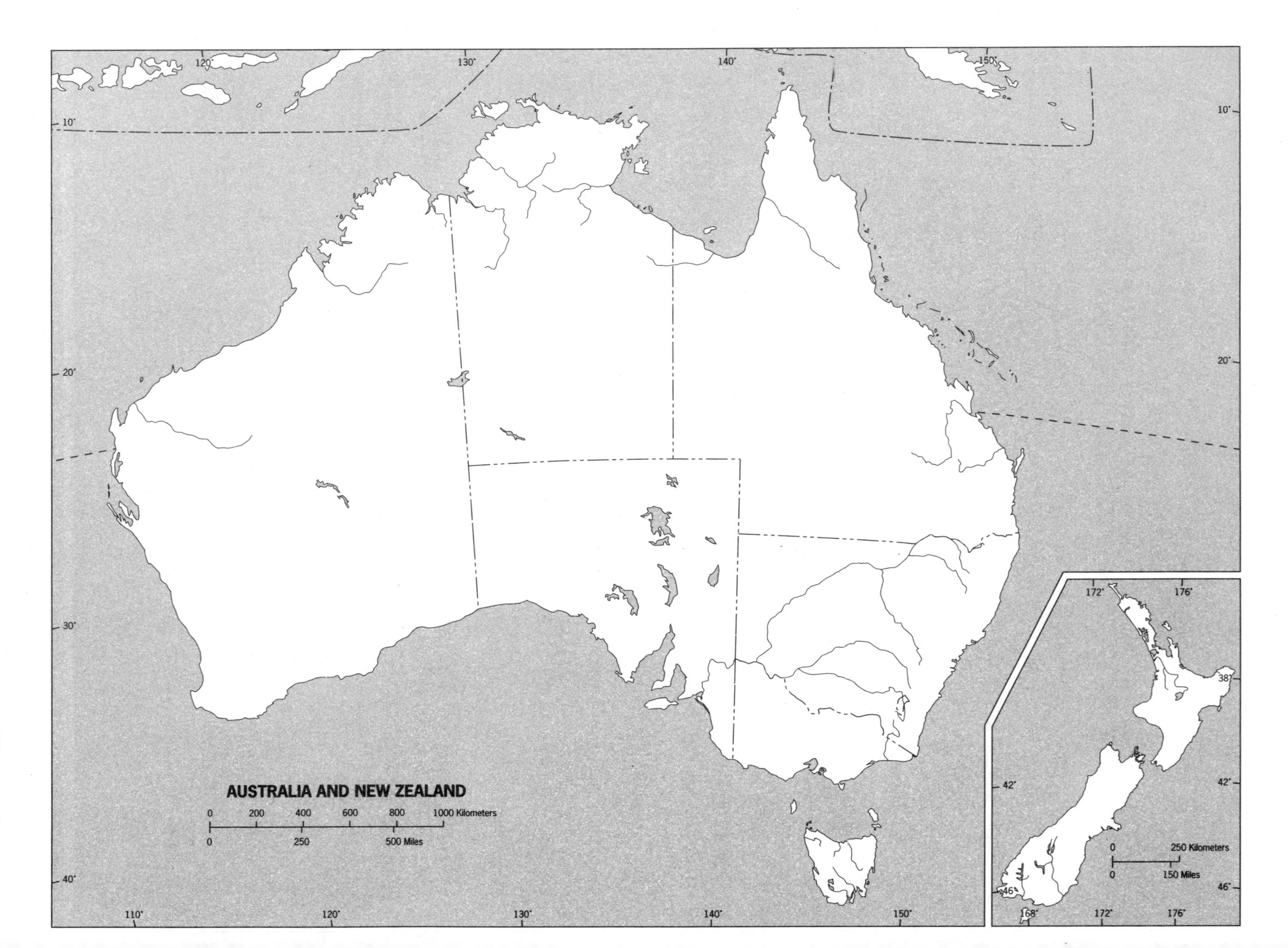
AUSTRALIA AND NEW ZEALAND
0 200 400 600 800 1000 Kilometers
0 250 500 Miles
0 250 Kilometers
0 150 Miles

VIRTUAL FIELD GUIDE

PART ONE
GEOGRAPHY, CULTURE, AND ENVIRONMENT

GOALS: To understand the nature of geography as the science of location and a core discipline that serves as a "bridge" between the social sciences and the physical sciences. With this, you, as a participant in the activity, will discern that the focus of geography is not so much the study of certain content material, as much as it is the spatial perspective of examining phenomena on our planet. You will appreciate the two-way interaction between humans and their environment. In view of the educational reforms taking place at the state and national levels, you will acquire an understanding about how an increased awareness of geography will help to develop a more responsible and enlightened citizenry that can solve both local and global spatial problems.

ACTIVITIES: Constructing hometown geographies, debating cultural imperialism, tracing the diffusion of rock & roll, and playing roles in a discussion of acid rain.

ACTIVITY 1.1: "Thinking Globally, Acting Locally!"

INTRODUCTION: Many students taking human geography as a college general education requirement have not had a formal geography course, *per se*, since junior high school perhaps. In many schools across the United States, geography got "lost" in the social science shuffle of the 'sixties era. As a result, a fair amount of incoming American college students have the false impression that geography is a "*trivial pursuit*," as their concept of what constitutes geography is shaped largely by the successful board game of that name, or what is listed under the geography category on the popular television show *Jeopardy*! But in 1985, the organization known as *G.E.N.I.P.*, or, the Geographic Education National Implementation Project, was formed to institute, update, and enrich geography programs in grades K-12 in American schools. *G.E.N.I.P.* is a collaboration between the major organizations in the field of geography: the National Council for Geographic Education, the Association of American Geographers, the American Geographical Society, and the National Geographic Society. Read about *G.E.N.I.P.* and the resources it offers at the ***National Council for Geographic Education*** Web site (WWW 1.1).

The *G.E.N.I.P.* collaboration has organized the study of geography around what are popularly referred to as "The Five Fundamental Themes of Geography." The themes are:

1) Location (both specific and relative)
2) Characteristics of a Place (both physical and human)
3) Human/Environment Interaction (a two-way street)
4) Movement
5) Regions (physical, cultural, economic, political; formal and functional)

For an elaboration of these themes, see the ***U.S. Department of Education*** Web site (WWW 1.2). These fundamental themes may be used to study geography at both local and global levels of analyses. A commonly used slogan among geographers is "*Think Globally, Act Locally.*"

Let us begin our study of human geography at the local level. Using the five fundamental geography themes, compose a typed, detailed outline of approximately two pages in length, describing the geography of your hometown, or another familiar place. If you live in a large city, you may choose to describe just your neighborhood within the city. The outline should be organized with the five themes listed as the major outline headings (i.e., Roman numerals). Your three or four subheadings per theme should be a sufficient introduction to the basic geography of the place.

The instructor *may* require that you use this outlining activity to learn basic geographic concepts, or may increase the requirements of this activity and assign it as a "capstone" research paper that integrates what you have learned and researched in your human and cultural geography course throughout the semester.

It would be appropriate to design a map to accompany your outline. The map should include the location of places mentioned within the outline/paper (for example, note in the southeastern corner of the city a water treatment plant that you have possibly mentioned in your outline). To do this part, you could use the ***Mapquest Web Site*** (WWW 1.3) to locate a street map of the location you will report on.

Focus on the geographic (i.e., spatial) aspects of the place. Minimize the historical, political, and social aspects of your town, unless they are examined for their geographic attributes or connections. You should use some combination of data sources (federal, state, and local government agency documents; regional newspaper articles; chamber of commerce materials; planning agency documents; utility reports; real estate agency data sheets; topographic maps; etc.). Most of these sources can be accessed through the Internet. Many towns and cities now have their own home page. That should be the first place to look for information for this activity. The federal government and state governments will provide additional links to excellent data sources for this assignment. Here is a list to get you started:

United States Census Bureau (WWW 1.4)

Federal Agency Statistics (WWW 1.5)

City & County Data Book (WWW 1.6)

United States Geological Survey (WWW 1.7)

Population Reference Bureau (for state-level environmental data) (WWW 1.8)

Massachusetts (as an example of a state data source) (WWW 1.9)

Here is a guideline with examples for the kinds of information that you may include in your outline and paper:

1. Location:
    a) specific:
        - latitude and longitude of the center of town or town hall
        - the intersection of specific highways
        - the main site feature of the place (e.g., at the confluence of two rivers)
    b) relative:
        - a location half-way between two big cities
        - a location in the southeastern part of your state
        - about an hour's drive from the state capital

2. Characteristics of a Place:
    a) physical
        - climatic classification
        - soil classification
        - landform classification

b) human:
- population characteristics (age, gender, race, ethnicity, etc.)
- religious affiliations
- languages spoken
- occupations (blue/ white collar; primary, secondary, tertiary, etc.)
- political affiliations (Democrat, Independent, Republican, etc.)

3. Human/Environment Interaction:
   a) water supply and treatment
   b) waste disposal
   c) pollution
   d) hazard preparedness

4. Movement:
   a) transportation modes and routes
   b) physical movements (primary wind direction, ocean currents, etc.)
   c) migrations
   e) diffusion (innovations, beliefs, customs, etc.)

5. Regions:
   a) Physical
      - landform
      - climate
      - geologic plate
   b) Cultural
      - ethnic
      - religious
      - language
   c) Economic
      - sectors of the economy
      - trade
      - major resources
   d) Political
      - zoning
      - township
      - county
      - Congressional District
   e) Formal
      - Corn Belt
      - Manufacturing Belt
      - New England
   f) Functional
      - watershed
      - commuter field

ACTIVITY 1.2: We're # 1! Cultural Imperialism

INTRODUCTION: Cultures can be many things, but they are certainly not static. Cultures can be changed through innovations and inventions, diffusion, acculturation, and revitalization. With the twentieth century advancements in communications, transportation, and trade, cultures in many parts of the world have become increasingly dynamic. Some nations fear an eventual loss of cultural identity with ever-increasing global interconnections. *Cultural imperialism* has been defined as the emerging global culture dominated by the world's superpower, the United States. Some argue that U.S. cultural influence is at least as strong as its military influence. Industrialized nations have responded in various ways to America's cultural dominance. France has become particularly wary of U.S. influence (e.g., *la loi Toubon* of 1994, a law which forbids French public entities and corporations engaged in public activities from using English expressions where there is a French equivalent). Canada has "allowed" considerable American cultural influence (e.g., most of the current National Hockey League franchises are now located in the U.S.). Since World War II, Japan has incorporated whole segments of American culture (e.g., baseball & fast food), yet has remained distinctively Japanese. The less industrialized nations have also had different responses to American cultural dominance. Many of the Islamic-dominated nations of the Middle East have little tolerance for American cultural influences and use censorship and other tactics to keep this influence to a minimum. Some additional cultural conflicts between less developed nations and the U.S. grew out of the Cold War which often pitted "godless communists" versus "corrupt capitalists."

This activity raises several opinion questions. 1) Does U.S. cultural imperialism exist, and, if yes, in what ways? 2) If no, are we simply witnessing the development of a "global" culture that currently happens to be largely influenced by the United States? 3) Or, will increased nationalism maintain separate and distinct cultures, with no one culture being dominant?

> ReseAnne Sims' "The United States vs. the World: A Theoretical Look at Cultural Imperialism," at the site of ***The University of Texas*** (WWW 1.10).
>
> Former U.S. Ambassador to Finland, Derek N. Shearer's "Hollywood: It's Not Cultural Imperialism, It's World Culture," see the ***U.S. Embassy*** Web site (WWW 1.11).
>
> David Rothkopf's "In Praise of Cultural Imperialism," at the ***Mt. Holyoke College Web site*** (WWW 1.12).
>
> Douglas Rushkoff's "Let Them Eat Apple Pie? Cultural Imperialism and the Internet," at the ***Arkzin*** Web site (WWW 1.13).
>
> Berlingeri, Brett, & Gokyigit's "Cultural Imperialism," at the ***Harvard University*** Web site (WWW 1.14).

After you have decided which point of view you wish to support, collect information in the virtual field to support your argument. You then might join like-minded students in one section of the room to work together to strengthen your argument in order to discuss and debate with the individuals and groups taking the other two perspectives.

ACTIVITY 1.3: Rock & Roll Is Here To Stay!

INTRODUCTION: Although the United States has been called a "*melting pot*" because of numerous ethnic influences from its wide range and history of immigration, one aspect of American culture that originated in the United States is that of rock and roll music. The world-wide exposure of this native American musical style is a classic example of cultural diffusion. Simply defined, diffusion is the spreading of ideas and objects by whatever means. Diffusion can occur through direct observation, word of mouth, the written word, or recorded sights and sounds. Human geographers are primarily interested in the spatial aspects of diffusion. Some of the key questions that geographers ask about diffusion of some cultural phenomenon include:

1. Where and when did the idea or item originate?
2. How far did this idea or item spread?
3. How long did it take this idea or item to spread?
4. By what means did it spread?
5. Did anyone or anything slow or prevent its movement?
6. Was this a contiguous or non-contiguous movement?
7. Was the concept or idea altered as it diffused?
8. Which segments of the population accepted this concept or idea?

In this activity, use the Internet to research and respond in short-answer format to the eight short-answer questions posed above, using rock and roll music as the subject in this study of diffusion. The following sites may be used to answer these questions:

Visit the **Rock and Roll Hall of Fame** in Cleveland, Ohio (WWW 1.15).

Refer to the ***History of Rock and Roll*** (WWW 1.16) Web site.

Travel back half a century to ***The Fifties*** (WWW 1.17), for information from the rock and roll's early years.

To focus on rock and roll's original artists, see the Web site ***Biddeford*** (WWW 1.18).

See the Rock & Roll series on the ***Public Broadcasting System*** (WWW 1.19).

To see how TV impacted this musical style, see the ***House of Music*** (WWW 1.20).

ACTIVITY 1.4: Rain Of Terror

INTRODUCTION: The interaction between humans and their environment is one of the five fundamental themes of geography. This interaction is a two-way street. Greater numbers of humans than ever before are exposed to deadly natural hazards (e.g., earthquakes, hurricanes, tornadoes, etc.). With the world's population at approximately six billion inhabitants, the negative impacts caused by increased human activity on the natural environment are also greater than ever.

This role-playing activity focuses on just one environmental impact created by human activity: acid rain. Using information provided in Web sites established by the United States Environmental Protection Agency and state environmental agencies, conduct some field work that will help you prepare for one of the roles listed below. Be prepared to talk about the effects acid rain may have on your character, and to present arguments for, or against, policies to control acid rain.

U.S. Environmental Protection Agency program on acid rain (WWW 1.21).

Massachusetts Department of Environmental Protection
(an example of a state environmental agency) (WWW 1.22).

Choose one of the following roles for the class discussion:
1. farmer
2. coal miner
3. factory owner
4. recreational fisherman
5. forester
6. architect
7. municipal health agent
8. resident of southeastern Canada
9. resident of a steel producing city

The instructor may wish to group individuals to jointly prepare a mock public hearing. Those individuals who play roles where their livelihoods could be negatively impacted by strict environmental regulations regarding acid rain may comprise one group. Another group could be those whose livelihoods could be positively impacted with more stringent regulations. A third group might approach the debate from a personal health perspective. Another group of may represent the regulating authority that would rule whether or not the environmental regulations should be strengthened.

ADDITIONAL WEB SITES FOR STUDYING ABOUT GEOGRAPHY, CULTURE, AND THE ENVIRONMENT:

The Web site for the ***Association of American Geographers*** contains information on the nature of geography, educational resources, and careers in geography. (WWW 1.23).

For a complete listing of the ***National Geographic*** sponsored Geographic Alliance Network sites. (WWW 1.24).

Worldwatch Institute is one of the leading non-profit public environmental policy research organizations in the United States. (WWW 1.25).

ADDITIONAL READINGS:

deSouza, Anthony R., et. al., *Geography for Life*, (Washington, D.C.: National Geographic Research & Exploration, 1994),

Huntington, Samuel, *The Clash of Civilization and the Remaking of the World Order*, (New York: Simon & Schuster, 1996).

McLuhan, Marshall, and Powers, Bruce, *The Global Village: Transformation in World Life and Media in the 21st Century*, (New York: Oxford University Press, 1993).

Postel, Sandra, *Air Pollution, Acid Rain, and the Future of Forests*, (Washington, D.C.: Worldwatch Institute, 1984), Worldwatch Paper #58.

PART TWO
POPULATION PATTERNS AND PROCESSES

GOALS: To become aware of various world population issues, and see how population problems can impact the development of cultures and influence human/environment interaction.

ACTIVITIES: Interpret population pyramids, construct population pyramids, and map the allocation of food resources.

ACTIVITY 2.1: Bar Hopping Around The Pyramids.

INTRODUCTION: Population pyramids (also known as age-sex pyramids) are specialized bar graphs that display an area's population by age and sex (gender) for a particular point in time. Pyramids are usually standardized to display the male population age brackets on the left side of the graph, female population age brackets on the right, younger age brackets at the bottom, and older age brackets at the top. Ideally, five-year age brackets are shown (e.g., ages 0-4, 5-9, 10-14, etc.). Pyramids have the top bar on each side of the graph represent some cutoff point age-bracket (e.g., sixty-five and above, seventy-five and above, etc.). The bottom of the graph is typically scaled to read the bars as percentages of the total population, or sometimes the actual number of people is shown on the scale, which is the case for the United States age-sex pyramid. If the bars are scaled to represent percentages of the total population, which is preferred in this virtual field activity, places of all population sizes can be easily compared (e.g., Canada and China), since the sum of the lengths of all the bars for each area examined will be the same (i.e., 100%). The term "pyramid" is used because, historically, most areas typically had a large young population, a somewhat smaller middle-age population, and an even smaller older population. Therefore, the graphs were usually quite broad at the base, and tapered steadily to a narrow peak, just as a true pyramid is shaped.

You will see that in today's world, population pyramids for different countries, states, and cities show a myriad of shapes. Most of the developing nations today still have age-sex graphs that are shaped like a pyramid. However, some of the more developed nations in Western Europe have shape profiles that are almost vertical, meaning that no one age cohort dominates the graph. The age-sex graph representing the state of Florida will be "top heavy" due to its large retirement population, whereas Utah's pyramid will have a much broader base reflecting the relatively high birth rate among the Mormon population, which represents a majority of the state's residents. One could construct a single population pyramid for an entire city, which would have a particular shape, or produce a dozen or more differently-shaped population pyramids showing various neighborhoods within the city, which also may be differently-shaped. Neighborhoods with colleges, prisons, military bases, retirement communities, and Veteran Administration hospitals reveal considerably different demographic profiles than a residential community.

Activity 2.1 Field Work

Start your field work by visiting the Web site for ***Mining Company*** (WWW 2.1).

Once there, select the Net Links option, and connect to the World Population. From World Population, go to International Population Pyramids. This is a direct link to the ***U.S. Census Bureau*** Web site (WWW 2.2) Here, countries are located alphabetically. Pyramids are available for various time periods, depending on the country chosen. Under "Type of Output," students can choose either "summary" (pyramids for 1997, 2025, & 2050), select years (e.g., pyramids for the United States for every year between 1950 and 2050), or dynamic (and visualize a country's population as the pyramid changes from year to year up to the year 2050). Please note that population pyramids can be important planning tools because predictions can be made regarding such impacts as certain age cohorts on school enrollments, work-force size, health concerns of an aging population, and retirement issues.

Let's compare the "summary" pyramids for the United States, China, Germany, and Bangladesh. First, examine the United States pyramid. Locate the bulging "Baby Boom" generation on the graphs (those born between 1946 & 1964). In 1997 they are found in the 30-50 age brackets. When they were in their pre-school years (1946-1970), baby boomers created huge markets for baby products (diapers, cribs, baby food, etc.). From ages 5-18 (1951-1982), they impacted pre-collegiate school enrollments. The past quarter-century is marked by the baby boomers' impact on the U.S. work force.

The United States

1. What are some of the likely impacts baby boomers will have on American society when they retire and achieve senior citizen status?
2. Why do females continue to outnumber males in the older brackets?

China

1. Why do Chinese men greatly outnumber women, particularly at the younger age brackets?
2. What do you think caused the large indentation in the 35-39 age bracket in China's 1997 population pyramid?
3. Why does China's 2025 pyramid look so markedly different from the 1997 pyramid?

Germany

1. What do you think caused the large indentation in the 50-54 age bracket in Germany's 1997 population pyramid?
2. Is Germany's total population expected to decline between 1997 and 2025 and beyond?
3. Which bracket is predicted to be the largest for Germany in 2050?

Bangladesh

1. Why is its 1997 pyramid so different from the U.S. and Germany pyramids?
2. How many people in Bangladesh were under age 5 in 1997?
3. Is Bangladesh's population expected to exceed 200 million in 2050?

The ***U.S. Census Bureau*** Web (WWW 2.3) also features "population clocks," which display its estimated population totals for the United States and the world at the moment you log on! Check from one day to the next to note any changes. On August 2, 1998, the estimate for the population of the United States was 270,259,165. The World Population Estimate on that date was 5,933,543,609. How have the numbers changed?

ACTIVITY 2.2: Shape Up!

INTRODUCTION: , Using data from various sources found in your college or town libraries, you can construct population pyramids of your home state, home town, or the municipality in which your college is located. Data can also be ordered directly from the ***U.S. Census Bureau*** Web site (WWW 2.4). Students interested in studying Canada can find population pyramid data at the ***Statistics Canada*** Web site (WWW 2.5).

Choose an area to study, and construct a detailed population pyramid by using the Data Table

(Table 2.1) and Pyramid Construction Table (Table 2.2). Write a one page analysis of the pyramid's shape, comparing it to other pyramids (e.g., the 1997 United States population pyramid examined earlier), and hypothesize reasons for any particular "bulges" on the pyramid.

Table 2.1. Population Pyramid Data Table

Place or Municipality:
Total Population: **Year of Data:**

Ages	Total Number	Number of Females	% Female	Number of Males	% Male
0-4					
5-9					
10-14					
15-19					
20-24					
25-29					
30-34					
35-39					
40-44					
45-49					
50-54					
55-59					
60-64					
65-69					
70-74					
75-79					
80-84					
85 and up					
Total					
Median Age					
	Combined	**Female**		**Male**	

Table 2.2. Population Pyramid Construction Table

Place: ____________________

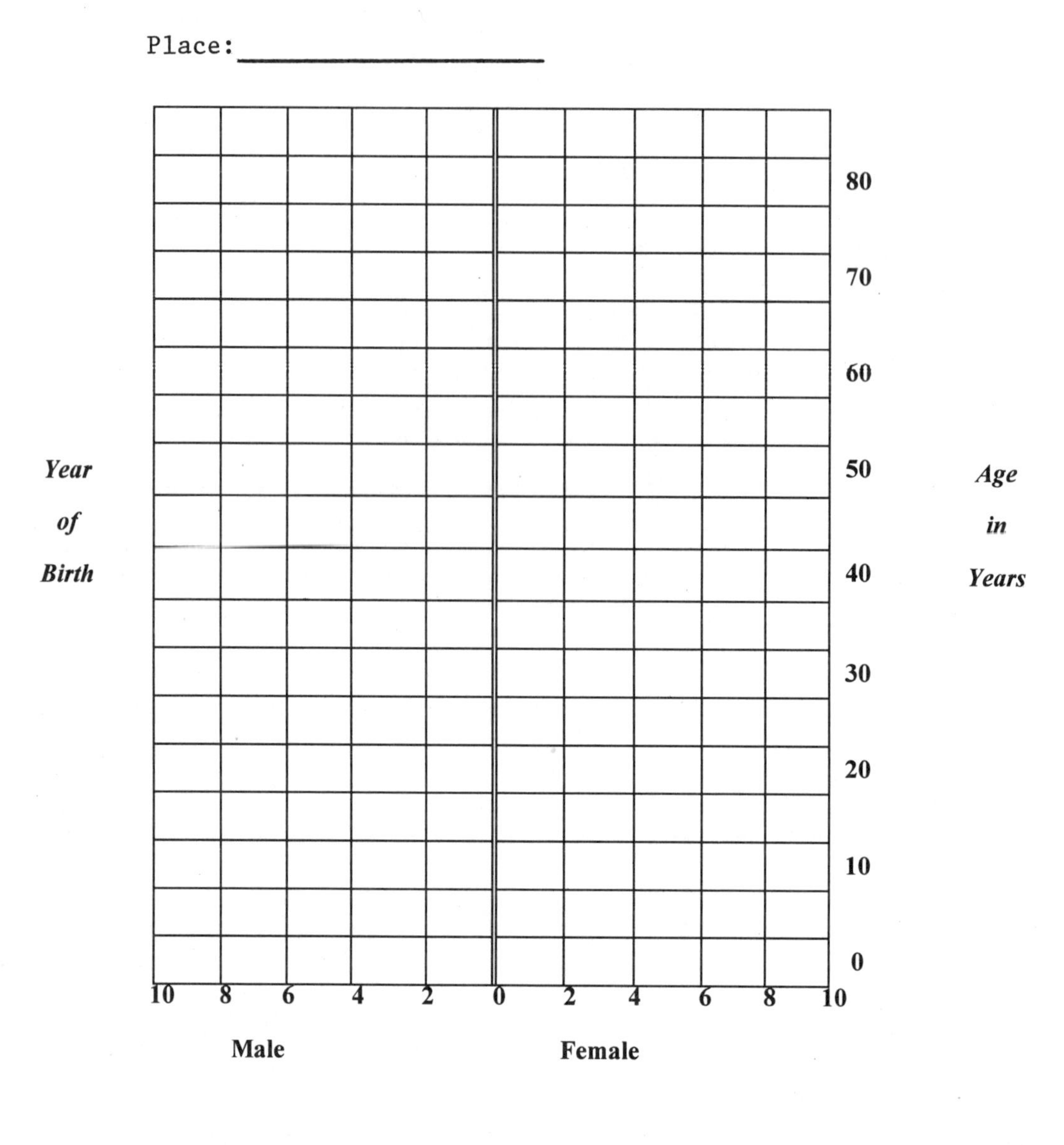

Med. Age:  Med. Age: _______

ACTIVITY 2.3: Let Them Eat Cake?

INTRODUCTION: To get a better understanding and appreciation of the variety of cultures that are present throughout the world, one needs to be aware of the day-to-day population-related issues and pressures that many people face. When will their next meal take place? Where can they go for medical treatment? Who will employ them? Why do thousands of people die in "ordinary" coastal storms? What will happen to a country that doubles in population in just one generation?

For an example, let's look at the Peoples Republic of China. Here is a nation that is just slightly larger than the United States in territory, yet it has five times the population of the United States to feed, with only about half as much farmland! Literally millions have died in China this century due to starvation. The late 1950s were particularly disastrous. Millions starved due to Mao's program called the "*Great Leap Forward.*" This human catastrophy is revealed on the negative "blip" on the graph on "Annual World Population Change: 1950-2050," shown at ***U.S. Census Bureau*** (WWW 2.6). Does this help you better understand why China instituted a one-child per family policy in 1982? Are the Chinese people more willing to accept this restrictive policy because, under communist culture, the rights of the individual often are forsaken for the benefit of the whole nation? Does the ancient Confucian emphasis on *"the here and now"*, which is still prevalent in China, remove many of the concerns that the Chinese people might normally have over the long-term consequences of this restrictive policy? This is just one of many examples where a country's culture is influenced by population pressures.

Locate the Web site for the ***Population Reference Bureau*** (WWW 2.7). It contains a classic and appropriate exercise to examine population pressures, which is entitled *"Food for Thought."* In this activity, participants form groups to represent the six major regions of the world according to the region's proportion of total world population. The six regions are North America, Latin America, Africa, Europe (including Russia), Asia (excluding China), and China. On a large, cleared floor space, participants use yarn to illustrate (map) the shape and relative area of the six major regions of the world, and then stand in their designated regions according to the proportion of the region that is agricultural (rural) and urban. This simple, but effective illustration, can be used to appreciate the concepts of arithmetic population density, physiologic population density, and the uneven distribution of resources.

Activity 2.3 Field Work

Part A

1. How will less developed nations improve their standard of living unless the population growth rate is sharply reduced?

2. Even if enough food can be grown to feed the world's growing population, where will these people find meaningful work in a more-automated society?

3. As countries reduce their population growth rate with the hope to raise their relative standard of living, how will the increased energy demands be met?

4. To what extent is population growth responsible for some of the environmental problems we see today on our planet? This question can be explored more fully by visiting the following Web sites on environmental problems in China and Bangladesh.

For a look at the controversial Three Gorges Dam project in China, go to the ***International Rivers Network*** Web site (WWW 2.8). Why does the title of the press release say that the Three Gorges Dam is not the answer to China's reoccurring flooding? What are some of the geological problems with building the dam? For a virtual pictorial tour of the dam project on the Yangtze River, go to the Web site ***Yangtze River Three Gorges Tour*** (WWW 2.9).

For a virtual pictorial tour of monsoon flooding in Bangladesh in 1988, go to the Web site ***Earth Base*** (WWW 2.10).

Part B

1. What percentage of Bangladesh was submerged in the 1988 flooding?
2. How many people were made homeless?
3. How many people died because of the flooding?
4. What four items combined are listed as causing this tremendous disaster?

ADDITIONAL WEB SITES FOR STUDYING POPULATION ISSUES:

For an educational module that introduces users to some of the fundamental questions about the connections among population, resource and energy use, and environmental impacts, see the website for the ***Association of American Geographers*** (WWW2.11). From the publications option, link to the Human Dimensions of Global Change page.

For United States health statistics, see the site for the ***Centers for Disease Control*** in Atlanta (WWW 2.12).

For world health statistics, see the site for the ***World Health Organization***: (WWW 2.13).

ADDITIONAL READINGS:

Brown, Lester R., *Who Will Feed China?*, (New York, NY: W.W. Norton & Company, 1995).

Brown, Lester R., Flavin, Christopher, and Norman, Colin, *The Future of the Automobile in an Oil Short World*, (Washington, D.C.: Worldwatch Institute, 1979), Worldwatch Paper #32.

Newland, Kathleen, *Women and Population Growth: Choice Beyond Childbearing*, (Washington, D.C.: Worldwatch Institute, 1977), Worldwatch Paper #16.

PART THREE
THE GLOBAL LINGUISTIC MOSAIC

GOALS: Gain an appreciation that language is an essential element of culture. Develop an awareness that most countries in the world are grappling with language problems as a result of being multilingual, and that different countries are trying various solutions to attempt to overcome some of the linguistic problems.

ACTIVITIES: Translate place names, compare words and dialects, debate the establishment of an official language of the United States.

ACTIVITY 3.1: What's In A Name? Ethnic Place Names and Geographic Place Names

INTRODUCTION: In many parts of the United States, local place names are often a good indicator of the dominant ethnic groups that originally settled an area (e.g., Spanish in the Southwest, Germans in southeastern Pennsylvania, French in Louisiana, British in New England). For example, if a place name ends in *-mann, -burg, -berg, -lich, -stein, or -t(h)al*, it is a likely indication that the name is of German origin. Using the ***IUPUI Max Kade German-American Center*** Web site (WWW 3.1), identify the original geographic locations of the following German word endings:

1. *-burg* ______________
2. *-bruck* ______________
3. *-furt* ______________
4. *-berg* ______________
5. *-rode* ______________

Using a U.S. map or road atlas, compare the place names in their own region of the country with those found in other sections of the country. Determine what the most common language of origin was for these regional place names.

Another option is to speculate on place name origins. Go to the ***Canonical List of Interesting Town Names*** *Web site* (WWW 3.2), and locate your state (or nearby state, if your state isn't listed). Choose one interesting town name and speculate on the origin of that name.

In China, Mandarin Chinese place names are often determined by their geographic location. For example, the city of Beijing's English translation is "*north capital.*" China has had several capital cities throughout its long history, and Beijing truly is the "north capital," compared to Nanjing and Xian, former Chinese capitals. Given the following directory of comparable Chinese and English words, translate a selection of Chinese place names into their English equivalents. (The Chinese words are the pinyin spellings, not the former traditional spellings.)

	Chinese	English
Locations	bei	north
	nan	south
	dong	east
	xi	west
	zhong	middle
	shang	up
	xia	down
Landforms	shan	mountain
	ling	range
	feng	peak
	guang	vast flat plain
Water Bodies	he	river
	jiang	river
	chuan	river
	hu	lake
	tai	bay
	kong	harbor
	hai	sea
	yang	ocean
	haitan	beach
Colors	hong	red
	huang	yellow
	lan	blue
	bai	white
	hei	black
	kafei se	brown
	lu	green
	juhong se	orange
	zise	purple
Numbers	yi	one
	er	two
	san	three
	si	four
	wu	five
	liu	six
	qi	seven
	ba	eight
	jiu	nine
	shi	ten
Other	da	large
	xaio	small
	chang	long
	tian	heaven
	di	earth
	jing	capital
	zhou	province (state)

Translate the following Chinese place names into English.

Cities	Shanghai	Sichuan
Provinces	Hunan	Shanxi
Rivers	Chang Jiang	Huang He
Mountains	Nan Ling	Changbai Shan

To look into how some of these places received their geographic names, refer to the ***University of Texas Web site's*** map of China (WWW 3.3).

ACTIVITY 3.2: Was It Something I Said? Dialect Word Comparisons

INTRODUCTION: Sometimes misunderstandings occur because many words have multiple meanings, and because meanings can change over time due to the dynamic nature of language. English is a language with an extensive vocabulary, and English words used in Great Britain may have quite different meanings when used in the United States or Australia.

Visit the Web site for ***BritSpeak*** (WWW 3.4) Go to the page called *"American-British Dictionary."* Translate the following British sentences into American English by changing the underlined words:

1. The Yanks called in a dear sparky to fix the broken lift in the block of flats.

   ____

2. In the refectory, the homely lass had bubble and squeak, aubergine, and afters.

   ____

You may also want to examine the page called *"Problem Words"* to find words that have directly opposite meanings depending on which side of the Atlantic Ocean one is located.

Not only are there differences in the English language between Great Britain, Australia, and the United States, but there are also regional differences within the United States as to what to call certain items.

What names do you use for the objects listed below? (First specify in which region of the United States you were raised.)

United States Region: __________________

1. cold cut sandwiches served on long rolls:

   ____

2. the collective name for carbonated beverages, such as Coke and Pepsi:

____

3. a beverage made in a blender with ice cream & milk, and flavoring:

____

4. a small, linear body of water that may flow into a river or other water body:

____

Note any other regional language differences that you have noticed since attending college:

____

____

ACTIVITY 3.3: E Pluribus Unum? Language in the United States

INTRODUCTION: The United States, with over a quarter of a billion people and counting, is a multilingual nation with an increasing number of international languages being spoken. The political organization, *U.S. English, Inc.*, was created to address the language issue in the United States. Founded in 1983 by the late Senator S.I. Hayakawa of California, *U.S. English, Inc.* now has over one million members nationwide. One of the stated goals of *U.S. English, Inc.* is to keep the United States unified through a common language.

Call on *U.S. English, Inc.* by visiting its Web site (WWW 3.5).

Go to the page entitled "U.S. English Quiz." Answer the ten questions (repeated below) and check your score. Which answer surprised you the most? Were you aware of this organization before this exercise?

1. The Constitution makes English the official language of the United States.
_____True _____False

2. According to the 1990 Census, how many languages are spoken in the United States?
__ 29 __ 129 __329 __1029

3. The IRS spent $113,000 to print and distribute 500,000 tax forms and instruction books in Spanish. Only 718 were returned.
_____True _____False

4. U.S. English was founded by an immigrant, and the current chairman of *U.S. English, Inc.* is an immigrant.
_____True _____False

5. After the people of Arizona voted to make English the official language of Arizona, a bilingual state employee filed a lawsuit claiming she had the right to create legally binding documents in Spanish, even if her supervisor didn't speak Spanish.
_____True _____False

6. On average, after learning English, an immigrant's income will increase by what percentage?
__5% __10% __15% __over 20%

7. U.S. Citizenship tests are offered in multiple languages.
_____True _____False

8. According to the 1990 U.S. Census, 97% of the U.S. population speaks English "Well" or "Very Well."
_____True _____False

9. French is the official language of the state of Louisiana.
_____True _____False

10. From 1980 to 1990, how much did a dual language government policy cost Canada?
__ $6.7 million __$67 million __$670 million __$6.7 billion

The U.S. English movement is not without its opposition. Do you think the United States should have an official language, or languages? If yes, what language(s)?

Prepare to debate this language issue by conducting some virtual field work using the following websites:

See the ***Public Broadcasting System*** Online News Hour: *"Double Talk: Bilingual Education."* Hear well-known people state their views on this issue (WWW 3.6).

Tom Murray, an English professor at ***Kansas State University*** presents an argument for why English should be the official language of the United States. (WWW 3.7).

The ***Yahoo!*** Bilingual Education page links several sites that disagree with the point of view of the U.S. English (WWW 3.8).

ADDITIONAL WEB SITES FOR STUDYING LANGUAGES:

For an introduction to Bengali, the language of the majority of people in Bangladesh, see ***Virtual Bangladesh*** (WWW 3.9). This site contains a Bengali tutorial which includes a transliteration schema and an on-line English/Bengali dictionary, as well as sample phrases and sounds. See an example of the Bengali script which is cursive, with 12 vowels and 52 consonants. With the proper hardware on your computer, you can also hear it spoken.

To find out about the impact of the French language on culture in Quebec, Canada, see ***Association of Quebec Advertising Agencies*** (WWW 3.10).

Interested in Native American languages? See ***University of Texas Health Science Center*** (WWW 3.11).

Do students test higher with English as a second language, vs. English-only? See ***Los Angeles Times*** (WWW 3.12).

To learn about Esperanto, a language developed in 1887 with the specific intent of creating an international second language, see ***Esperanto*** (WWW 3.13).

ADDITIONAL READINGS:

Axtell, Roger E., *Do's and Taboos Around the World*, (New York, NY: John Wiley & Sons, Inc., 1990), 2nd ed.

Gates, Gary, *How to Speak Dutchified English*, (Intercourse, PA: Good Books, 1987).

Patinkin, Mark, *The Rhode Island Dictionary*, (North Attleboro, MA: Covered Bridge Press, 1993), illustrated by Don Bousquet.

PART FOUR

THE GEOGRAPHY OF RELIGION

GOALS: To understand the far-reaching influence of religion on human/cultural geography, and gain a sense of the complexity of the geography of religion. Religion still dominates the lives of billions of people in many parts of the world. How people dress, what people eat, when people work, with whom one associates, may all be prescribed by religion. Differences in religious beliefs are also one of the major sources of conflict in several parts of the world.

ACTIVITIES: Compare the religious makeup of countries, construct a cartogram illustrating religious membership in the United States by state and by denomination, examine the Amish lifestyle and cultural landscape, trace the spatial history of the Mormon church within the United States, take a virtual tour of two Nazi Holocaust sites, examine other historic or current ethnic and religious prejudices and genocides.

ACTIVITY 4.1: Where In God's Name?

INTRODUCTION: Many of the world's regions have fairly distinctive religious spatial patterns (e.g., Latin America is primarily Roman Catholic, Southeast Asia is largely Buddhist, Northern Africa is primarily Islamic, etc.). Several sources of world data list a country's religious makeup. One of the best sources of comparative world data is the United States' ***Central Intelligence Agency*** Web site (WWW 4.1).

Using this Web site, list the dominant religion and corresponding percentage for each of the following countries in Table 4.1.

Table 4.1

Country	Dominant Religion	Percent of Total	Major Religious Holidays	Religious Disputes
Iran				
Indonesia				
Italy				
India				
Israel				
Iceland				

Now check the ***Central Intelligence Agency*** site for the religious holidays observed in these countries, and also note if there are religious disputes taking place within the country, or between it and other countries. You might also want to consult the ***Atlapedia***

Web site (WWW 4.2), which covers religious disputes for individual countries under the section "Modern History".

The United States has often been referred to as a *"melting pot"* or *"tossed salad"* because of the heterogeneous backgrounds of its residents. This ethnic heterogeneity also gives rise to the diversity of religions found in the United States. Just as a world map of religions shows areas that are dominated by a particular faith, so, too, does the map of religion in the United States.

Take a virtual field trip to the ***Pennsylvania State Data Center*** and consult its data table on church membership in the United States in 1990 (WWW 4.3). Connect to the page "data and maps."

Take a piece of graph paper, preferably 10 squares/inch, and construct a cartogram of churches or membership for one of the major religions found in the United States. Be prepared to explain why you think this particular religion has the spatial pattern it does, based on the ethnic groups and migrations may be involved.

ACTIVITY 4.2: If It Looks Like A Duck ...

INTRODUCTION: Religious affiliation can be highly evident on the cultural landscape. This includes the beliefs and customs, as well as the sights, sounds and aromas that are identified with certain cultures, and which often are strongly influenced by religion. One of the most distinctive religious cultural landscapes in the United States is that of the Old Order Amish. Their oldest and best-known settlement is located in Lancaster County, Pennsylvania.

Take in the cultural landscape of the Amish by connecting to the ***Pennsylvania Dutch*** Web site (WWW 4.4). You will see most of the questions below during your visit. The site also contains an interactive service that allows you to ask your own questions about the Amish and have them answered by experts.

Activity 4.2 Field Work

Part A

1. Who are the Amish?

2. Are they the same as the Pennsylvania Dutch?

3. What is the history of the Amish?

4. Why don't they accept modern ideas and innovations?

5. Do they speak English?

6. Why do they dress the way they do?

7. What's an Amish wedding like?

8. Do Amish children go to school?

Part B

1. How many years of schooling do the Amish typically complete?
2. On which days of the week do Amish weddings usually take place?
3. In which month do most Amish weddings occur?
4. What is the most common color of an Amish woman's wedding dress?
5. How many languages do most adult Amish know?
6. In what year did the Amish religion split from the Mennonite religion?
7. Amish women are usually buried in their wedding dress. **True/False**
8. The Amish try to avoid the use of buttons on their clothing. **True/False**
9. Old Order Amish send their children to public schools. **True/False**
10. The Amish men grow beards and mustaches after they marry. **True/False**

If you are artistically-minded, you could sketch pictures showing some of the visual elements of the Amish cultural landscape. Another option is for you to write a summary essay on the Amish cultural landscape, by including the following elements: dress, modes of transportation, languages, beliefs, lifestyle, architecture, and occupations.

The Amish lifestyle is quite different from that of most other Americans. To better appreciate the distinctive lifestyle of the Amish, go to the ***Amish-Heartland*** Web site (WWW 4.5).

You may also experience the daily life of one Amish woman via her personal, one-month diary. Katie Schlabach is a married Amish woman who lives in Holmes County, Ohio, which currently is the largest Amish settlement in the world.

Here are some questions to think about as you read her diary:

1. What activities does she do on a daily basis?
2. What occupies most of her working days?
3. How does she travel?
4. What is the church service like?
5. How important is family life to her?
6. Compare your own lifestyle with that of Katie Schlabach.
Would you like to trade places with her? Why, or why not?

ACTIVITY 4.3: Why Can't We All Just Get Along?

INTRODUCTION: Religion has been at the heart of many of the world's great conflicts. How many people have suffered or been killed in the name of religion throughout human history? While many people came to the United States to escape religious persecution, one religion that originated in the United States was forced to relocate within the country to avoid religious persecution. Pay a call on the Mormon church (formally known as the Church of Jesus Christ of Latter-Day Saints or the L.D.S) at their ***Mormons*** Web site (WWW 4.6).

Read the essay on Mormon history by Richard H. Jackson. You can locate sites that are of historical significance to the Mormon church by using the state maps feature at Web site of the ***National Geographic Society*** (WWW 4.7). When you click on a state, a small map of the state should appear, along with information on the state. If you then click on the small map, it will enlarge.

One of the greatest atrocities in human history occurred in the twentieth century with the genocide of European Jews during the Nazi Holocaust. All the written accounts, photographic exhibits, and cinematic depictions, collectively, could never entirely capture the magnitude of crimes committed, and the incredible misery experienced, during the Nazi Holocaust. Nevertheless, it is necessary for people to try to describe the enormity of this suffering, and it is essential that *"we must never forget."*

Travel to ***Remember*** (WWW 4.8), Stuart C. Nichols' virtual tour of the Polish concentration camps called Auschwitz and Birkenau. This is a written and photographic record of the five days he spent visiting these notorious death camps in September 1993.

Note: Part of this document will change over time. New or revised graphics will appear from time to time. Remember that the graphics take time to load on the Web, so please be patient. Also, if you can't see a picture, it is probably because most of these files are *JPEGS*. They were selected for quality, but some browsers have trouble reading them.

Now identify and consider another of the world's current genocides or religious conflicts via the ***Cable News Network*** website (WWW 4.9) or another online news service. Research the conflicts' history and familiarize yourself with the central issues.

Activity 4.3 Field Work

Conflict under study:

1. Is this a relatively new conflict, or has it been going on for a long time?

2. What groups are involved?

3. Has a third party (nation, international organization, etc.) intervened?

4. Do you see any hope for peaceful resolution to the conflict in the near future?

5. What is the United States' position on the dispute?

ADDITIONAL WEB SITES ON RELIGION:

To find out more about Mormon doctrine and beliefs, see ***The Church of Jesus Christ of Latter-Day Saints*** (WWW 4.10).

Yahoo! (WWW 4.11) indexes both large and small faiths and religious practices.

ADDITIONAL READINGS:

Hostetler, John A., *Amish Society*, (Baltimore: The Johns Hopkins University Press, 1993), 4th ed.

Kraybill, Donald B., *The Riddle of the Amish Culture*, (Baltimore: The Johns Hopkins University Press, 1989).

PART FIVE: LAND AND LAND USE IN THE RURAL SECTOR

FOOD AND SHELTER: GETTING DOWN THE BASICS OF LIFE

GOALS: To experience different cultural and economic conditions in rural regions with an emphasis on the diffusion of domesticated animals, traditional rural housing, and how commercial agriculture meets the global food needs.

ACTIVITIES: There are three activities for Part Five. First, you will travel the continents and study the domestication of animals. The focus of the second activity is a field study of folk architecture in the Great Plains. The third section allows you to take a look at the human and environmental impacts of aquaculture as a growing segment of world agribusiness.

ACTIVITY 5.1: How Now, Black and White Cow? Livelihoods of Rural People.

INTRODUCTION: Have you ever wondered why it is that most of the dairy cattle you see are black and white spotted Holsteins? For many of us living in industrialized societies, the closest we get to livestock is taking a Sunday drive along a country road on the fringes of suburbia. If you have (and you can admit this) mooed at a cow standing along a fence line chewing its cud, chances are you were not raised on a farm. In fact, less than three percent of the U.S. labor force lives on farms.

Urbanites are dependent on rural dwellers for food supplies and for most of us, the closest we get to harvesting our food is picking a can of peas from the grocers shelves or selecting an anonymous cut of meat from the butcher counter. Unless you were born in an agricultural region, you are probably unfamiliar with livestock and how they developed and diffused from their source regions. To learn more about the diffusion of livestock from Ankole-Watusui (cattle) to Zhongwei (goats), visit Oklahoma State University's ***Breeds of Livestock*** Web site (WWW 5.1) This informative site will allow you to travel all over the world and discover how environmental conditions as well as the influences of local resources, diffusion, and historical inertia have contributed to the contemporary character of domesticated animals that provide food and fiber to billions of people.

Once at the ***Breeds of Livestock*** site, connect to the Regions page. Scroll down to the bottom of the page and click on Breed Home Page and read through this short introductory section. Then step back to the main page and click on the map in the area you are want to study. Your choices include: Africa, Asia, the British Isles, Continental Europe, North America, South America, and Oceania. You may select any or all of these regions and read about the types of livestock found in these areas, their origins and diffusion, as well as view images of each breed. While you may go into greater detail in your discussion of global livestock, we have selected some examples to consider for each region. Each breed selected here has distinct geographic qualities and provides greater insight into the dynamics of animal domestication and diffusion. Certainly all of the breeds mentioned in this web site are interesting and, as time allows, you may wish to do some further exploration of the site on your own. When you have completed your research in each region, you should consider the following general questions.

Activity 5.1 Field Work

1. How have natural environments influenced the domestication and development of animal breeds?

2. How has diffusion changed the distribution of animals within regions and across throughout the world?

3. How have cultural preferences and changing economies affected breed popularity and distributions?

AFRICA

Cattle

Ankole (known as Ankole-Watusi in North America) ***Can Cows Really do the Bossy Nova?***

1. How did the Ankole-Watusi earn its name---can they really dance? How are they related to the Ankole cattle of Africa and how are they similar or different?

2. Why have Ankole-Watusi cattle been raised mainly for their milk rather than their meat? How are milking practices between the two breeds different and why?

3. What role did zoos and game parks play in the diffusion of the Ankole-Watusi? What roles have the natural environment and cultural traditions played in the diffusion and development of the Ankole in Africa?

4. The photo of the Ankole-Watusi shown on this page gives you a good example of the large horns characteristic of this breed. How and why did this physical trait evolve? Why are the Ankole horns important to African cattle raisers?

N'dama ***Fly By Night Cattle?***

1. How are these cattle different from the Ankole-Watusi in their physical characteristics as well as their geographic distribution?

2. Why is it important for African cattle raisers to improve their herds with trypanatotolerant breeds?

Goats

Boer Goat ***A 300 Pound Goat --- We're Not Kidding!***

1. How did the Boer goat earn its name and what is its primary use?

2. Why do goats and cattle make a good combination when raised together in South Africa? Why didn't this livestock combination emerge in North America?

Sheep

Damara ***Where Are Ewe?***

1. How did the environmental conditions of Namibia influence the development and utility of this breed?

ASIA

Cattle

Hallikar, Hariana, Kankrej, Sahiwal ***We Have Four Kinds of Cattle on Draft***

Consider each of these south Asian cattle breeds, and answer the following questions.

1. If you were in need of a speedy long distance draft animal, which of these breeds would you select?

2. Why would draft cattle be so popular in this part of the world?

3. What makes the Sahiwal breed more versatile than the other three? Why has this breed experienced wider diffusionary patterns than the Hallikar, Hariana, or Kankrej?

Kholmogory ***Hurry Up---These Cattle Are Russian!***

1. The photo example of the Kholmogory stands in stark constrast to the previous four breeds found in south Asia. What are the major environmental and use differences between the Kholmogory and the previously mentioned Asian cattle breeds?

Sanhe ***So That's Where Ice Milk Comes From!***

1. What might the Sanhe and the Kholmogory share in terms of their adaptiveness to harsh environments?

2. How have the climatic effects of continentality in Inner Mongolia resulted in the hardy nature of Sanhe cattle?

Goats

Zhongwei ***Getting Fleeced in China***

1. Goats are often associated with two things---poverty and poor agricultural areas. Why might the Zhongwei goat be well-suited to the physical geography of the Chinese steppe?

Other Asian Animals

Bactrian Camel, Dromedary Camel, Yak ***Would You Walk a Mile for a Camel or a Yak?***

1. What are the major differences in environments between the animals commonly referred to as ships of the desert and those thought of as ships of the plateau?

2. Which type of camel are found in China? How are these camels different from those developed in Turkmenistan?

3. Why do you think there is no mention of Dromedary camels being use for meat?

4. Why would it not be a good idea to attempt to raise Dromedaries in the cold, moist climates in which Yaks might thrive?

5. How have each breed type contributed to their respective regions' demands for meat, milk, fiber, and transportation?

BRITISH ISLES

Cattle

Belted Galloway, Guernsey ***Bring on the Cookies and Milk!***

With the Belted Galloway resembling a popular chocolate sandwich cookie and the Guernsey famous for their milk production, these two breeds seem like a natural combination! But, in fact, these two breeds are quite different.

1. Why have Geurnsey cattle been popular as milk producers and how did religion and soil bring this breed into existence?

2. What advantages do Galloway cattle have over other breeds and how have they adapted to their environment?

Goats

Bagot ***Why It Is In Your Best Interest to Treat This Goat With Kid Gloves***

While Britain may not be as well known for its goats as it is for its sheep, the Bagot have an interesting and long history associated with the region.

1. How did the Bagot most likely develop in the British Isles and how did the breed influence local belief systems?

Sheep

Cotswold ***Pulling the Wool Over Their Isles***

1. With over four dozen sheep breeds originating in the British Isles, you have many types to choose from. Many of these animals have names that double as toponyms and Cotswold sheep are just one example. How did this breed end up with this name?

Swine

Hampshire, Yorkshire ***Hog Wild: Pigging Out in Britain***

The stories of both of these swine breeds echo that of native development and global diffusion. Both named for regions in England, they have had a profound influence on food production in many parts world, especially the United States.

1. How did the Industrial Revolution and hog production go ham in hand? Can you see any linkages between the development of factories and English agriculture such as the raisers of sheep and swine livestock?

2. How did the export of Hampshires to the United States affect the swine industry of the American Midwest?

CONTINENTAL EUROPE

Cattle

Herens, Holstein, Simmental ***Cattle Call***

1. Many cattle breeds were developed in continental Europe with diverse purposes and histories including Herens, Holsteins, and Simmentals. Which of these might be best named demolition derby cattle and why are their numbers declining? Do you think this indicates a decline in transhumance as a grazing practice in Europe?

2. Today in the United States, Holsteins are the most numerous breed of dairy cattle. Where were Holsteins developed and how did they become so popular in the U.S.?

3. Let's say you decide to keep a Holstein cow for milking purposes. Based on the average per cow production in the United States, how many eight-ounce glasses of milk would your single black and white spotted cow produce during it's natural productive life (hint: a pound of milk is equal to a pint which is 16 ounces)? How does this help explain the chronic problem of over-supply of fluid milk on American markets given there are over nine million dairy cows in the United States?

4. Create a timeline of Simmental diffusion by starting with the first exports from Switzerland. Why has this breed spread throughout the world with greater success than any others?

Sheep

Bovska ***The Ups and Downs of Alpine Sheep Raising***

1. Why have the numbers of Bovska sheep declined since the 1950s?

2. What do geography and ears have in common when referring to the Bovska breed?

Swine

Swallow-Bellied Mangalitza ***Living Low On The Hog***

1. The popularity of domesticated animals is often determined by changing consumer tastes and preferences. How has the popularity of the Swallow-Bellied Mangalitza been affected by contemporary diets?

NORTH AMERICA

Cattle

Corriente, Senepol ***Rope 'Em If You Got 'Em***

1. Corriente and Senepol cattle are good examples of how colonialism and animal diffusion are interrelated. Where did each breed originate and where in North America did they develop?

2. What are some of the unique marketing conditions on St. Croix and why, even though cattle were present, did the island fail to develop any stockyards?

3. Where would you find descendents of the original Corriente cattle today and why?

Goats

Myotonic, San Clemente ***Goats for the Faint of Heart***

1. If you raise meat goats in Tennessee, why might they volunteer to faint?

2. It was recently announced that the United States Navy is phasing out their dairy farm operations near Annapolis, Maryland. But how did the Navy get their goats---or better put, how did they get rid of them?

Sheep

Hog Island, Tunis ***Mutton Honey!***

1. Both Hog Island and Tunis sheep have their origins in colonial times but their fates have been quite different. Which of these two American breeds is more rare and why? Do you see any irony in the role played by the Nature Conservancy on Hog Island and the decline of this breed?

2. Is sheep raising an important livestock industry in your region of the country? When was the last time you ate lamb or mutton---or have you ever?

SOUTH AMERICA

Cattle

Nelore ***Brazil is Nuts for Nelores***

1. What environmental similarities between Brazil and India have contributed to the success of the Nelore in South America?

Llama

Llama ***The Fiber of Their Being: The Multi-Purpose Llama***

1. Llamas today are popular as pets although their heritage is much less glamorous. Why would the llama have been a useful animal to have on hand over that past 5,000 years?

OCEANIA

Cattle

Murray Grey ***Getting Bullish on Australia***

1. How did one man's prejudice against grey calves end up as the force behind the development of the Murray Grey?

2. Where is one of the most favorable export markets for Murray Greys?

Sheep

Priangan ***A Professional Athlete in Indonesia: Ram Merino?***

1. What do Priangan sheep have in common with the Herens cattle of Switzerland? Do you have any ideas on why neither of these breeds have been popular outside their regions of origin?

Romney ***Spinning a Sheep Tail***

1. What are the qualities developed in the Romney breed that facilitated its success in New Zealand and the Falkland Islands and later to the United States?

Swine

Kuenkune ***Pets or Meat?***

1. Compare the Kuenkune to North America's Potbellied Pig. How did each of these breeds evolve from primarily rural meat animals to popular suburban pets?

Activity 5.2: There's No Place Like Home on the Range; Rural Settlement Forms

INTRODUCTION: Most often, folk (vernacular) architecture reflects localized geographic conditions in the types of building materials used, house style, as well as the arrangement of buildings and structures. Traditional homes may be made of adobe, thatch, hewn logs, or even animal hair. History, ethnicity, and the physical environment play a large role in the form and function of folk architecture.

Have you ever wondered why anyone would build a house out of sod? Could it be that there are no other alternatives? If you are accustomed to living in an urban setting, chances are your residence is constructed of modern building materials such as brick, concrete, block, metal, dimension lumber, or any combination of these. Your home may even have been made in a factory and delivered to you. These conveniences of industrialized societies are not common in most parts of the world. Most of the world's population live in structures that were made by hand (often their own) and out of materials that are locally available to them such as mud, wattle, sod, handmade bricks, or even cloth.

Since most individuals have never lived in a sod house, we will use this type of construction as an example of folk architecture. Sod houses played an important role in the settlement of the northern Great Plains region. To view some images of sod houses, go to the ***Pioneer Camera*** home page (WWW 5.2) and begin reading each description of the houses listed by clicking on Enter the Exhibit and selecting Sod Houses. Be sure to click on the "full page" option to see a larger and clearer image of each house, and to follow any links that are included in each narrative. For a complete picture of rural life in the Dakotas in the late 19th and early 20th

centuries, be sure to take a few minutes and go to the Farming Life and Prairie Society links on the Exhibits page.

1. List the year in which each of the five houses was photographed. Which was the most recent and how was it different from the other examples of sod houses?

2. How would you describe the ethnicity of the sod house dwellers? Why do you think these people came to settle in the Dakotas? Would you expect to find sod houses in their respective homelands? Why or why not?

3. How did sod house dwellers on the plains demonstrate social stratification? In other words, what sorts of examples of social status and home improvements were they making to their sod houses to keep up with the Olsons?

4. Other than the Great Plains of North America, where else might you expect to find regions with sod houses as part of the cultural landscape?

Activity 5.3: Commercial Agriculture; There's Something Fishy Going On Here

INTRODUCTION: This chapter focuses on the dynamics of commercial agriculture. The activities listed below focus on aquaculture as an expanding sector in global agribusiness.

One of the most promising ventures for producing high protein food sources for the world is aquaculture. Since protein is one of the most important dietary components and is often missing or in low supply in the grain-based diets that are most common throughout the world, commercial fish production may help fill this critical need. Agribusiness expansion in aquaculture has been accelerating since the 1980s and should continue to do so as global demand continues to increase and fish harvests from natural water sources such as oceans and rivers continues to decline.

Aquaculture in the United States

Louisiana leads the United States in aquaculture with over 3,000 producers of fish for commercial purposes. Many other states have significant fish-farming agribusiness. For statistics on aquaculture for your state or the entire country from the United States Department of Agriculture, go Portland State University's ***Government Information Project, Census of Agriculture*** Web site (WWW 5.3). You may click on any state or "United States", which is highlighted in a box on the map. This information is also available at the county level if you choose an individual state. When the census data for the location you have chosen appear, select Table 23 Fish Sales and answer the following questions.

Activity 5.3 Field Work Questions

Part A

1. List the types of fish that are produced in your state and county. If your state has no aquaculture activities, go to Question 3.

2. What is the total dollar value of aquaculture in your state? How important do you think fish farming is to your state's economy?

3. If there is no aquaculture in your state, why do think this is the case?

4. If you want to see how your state or region fits within the broader aquaculture picture in the United States, go to the ***United States Department of Agriculture Extension Service*** Web site (WWW 5.4). This page will give you a brief overview of everything from crayfish crops in the Louisiana bayous to how to raise bass in Indiana on soybeans.

5. One of the largest fish crops in the United States in farm-raised catfish. More than five million pounds of the popular fish are produced each year. The ***Catfish Institute*** Web site (WWW 5.5), is baited with all sorts of information on catfish production and consumption. Visit the Catfish Institute to see how cat fish consumption varies by geography. Is your home state listed as one of the top consumers of catfish?

6. For a step by step illustrated tour of catfish farming, visit the Fish Pond at the Catfish Institute. In which four states are 95% of all farm-raised catfish produced? Are those the same top four states for consumption? Why do you think the patterns of production and consumption are different?

Part B

Global Aquaculture

Aquaculture is becoming an increasingly attractive agribusiness sector throughout the world as the demand for fish grows with populations and changing diets. To experience how the fish-farming industry is meeting market needs, go to the ***Aquaculture Magazine*** Web site (WWW 5.6) and click on the link for the World Aquaculture.

Select any of the articles listed below and answer the corresponding questions or discuss them as a group.

Australian Aquaculture Influenced by Asian Contracts

1. How has immigration changed the food culture of Australia and what has been the role of aquaculture in this dietary shift?

2. Which types of fish are being raised in Australia and what are some of the environmental problems that have been encountered?

Mexico's Shellfish Aquaculture

1. How has the physical environment both fostered as well as hindered the development of Mexican aquaculture?

2. What roles have politics (such as NAFTA) and education played in the expansion of fish-farming activities in Mexico?

Shrimp Farming Development in India. An Overview of Environmental, Socio-Economic, Legal and Other Implications

1. Where are shrimp produced in India and where are their export markets?

2. How has remote sensing been used to track aquaculture land use?

3. While the demand for shrimp is high in India, so are the environmental costs. Many examples are given in this article, list and discuss what you consider to be the three most significant problem areas.

Salmon Still A Major Part of Chile's Aquaculture Success

1. Where is Chile's aquaculture region? Why has this part of the country been so favorable for salmon production? (For additional background on the Chilean salmon industry, visit Web site WWW 5.7).

2. How have environmental conditions as well as infrastructure presented problems for aquaculture in Chile?

3. Why does Chile mainly focus on export markets for its fish products?

For an overview of world aquaculture, go to the ***Food and Agriculture Organization*** (FAO) site (WWW 5.8), select Fisheries and link to Review the State of World Aquaculture. After reviewing the article, you could write a short essay on the positive and negative impacts of aquaculture on the natural environment and the significance of aquaculture to rural areas and developing countries.

PART SIX
THE URBANIZING WORLD
ATTENTION ANY-MART SHOPPERS!

GOALS: What is "at issue" in the urbanizing world is the seemingly inevitable shift of commercial activities away from the central business district (CBD) and toward the suburbs. One of the largest segments of the economy that has steadily exited the downtown since the 1950s in favor of the suburbs is retailing. Through activities contained in this part, you will gain a better understanding of how your behavior as a consumer shapes the retail landscape and why "Main Street" retailers are disappearing from the shopping horizon.

ACTIVITIES: There are two major activities included for Part Six. The first section is devoted to exploring issues related to the decline of downtown shopping districts and strategies for their revival through Main Street programs. The second activity involves students conducting surveys of their personal shopping patterns and combining that data with the results for the rest of the class. After the group data is determined, students may choose to share their class results with students at other colleges and universities by posting their data to the ***Virtual Field Guide*** web site.

Activity 6.1: Main Street Gets Malled by the "Burbs"

INTRODUCTION: Shopping. Love it or hate it, we still have a need to shop. Some of us shop for reasons other than to obtain the necessities of life. For many, shopping is as much recreational as it is utilitarian. Prior to mass exodus of population and businesses from the CBD, when the majority of urbanites lived in a "walking city," virtually all shopping was oriented toward the downtown. Living and shopping on Main Street is getting more difficult to do these days. Through competition with the suburbs for shopping, employment, and entertainment dollars, many downtowns have become commercial relics. Those downtowns that continue to thrive have done so by capitalizing on their uniqueness as the historical heart of the region and by changing with times. Where you once had storefronts displaying shoes, furniture, or even groceries on Main Street, you now find gourmet coffee shops and upscale boutiques.

If you live in an area where you shop primarily in a downtown setting you are in a distinct minority. With the most common commuting pattern these days being from suburb to suburb, and the majority of the American population since 1990 living in suburbs, urban retailers are at a distinct disadvantage. The population shift to the suburbs has decreased foot traffic on downtown streets and directed consumer spending to malls, shopping centers and "big boxes" (e.g. large general merchandisers or large specialty stores with great depth of product lines). Downtowns do, however, have something to offer which suburban shopping centers and malls do not---historical context and organic character. When you visit a mall, think about how the form fails to follow function. For example, can you think of any shops inside your favorite mall with awnings or shutters on their storefronts? How about trees, fountains, or park benches---does your mall have any of these along its "main street?" What mall designers are attempting to do is replicate the outdoor downtown experience in an enclosed, climate controlled setting, often with plenty of free parking.

If we recreate the CDB in the form of a mall, why don't we just go back to shopping in the real downtowns and forsake the artifice of suburban shopping centers? Can traditional downtowns once again become a mecca for shopping and entertainment as well as employment? One organization that is keenly involved with strategies to rejuvenate downtowns is the National Main Street Center, a branch of the National Trust for Historic Preservation. "Main Street" programs have been adopted by over 1,000 communities as ways to bring residents back to downtown. As you work through the problems in the following section, keep in mind the downtown situation you are most familiar with and compare its problems and progress with those in other locations.

Activity 6.1 Field Work

Part A

Using the ***National Main Street Center (NMSC)*** Web site (WWW 6.1) as your guide, work your way through this activity keeping in mind how the Main Street approach may or may not work in your community. Click on About Main Street and read the introductory section. Then follow the links for The Main Street Approach, The Decline of Main Street, The Importance of Downtown, and Main Street Communities. After reading through these sections, consider the following:

1. According to the NMSC, what element of the infrastructure has done the most economic damage to downtowns? Can you think of any local examples in your community where small towns have suffered due to changes in the transportation network?

2. Do you see the visual appearance of your downtown as a positive or negative force in its maintaining its economic significance?

3. Do you shop in a downtown setting? If so, what types of goods or services do you purchase downtown? Do you go downtown primarily to shop or for other purposes?

4. Do you know of any Main Street programs in your area? What, if any, differences do you see in the downtown since the program has been implemented?

5. Which of the three communities (Burlington, IA, Holland, MI, Port Gibson, MS) is most similar to your hometown? Do you think any of the approaches used by these cities would work well in your downtown area? Why or why not?

For many of you, when someone asks if you want to go shopping they perhaps are implying a trip to the local mall or shopping center and not the downtown. While Main Street programs have assisted in the revitalization of many downtown retail districts in the United States, most consumers still shop for such items as clothing, shoes, hardware, and household goods in suburban centers. Main Street programs are not panaceas for all downtowns. Some towns may be too small or too large for the Main Street approach or in some cases, the downtown revitalization effort lacks grassroots support and other crucial resources.

Have you ever thought about how your choices as a consumer and commuter help shape the landscape? Do you have any idea how many miles you drive everyday or how many shopping trips you make in a given day or week? Have you ever made a concerted effort to go out of your way to shop at locally owned stores rather than large chain retailers? Are there many "hometown" stores that survive in your town in the shadow of the Wal-Marts and Home Depots of the world? Begin thinking about a mental map of your shopping travels and later we will create a real map detailing your shopping habits and those of your fellow students.

Part B

For this section of Activity 6.1, explore your local retail landscape and create a shopping profile for you and your class. There are three things you will need to do. First, record you answers to the following questions about shopping in your community. Second, you will create a map of the local retail landscape. Third, combine your results with other class member and post these results to the ***Virtual Field Guide*** Web site so you can compare your experiences with students in other locations.

To begin, we need to identify the types of shopping opportunities you have in your region by linking to the ***International Council of Shopping Centers' (ICSC)*** Web site (WWW 6.2). Click on the "Research" link, select Library and then at the bottom of the page choose Shopping Center Definitions. Scroll down toward the end of the page until you reach the "Shopping Center Table." For each of the retail centers listed in Table 6.1 below, name any local examples as well as their locations that fit the descriptions. After you have listed the locations, note how many times you have visited these types of shopping centers in the past week.

Table 6.1

RETAIL CENTER	LOCAL EXAMPLES	LOCATIONS	TIMES VISITED THIS WEEK
Neighborhood Center			
Community Center			
Regional Center			
Superregional Center			
Fashion/Specialty Center			
Power Center			
Theme/Festival Center			
Outlet Center			
Downtown Stores			

Now that you have an inventory of local shopping centers, add to this list the downtown stores you have visited over the previous week.

Consider these questions:

1. Based on frequency of visits, which was the most popular shopping center (by name and type) for you and your classmates?

2. How did downtown shopping figure into the retail profile for this class? What were the most frequented stores by you and your classmates?

3. Do you feel the shopping opportunities in your town are satisfactory? What do you like best about shopping in your region? What types of changes if any would you like to see?

4. What is your favorite store to visit? Which is your least preferred and why?

5. On average, how many miles would you estimate you travel in a typical shopping trip?

6. Where do you normally shop for the following items (give store name and type of shopping center):

ITEM	STORE NAME	TYPE OF SHOPPING CENTER
Clothing		
Shoes		
Groceries		
Books (non-textbooks)		
Health and Beauty		
Home Electronics		
Music and Video		

The next step is to construct a map of these shopping center locations. Create a map of the area where you do the majority of your shopping. This will most likely be where you are currently living and where you regularly shop. Locate each of the shopping center types on the map. Then, draw circles around each, representing the primary trade area as defined in the tables on the ***ICSC*** Web page (WWW 6.2). You can use a simple compass to draw the circles but be sure to check the map scale to accurately delimit each trade area. You will need a map of your study area that can accommodate distances of at least 15 miles. If you do not have a ready-made map handy, you can create a map from various sites on the Internet including: the ***Map Blast!*** Web site (WWW 6.3) and the ***Maps On Us*** Web site (WWW 6.4).

Part C

When you have your map completed, answer the following questions:

1. Do any shopping center market areas overlap?

2. Is there any identifiable locational pattern of retailing that you can identify based on the map you have created (i.e., are the shopping opportunities located in certain areas or are they associated with specific transportation routes?)?

3. Why is it difficult for smaller shopping centers to compete against malls?

4. Do any of the shopping center market areas overlap a downtown retail district?

MAKING THE MOST OF YOUR CLASS RESEARCH

Now that you have created a shopping behavior profile for your class, you can compare your group to other college students by visiting the Virtual Field Guide web site. Go to the page for Part Six and click on the Travel Survey option. You will need to collect, summarize, and send the following information for your class by each of these categories:

University or College		
Percent Male		*These two should add to 100%*
Percent Female		
Average Age of Individuals in Class		
Percent On-Campus		*These two should add to 100%*
Percent Commuter		
Percent Who Use Transportation to Go Shopping		
- personal vehicle		
- public transportation		
- bicycle		
- other		
Most Frequently Visited Shopping Center Type		
Is There an Active Main Street Program in Your Town? (yes/no)		
Average Number of Miles Travelled per Typical Shopping Trip		
Most Popular Stores for:	Store	Type of Location
- clothing		
- shoes		
- books		
- health and beauty		
- home electronic		
- groceries		
- music and video		

You can e-mail your class results and they will be added to data from other college geography classes. After sending your information, compare the results to other classes if it is available. Is your group unique or fairly typical? Do you see any regional travel or shopping patterns across the United States? Do shopping habits vary depending on city size? How might urban geographers be able to use this type of information in transportation and land use planning? Are there any strategies downtown retailers could use to draw customers back from suburban shopping centers?

ADDITIONAL WEB SITES FOR STUDYING URBAN GEOGRAPHY

Urban Land Institute **(WWW 6.5)**
U.S. Malls Home page **(WWW 6.6))**
Mall of America **(WWW 6.7)**
King of Prussia Plaza **(WWW 6.8)**

PART SEVEN
THE GEOGRAPHY OF MODERN ECONOMIC CHANGE

GOALS: To classify countries according to their level of economic development and to see the correlation between development and the demographic transition. Second, to become aware of how industries adapt to change in order to survive in today's global economy. To recognize the range of basic business protocol in a selection of world cultures.

ACTIVITIES: Access and use data to classify countries by level of development, visit Ocean Spray Cranberries, Inc. in order to construct a corporate case study of adaptation and innovation, and study and test business protocols.

ACTIVITY 7.1: Are We There Yet? Classifications of Economic Development

INTRODUCTION: Countries of the world can be classified according to level of economic development, based on a broad array of socio-economic variables. Until fairly recently, many sources simply classified nations into *"developed"* and *"underdeveloped."* Sometimes they are referred to as the *"haves"* and *"have nots."* There are some problems using such a simple, two-category classification. First, there is the underlying implication of superiority and inferiority of the developed nations and underdeveloped nations, respectively. Secondly, many countries do not clearly fit into either of these two broad categories. For the purposes of this activity, the following four-fold classification will be used:

1. underdeveloped
2. developing
3. almost developed
4. developed

These economic stages correlate with the four stages of the demographic transition as outlined in Part 2, Chapter 5, of the de Blij and Murphy text.

Activity 7.1 Field Work

Choose a world country, and refer to ***Central Intelligence Agency*** Web site (WWW 7.1). Look up the requested data for your country, as per the categories of information in Table 7.1 below, and circle the numbers that apply to your country. Total the number of circles in each column.

1. Where does your country best fit in terms of level of development?

Notes: Some countries may fall on the "boundary" between two of these stages of development. Also, the addition or subtraction of one or more variables could change a country's position within this classification. If different data sources are used, you may find different values for a particular variable. You should also be aware that the data changes over time. Try to stick with a single source of information, if possible. You should note any significant differences between data sources. A follow-up exercise would be for your class as a whole to make a choropleth world map of development based on your findings.

Table 7.1. COUNTRY DEVELOPMENT CLASSIFICATION

Country: _____________ **Data Source Used:** ______________________________

Variable	Underdeveloped	Developing	Almost Developed	Developed
Population Growth Rate (%)	> 3	2.1 - 3	1 - 2	< 1
Birth Rate (per 1000)	> 45	31 - 45	20 - 30	< 20
Population under Age 15	> 40%	31 - 40%	20 - 30%	< 20%
Infant Mortality Rate (per 1000 births)	> 100	51 - 100	10 - 50	< 10
Life Expectancy	< 55	55 - 64	65 - 70	> 70
Literacy Rate	< 70%	70 - 79%	80 - 90%	> 90%
G.D.P. (dollars per capita)	< 200	200 - 1,900	2,000 - 15,000	> 15,000
G.D.P. % Agriculture	> 40%	21 - 40%	10 - 20%	< 10%
% of Labor in Agriculture	> 30%	21 - 30%	10 - 20%	< 10%
Persons per Television*	> 500	101 - 500	10 - 100	< 10
TOTAL CIRCLES				
Conclusion (Check one)				

*** Calculate Persons per Television Set by dividing the Total Country Population by the number of televisions.**

ACTIVITY 7.2: "Berry" Good Business! Adapting to Change in the Business World

INTRODUCTION: In order to survive in today's competitive business world, corporations must constantly adapt to ever changing demographics, markets, preferences, trends, and technological innovations. One of the better examples of market adaptation is the story of Ocean Spray Cranberries, Inc. This is a Fortune 400 company that made a $1.4 billion business out of a tiny, bitter berry. Compile a case study of the company by visiting ***Ocean Spray Cranberries, Inc.*** (WWW 7.2).

Part A

Click on their *"Timeline of Innovation."* List what key innovations occurred in the following years:

1930: ______________________________

1939: ______________________________

1942: ______________________________

1951: ______________________________

1952: ______________________________

1963: ______________________________

1977: ______________________________

1981: ______________________________

1993: ______________________________

1995: ______________________________

Part B

Click "*Company Profile*." Go to the last section that lists where Ocean Spray's facilities are located. On figure 7.1.a, label the U.S. states that have cranberry receiving stations. On Figure 7.1.b, label the states with processing and bottling plants. Why do you think these areas stand out on both maps?

Figure 7.1.a States with Cranberry Receiving Stations

Figure 7.1.b States with Cranberry Processing and Bottling Plants

Part C

Read more about the cranberry by clicking on the page "*Cranberries and Citrus*," and then go to the page "Cranberry Fun Facts" to complete the Cranberry Quiz.

1. True/False: Cranberries are a native American fruit.
2. Why did sailors in colonial days keep cranberries on board their ships?
3. Cranberries grow well in what type of soil?
4. True/False: Cranberries grow in water.
5. How many states are major cranberry producers?
6. Which country in South America grows cranberries?
7. What is the average number of cranberries per pound?
8. What percentage of cranberries are consumed during Thanksgiving week?
9. What percentage of the world's cranberries are sold by Ocean Spray?
10. True/False: Cranberries are quite suitable for wine making.

In summary, the cranberry industry is a good example of adaptation and innovation. Can you cite other industries that have had to adapt to change? In what ways have they adapted?

ACTIVITY 7.3: Sayonara To Faux Pas!

INTRODUCTION: In today's world, many businesses compete in the global market. This greater exposure to foreign cultures has led to some embarrassing business *faux pas* (blunders).

This activity demonstrates a few of the cultural *"land mines"* that one could accidentally step on when conducting business abroad. Remember, no one culture is *"right,"* or *"better"* than another. But customs and expectations of foreign hosts are often different from our own. Those who have taken the time to learn about the cultural differences stand a much greater chance of business success.

Activity 7.3 Field Work

Take ***Interface JAPAN*'s** simple yes/no five-question *"Intercultural Training and Business Protocol Quiz"* :

1. Is it appropriate to arrive 10 minutes early to a business appointment in Japan?

   ____ YES ____ NO

2. In a meeting with Japanese business people, you make a joke in English and laugh. Is this behavior appropriate?

   ____ YES ____ NO

3. When your Japanese friend asks you to go to a bar after work, you say, "I can't because I want leave soon." Is that a reasonable response?

   ____ YES ____ NO

4. Visiting a Japanese company,you exchange business cards with your Japanese colleague and then sit down. Have you followed the correct business etiquette?

   ____ YES ____ NO

5. At a presentation with Japanese people you ask, "Do you understand?" Is that a polite question?

   ____ YES ____ NO

To check your answers, go to the ***InterfaceJAPAN*** Web site (WWW 7.3).

How many out of the five did you have as correct? _____

If you answered all five correctly, *Subarashi!* (Great!) This quiz focused strictly on Japanese business protocol. Here are some other brief guides to follow when you are conducting business in other parts of the world according to the celebrated international business expert Roger Axtell in his best-selling book: *Do's and Taboos Around the World*.

Europe: What would be mildly bad manners at home (gum chewing, talking with hands in pockets, back slapping, etc.) are cardinal sins on the Continent. Europeans tend to be more formal than most Americans. Punctuality is a must, especially in Northern Europe.

Africa: This continent is divided into three sub-regions: northern nations bound together by language (Arabic), religion (Islam), and resources (oil); middle Africa (black multicultures); and South Africa (long time Dutch/English orientation). North Africa generally follows Arabic protocol, gestures, etiquette (don't use your left hand!), and behavior. The nations in middle Africa are oriented to a myriad of black multicultures, and it is impossible to generalize about such a complex region. Because of the recent downfall of the apartheid system, the once strong European (Dutch/English) cultural connections are in a state of flux.

Asia & the Pacific World: No region of the world has a greater variety and diversity of languages, races, and religions, than Asia. Most Asians are extremely polite. The worst mistake one could make in business is to allow your foreign host to "lose face." Business cards are swapped at a pace that put children trading baseball cards to shame! Cards should be printed in both English and the local language. You should be punctual for appointments, but don't be offended if your hosts are late. When doing business in Japan, it is often essential to have a strong contact with an established Japanese firm. Due to the cultural origins, directness, and informality of its citizens, Australia is probably the one nation in this region where Americans feel the most "at home" when conducting business.

Central & South America: Although we tend to over-generalize about Latin America, do recognize that there are many differences in customs and behavior. One behavioral aspect that takes some getting used to by U.S. citizens is that Latin Americans tend to stand close during conversations. Latin Americans are warm and friendly people. Punctuality is not closely adhered to in this region.

The Caribbean: This is another region with considerable diversity in languages, races, and cultures. Casual dress and less formal behavior are commonplace.

Canada: Canada is comprised of many different ethnic groups, and while customs are generally similar, there are some differences. This is particularly true in Quebec, where language is a very sensitive issue. Most Canadians tend to be somewhat more conservative than most U.S. citizens.

Having read these protocol summaries, have you noticed any of these behaviors depicted on television or in the movies? Have you had any personal experiences where you personally made a mistake in protocol? Here's a tip when hosting an English guest: Don't serve corn with a meal. The English view corn as animal feed! To avoid these kinds of mistakes, see

> Brad Bowerman's ***Geography World*** site for a huge list of links to cultural sites (WWW 7.4).
>
> View the site ***Gestures in Cultures***, to learn about body language around the world (WWW 7.5).

ADDITIONAL WEB SITES ON THE GEOGRAPHY OF MODERN ECONOMIC CHANGE:

For a listing of many sites on China's business and trade, see ***China on the Net*** (http://www.kn.pacbel.com/wired/China/hotlist) (WWW 7.6).

For a good example of how a community advertises itself to compete for industrial economic development, see the informative website for ***Taunton, Massachusetts*** (http://www.ci.taunton.ma.us/info.htm) (WWW 7.7).

Need detailed, up-to-date information on a particular country's economic structure and trends? View the ***World Bank*** website's "*Country Briefs*"

ADDITIONAL WEB SITES ON THE GEOGRAPHY OF MODERN ECONOMIC CHANGE:

For a listing of many sites on China's business and trade, see ***China on the Net*** (WWW 7.6).

For a good example of how a community advertises itself to compete for industrial economic development, see the Web site for the town of ***Taunton, Massachusetts*** (WWW 7.7).

Need detailed, up-to-date information on a particular country's economic structure and trends? View the "*Country Briefs*" page on the ***World Bank*** Web site. (WWW 7.8).

Pennsylvania's industrial trends are described in the Research Brief entitled "*Industry Trends in Pennsylvania*" on the ***Pennsylvania State Data Center*** Web site (WWW 7.9).

What is the impact of economic growth on a developing country? See "Exploring the Health Impact of Economic Growth, Poverty Reduction, and Public Health Expenditure," at the ***World Health Organization*** Web site (WWW 7.10).

ADDITIONAL READINGS:

Axtell, Roger E., *Do's and Taboos Around the World*, (New York: John Wiley & Sons, Inc., 1990), 2nd ed.

Axtell, Roger E., *The Do's and Taboos of International Trade*, (New York: John Wiley & Sons, Inc., 1991).

Jones, K., and Simmons, J., *The Retail Environment*, (New York: Routledge, 1990).

Renner, Michael, Swords Into Plowshares: Converting to a Peace Economy, (Washington, D.C.: Worldwatch, 1990)

PART EIGHT

THE POLITICAL IMPRINT
ALL NATIONS GREAT AND SMALL

GOALS: The purpose of these activities is to bring the relative abstraction of politics to the reality of everyday life. We will explore and discuss political boundaries, challenge the conventional notion of what makes a nation, and examine the tenuous existence of nations without states. All these topics should bring to you new perspectives on the dynamics of political geography and the role it plays in shaping your world.

ACTIVITIES: Our virtual tour of the political landscape includes three activities. First, we look at the lines that bind – the geography of boundaries. Next, prepare for a tour of some of the tiniest "nations" on earth as they exist in reality or only on mental maps. Finally, we look at stateless nations facing difficult political and geographic odds.

ACTIVITY 8.1: Political Culture and the Evolving State
Bounded and Determined: Taking Political Boundaries to the Edge

INTRODUCTION: Every single day, perhaps without any awareness on your part, you cross a variety of political boundaries. Would you know when you leave one local voting precinct and venture into another or traverse one Congressional District and enter another? The boundaries you are probably most familiar with are those of city limits, township, county, state and national boundaries. What you may not know is that most of those boundaries have changed over time and in the past, may have been a serious point of contention. If the only things certain in life are death and taxes, you might want to add boundaries to that list because humans are very territorial and that's where all the troubles start. The following questions all deal with identifying geographic boundaries at different scales. We will begin with boundary lines in your part of the world and expand our investigation to a global scale. Some of the questions require little more than using your knowledge of local conditions but when possible it is recommended that you back up your answers with maps or documentation. A local city, county, state, topographical or U.S. Census map may provide the verification you need.

Activity 8.1 Field Work Questions

Part A

1. Name your county of residence and all counties with which it shares borderlines. How would you best describe the character of the boundary? For example, does it appear that the boundaries are based on physical environment such as water courses or mountain ridges or are they geometric survey lines that do not follow any obvious natural features or perhaps a combination of both?

2. Do you know of any boundary disputes in your state, county or community? What part, if any, have the region's physical geography played in these disputes?

Part B

Boundary line disputes have played a major part in conflicts at many levels from family feuds to full-scale wars. The following list of web sites will provide you with some examples of how arguments over territory and boundaries have resulted in a variety of changes to the political landscape.

The Iowa and Missouri Dispute
The Iowa Honey War site (WWW 8.1) If you had never heard about a series in incidents in 1839 that nearly brought Iowa and Missouri to the brink of war you are not alone. With such battle cries as "Death to the Pukes" and armed with such lethal weapons as kitchen utensils, residents near the disputed boundary between the two states were prepared to do battle over honey. That's right— honey.

1. How did such a conflict develop and how was it resolved and why was the final agreement much sweeter for Iowa?

The U.S.-Canada Boundary in the Pacific Northwest: The Pig War
The National Park Service San Juan Island National Historical Park Web sites (WWW 8.2), (WWW 8.3), (WWW 8.4)

The United States and Canada share the longest unfortified border in the world. While on the surface it appears that the two countries are fairly comfortable with this peaceful relationship, in the past, the border has been a source of much contention. After the dispute over one section of the border involving British Columbia was resolved one piece of the United States ended up as an enclave within Canada.

2. Where would you find this unusual piece of real estate?

3. Can you think of any reason why the United States would fight in the "Pig War" to retain this relatively tiny chunk of territory?

4. What are the differences between "British" and "English" camps and what precipitated the name variations?

5. Do you think British and English should be used interchangeably—why or why not?

The Baarle-Nassau/Baarle-Hertog Dispute
Professor Barry Smith's *Baarle-Nassau/Baarle-Hertog* Web site (WWW 8.5) No, not the Nassau located in the Caribbean. These "islands" are on dry land in Belgium and the Netherlands.

6. What makes these enclaves so unique?

7. How were they formed and what attempts have been made over the past to resolve this conundrum?

Explore other border issues with the ***International Boundary News Database*** Web site (WWW 8.6) If there is a boundary issue somewhere in the world, it is probably cited in the International Boundary News Database. You can access the database by simply entering location names and submitting your search request. When database completes the search it will list all the boundary issues associated with the locations you have chosen. Read through the search results and list and discuss what you believe are the major border issues.

8. How would you classify the boundary you chose (see page 350 in your text for a discussion of "Origin-Based Classification)?

Activity 8.2: State Organization and National Power
Micro-Minis: Skirting the Issues of Statehood

INTRODUCTION: What does it take to create a country? Is it political or military power over a geographic territory? Do you need a minimum number of people to qualify? Or do you become a state because others recognize your legal right to exist? For some smaller states, retaining their identity, or for that matter creating one, can present some problems. Many states have populations of less than one million residents. These are ministates and despite their small size, they manage to function as fully legitimate political entities yet wield little influence in global affairs. Then there are the microstates. Microstates may or may not have any political or geographic raison d'etre, but exist nonetheless. Some microstates are self-proclaimed nations created by individuals, groups, or even corporations such as the "Republic of Ceurvo Gold," established by a tequila manufacturer. In fact, some microstates exist only in the minds of their creators or on the Internet such as the "Aeldarnian Empire." And then there is the "Kingdom of Talossa" which was created by a high school student and territorially consisted of his bedroom. Some say the world is getting smaller. Let's take a look and see.

Activity 8.2 Field Work

Prepare to take a magical mystery virtual field trip to an amazing variety of microstates.

To begin your journey, go to the ***Micronations*** Web site (WWW 8.7) and read the section titled, "What are Micronations?" Next, scroll down to the list of micronations and answer the questions for the micronations listed below.

1. Breckenridge: Why did this town declare itself a "kingdom?"

2. Christiania: Exactly how would you describe this "social experiment?" Would such a community survive in the United States? Why?

3. Conch Republic: How did Border Patrol action bring this microstate out of its shell? (Be sure to the visit the ***Cyber Conch*** Web site too. WWW 8.8).

4. Minerva, Republic of: Why did this "republic" fail to keep its head above water?

5. Morac-Songhrati-Meads, Republic of: Where is the "Humanity Sea" and exactly how human is it?

6. Mosquito Shore and Nation: Who have been the main political players that have wrestled for this territory for the past 300 years?

7. Navassa Island: What does the self-proclaimed king have to rule over on Navassa and why might the Coast Guard want to take his throne? Tour the island via its ***Navassa Island*** Web site (WWW 8.9) and follow the link for History for more information.

8. Seborga, Principality of: Seborga has been a microstate for over 1000 years. Why is it still struggling for recognition? Travel to the principality via its ***Principato di Seborga*** Web page (WWW 8.10).

9. Winneconne: What does Winneconne have in common with Breckenridge?

Activity 8.3: Multinationalism on the Map
States of Minds and Hearts: UNPO Members

INTRODUCTION: The Unrepresented Nations and Peoples Organization (UNPO) provides a forum for groups who are not represented in traditional supranational bureaucratic institutions such as the United Nations (UN). For those nations without a state, the UNPO offers assistance and guidance for self-help programs and adheres to philosophy of progress through non-violent measures. Who are the more than 50 members of the UNPO and what are they doing to ease the plight of their peoples?

Activity 8.3 Field Work

The ***UNPO*** Web site (WWW 8.11) is the starting point for this activity. Go to the UNPO home page and click on What is the UNPO?.

1. Based on what you have read, how is the UNPO different from the UN?

Next, go back to the main page and select Members of UNPO. Select any one of the member nations ***excluding*** those peoples who reside in the United States and answer the following questions (helpful hint: if possible, you should print the member's page for future reference).

Note the UNPO member you have chosen to study: ____________________

2. Describe the geographic location.

3. What ethnic group(s) are included in this area?

4. What types of economic activities take place in this region?

5. How did this group of people survive to this point and what are the major challenges for their future as a nation with or without a state?

6. Why do you believe the UNPO you have selected has not been given independence or been recognized as a nation and what geographic factors are involved?

7. Were you surprised to learn that there are UNPO members in the United States?

Go through the list of UNPO members and pick out those nations that are currently living within the U.S. borders. List those members below and answer the following questions.

8. List the UNPO member nations that reside within the political boundaries of the United States.

9. Where are these nations located within the United States?

10. What, if any, do these peoples have in common?

11. In the best case scenario, what do you see as the future for each of these groups? Do you think they will ever become nations with a state or will they continue to be assimilated into the host culture? Why do you think this is the case?

12. Are there any parallels you see between the UNPO members in the United States and the other member nation you selected? If so, what are the similarities as well as the differences?

PART NINE

SOCIAL GEOGRAPHIES OF THE MODERN WORLD -- GRRRL POWERLESS

GOALS: The focus of this section is on gender and the geography of inequality. There are three activities included for these subjects all of which are key points for Chapter 31 in Part Nine. Each of the activities is designed to challenge students to look deeper into cultural differences through the lens of gender.

ACTIVITIES: The first activity centers on gender and demographics, and examines the status of women in several countries. It asks students to compare their lifestyles to those in other locations. For example, Figure 31.1 in the de Blij and Murphy text illustrates the spatial differences between male and female life expectancies. Students will look for demographic clues in other statistics which help explain life expectancy patterns. The second activity follows up on the demographic study by examining female infanticide and other reproductive rights topics related to the status of women. The final part of this activity looks at women in the workplace with emphasis on women in the family economy and women laborers in the third world.

Activity 9.1: Gender and the Geography of Inequality; No Great Life Expectations

INTRODUCTION: A quick review of de Blij and Murphy's Figure 31-1, "World Female Life Expectancy over Males, shows that three countries, Bangladesh, India, and Pakistan, are the only countries in the world where females do not outlive males. Various factors have been attributed to life expectancy differences between males and females but generally the world pattern of longer lives for females have been explained by unhealthy lifestyle choices made by males. Why are females in these three countries not enjoying longer lives? Are some countries less favorable for female survival? What factors enable men to live longer than women? To explore these questions, let's proceed to the following activities that focus on the gender-based demographics of life expectancies.

ACTIVITY 9.1 Field Work
Follow the web links for each of these countries and be prepared to discuss your findings.

BANGLADESH: Poverty brings suffering to both males and females but in the case of Bangladesh, the effects on the lives of women are particularly harsh. For a brief introduction to some of the demographic variables that can be used to explain life expectancy differences by gender, go to the ***Novartis Foundation for Sustainable Development*** Web page on poverty in Bangladesh (WWW 9.1). After reading the short narratives and reviewing the data included in the two tables, answer the following questions.

1. What percent of the total Bangladeshi population live in rural areas? How does this contribute to lower life expectancies for women? Which of the factors found in the table titled, "Female-Male Gaps in Bangladesh" best supports your explanation and why?

2. How does the natural environment conspire with desperate social conditions to further lower the quality of life for both males and females in Bangladesh? Can you think of any solutions to help mitigate these hazards?

If there is one condition that is genderless it is hunger. No matter whether you are a woman or a man, when you are in need of food, the hunger pangs are equally debilitating. But due to the unique role of women in the family, they are in fact at greater risk to the effects of malnutrition. In Bangladesh, if a woman is not receiving adequate food, her children, born and unborn, as well as herself, are at higher risk. For more insight into the issue of hunger and gender, go to the "Women's Health and Nutritional Security in Bangladesh" page at the ***Novartis Foundation*** Web Site (WWW 9.2). After reading this article, answer the following questions concerning health, education, marriage, and the legal status of women in Bangladesh.

3. How have gender inequities in health care resulted in differing qualities of life for children? In Bangladesh, who eats "last and least"? Think about the role of gender and food in your home. Is this Bangladeshi culture trait similar to what you experience in your family? How?

4. According to the World Bank, what factors are responsible for the high maternal mortality rate suffered by Bangladeshi women? If you were hired as a consultant and were asked to target one of these variables that could be most easily remedied, which would you choose and why?

5. What is the maternal mortality rate in the United States? To find this statistic, refer to Table 3 on the UNICEF ***Country Estimates of Maternal Mortality*** Web site (WWW 9.3). What are some of the factors you believe account for the differences in maternal mortality rates between Bangladesh and the United States? List the countries with maternal mortality rates lower than those of the United States. Why do you think these countries are doing a better job of ensuring safer motherhood than the U.S.? Which countries have the highest maternal and lowest mortality rates and what factors do you think contribute to these conditions for women?

6. How does violence against women translate into a health and cultural issue in Bangladesh?

7. Was anyone in your family denied a public school education because of their gender? Why would this happen to young girls in Bangladesh? What are the long-term consequences of lack of adequate education for females in Bangladesh? How is denial of education justified in this culture? Have you ever heard these arguments against educating women in the United States and why?

8. How do religion, early onset of puberty, and the status of females combine to lower life expectancies and qualities of life for young Bangladeshi women?

9. Widowhood in any situation is very difficult, but why are Bangladeshi women at great risk if they lose their husbands?

10 . If Bangladeshi women are "equal" under the law, how is it they are burdened with great inequities?

11. Follow the Purdah link in the final paragraph of the ***Novartis*** Web site. What is Purdah and how does it affect the lives of Bangladeshi women (WWW 9.4)?

After reading the previous materials and giving considerable thought to the living conditions experienced by Bangladeshi women, what do you see as their future? Do you foresee life female expectancies to increase, decrease, or stay the same in the future and why?

ACTIVITY 9.2: Mothers and Daughters of India

INTRODUCTION: Many cultural, economic, and political factors influence family size and composition. Reproductive rights are not automatically associated with individual freedoms in many parts of the world. In regions where females are considered less than equals, and male children are preferred, women and girls often find themselves in perilous situations. Such is the case in India, where men outnumber women, an unusual demographic in a world where females generally experience longer life expectancies and sex ratios at birth are virtually 50/50. Why do males outnumber females in India? Part of the explanation lies in family planning decisions that are shaped by the status of women.

While working through the activities below, keep in mind how powerful cultural belief systems such as religion and the traditional role of women play in the composition of families and gender preference.

ACTIVITY 9.2 Field Work

Part A

We begin our journey to India by visiting the ***Women of the World*** Web site (WWW 9.5). Begin reading and click on Please begin with the introduction. When you reach the bottom of the page, begin your review of social conditions by clicking on India, read the Overview section then go back to the web links box at the top or bottom of the page and click on each of the following: Population and Family Planning, Contraception, Sterilization, Other Reproductive Health Matters.

1. What types of incentives does the Indian government offer those who are willing to participate in family planning programs? Why would this appeal to many communities in India?

2. How does the government and private industry work together to distribute contraceptives? Why might a similar program in the United States meet with some resistance?

3. Who are more likely to be sterilized in India -- males or females, and why do you think this would be the prevailing trend? How does the government reward persons who choose to be sterilized? Does the United States government reward its citizens in comparable ways for family planning decisions? (Hint: Think income taxes!)

4. What are "dowry deaths" and how is this representative of the status of women in India?

Part B

Dowry deaths are but one hazard to growing up female in India. Some girls never have the chance to be born because the fetus is aborted based on ultrasound tests indicating the unborn child is female. Selectively aborting fetuses by gender is called "foeticide". Female infanticide, foeticide, and other factors contribute to a growing problem of missing girls in India. Simply put, there are millions of females "missing" from the Indian population, women who statistically should be a part of the demographic profile of the country. For a cartographic representation of the unbalanced sex-ratio problem in India, go to U.N.I.C.E.F.'s Web Site that addresses ***Gender Equity in India*** (WWW 9.6).

1. What can you surmise about "missing women" from the spatial pattern on the map?

2. Which Indian state has the highest number of "missing women"? Keep this location in mind as you read the next section.

Part C

Next, go to the ***Hinduism Today*** web site and read, "Will India's Ban on Prenatal Sex Determination Slow Abortion of Girls?" (WWW 9.7), and answer the following questions. (Note: This site contains an entire collection of articles, but the following questions focus on just this one article.)

1. How have advances in medical technologies resulted in the proliferation of female foeticide in India and why are some ultrasound clinics going "underground?"

2. What reasons do "pro-selective abortion" advocates present when supporting female foeticide? Do you agree with any of these arguments and why?

3. How has emphasis on the male child influenced the status of girls and women in India? Do you see any parallels between these issues in India and China and why?

4. What is *stri dana* and how does the dowry system place females in peril in India?

5. Which state in India has the greatest prevalence of dowry practices? With the UNICEF "missing women" in India map you previously viewed, what do these two issues have in common?

6. Hinduism is practiced by hundreds of millions of Indians. How do Hindus view abortion and why does the practice continue despite the religious contradictions?

7. Step back from India for just a moment. Think about the different values placed on gender where you live. Do you believe males are valued above females in your country? If so, list some examples, and if not, explain why.

Part D

At this point, you should have a good understanding of the risks involved in being an Indian woman but what would a female visitor to India encounter as she travels the countryside? Become a virtual woman tourist in India by going to the ***Hot Wired*** Web page (WWW 9.8) You'll receive advice as a female traveler. Be sure to take a side trip and click on Indian Women near the beginning of the article and answer the following.

1. What sorts of interactions with Indian men are women tourists warned about and how are they advised to deal with unwanted social situations—or why you shouldn't go barefoot on a bus?

2. What is "Eve teasing" in India and are these behaviors unique to this part of the world?

3. Given the description of women in Indian society (Indian Woman), why do you think female foreigners are treated so differently?

4. While this article mentions many difficulties for women travelers in India, what, if any, are considered to be the perks? Based on this information, whether you are male or female, would you be interested in visiting India---why or why not?

ACTIVITY 9.3: Caution: Women at Work

INTRODUCTION: The majority of the world's work force is composed of women. Women work in fields, factories, mines, oceans, forests, deserts, and in the home. Working conditions vary wildly and are more commonly unfavorable than not. In most countries, female laborers are paid less and work more hours than their male counterparts thus having direct economic consequences on the welfare of families. To explore the challenges faced by women in the world labor force, we will examine the lives of women in Pakistan, women as food producers, and a case study of a female factory worker in Mexico.

ACTIVITY 9.3 Field Work

Part A

We begin by visiting the ***First to Rise Last to Sleep*** Web site (WWW 9.9), which details the lives of women in Pakistan. Consider the following questions.

1. How has geography affected the status of women in Pakistan and how is this reflected in the labor force?

2. How are prospects for urban women in Pakistan different from those living in rural areas?

3. Who are the women of the Pakistani middle class and how are their lives different from other women in the country?

Part B

Many women, including those living in Pakistan, make major contributions to the family economy. Whether she is assembling clothes in an apparel factory or canning foods for the family's consumption, women provide direct support for themselves and her families. Women as food producers are often overlooked as a part of the overall economy. For a closer look at how much of the world's labor is generated by a nearly invisible class of workers – women in the developing world – go to the United Nations' ***Food for the Future*** Web page (WWW 9.10). Read "Women as Food Producers" and consider the following questions.

1. What do you think accounts for longer working days for women versus men? Compare your own experiences to those mentioned in the article. Do you think women in your community work more or less hours per day than men? How do you think these work schedules affect family life?

2. How does the lack of a male head of household impact the welfare of many families in terms of malnutrition? Were you surprised by this revelation why or why not?

3. Why are men migrating to urban areas and how does the absence of men complicate land tenure issues?

4. How are reproductive rights and adequate access to food interrelated?

5. Why does the United Nations argue that the world is headed for an "absolute food shortage" and what solutions do they offer?

6. Why is it difficult for many rural women in Africa to qualify for credit and how would this affect food production?

Part C

Many women spend most of their days not in fields but on assembly lines. The diffusion of manufacturing from industrialized regions to developing areas in an effort to capture cheap labor, has resulted in a new class of working poor. In Mexico, "maquiladoras," low-wage, low-skill factories that locate along the U.S.-Mexico border, provide employment for thousands of women. The story of one such woman, Maria Ilbarra, is told in "The Life of a Maquiladora Worker" on the ***Pacific News Service*** Web site (WWW 9.11). Read of Maria's experiences and be prepared to discuss the following questions.

1. How much money (in American dollars) does Maria earn in a week working at Maxell? How would this compare with a minimum wage job in the United States? How many hours do you have to work to earn enough money to buy a gallon of milk?

2. Why was Maria afraid to confront her employers about her wages and working conditions? How did her manager react to her complaints?

3. What do you see as the future for Maria's sons and Maria herself? Do you think her life is much different from women who work as food producers in Mexico - why?

PART TEN

COPING WITH A RAPIDLY CHANGING WORLD HUMAN INTERACTION WITH THE ENVIRONMENT

GOALS: As the great global warming debate rages, and El Niño is blamed for just about every great calamity on the planet, some areas are receiving too much precipitation and others not enough. The drought of 1998 will be long remembered by Texans as one of the most brutal and deadly on record. But while Texas was toasting, China was experiencing catastrophic floods. Are humans to blame for global climate change? Is there really anything such as "normal" weather conditions? Can humans continue altering the natural environment to suit their own needs without long-term effects? The following activities will focus on the challenge of humans versus the environment and the consequences of the perpetual tug of war.

ACTIVITIES: You will be studying the dynamics of human and environmental interfaces at a variety of scales. First, you will conduct an inventory of local water resources and examine specific water issues faced by your community. The second activity will turn students into time travelers to explore how variations in precipitation have changed the human experience and the natural environment. The final part of this section takes at look at the earth from a different perspective -- from space -- through remotely sensed satellite images. In this section, you will study a series of images and maps that illustrate landscape change resulting from human and natural processes.

Activity 10.1: Streams of Consciousness: Local Water Resource Issues

INTRODUCTION: Water plays an important role in every community. What would you do without fresh water? Often, the problem with water is that there is either too much or not enough and what water you do have may have quality problems. You may have enough water for now but future water needs could be a problem. Most of us take water for granted but that is a serious mistake. Have you ever given any thought as to water resources in your community? Explore your water world.

Activity 10.1 Field Work

Part A

Using a local map of your choosing, make an inventory all surface water resources in your local community. Begin with the largest streams and list the features in a hierarchy from largest to the smallest tributaries (include any bodies of water too).

1. What is the source of your community's municipal water?

2. Is this water used for any other purposes such as recreation, navigation, industry or irrigation?

3. Are there any local water uses you believe are "conflicts of interest" and if so, what are they and what could be done to mitigate the situation?

Part B

To access background information on water quality issues in your state, go to the "Regional U.S. Water Supply Problems" page at the ***National Drought Mitigation Center*** Web site (WWW 10.1). Compare your state's situation to that of other states in your region.

1. How are the water problems in your state different or similar to the region?

2. Are most of the water resource issues in your region more a result of the natural environment or of land use choices and economic activities by humans?

Part C

Look at Figure 32.2 in your text, "Variations in the Moisture Index in the United States." What is the moisture surplus or deficit for your location as indicated on the map? Compare these data with current conditions on the Web site for the ***National Drought Mitigation Center***, using the current soil moisture map (WWW 10.2). Click on Current Standardized Precipitation Index Maps.

1. What are the soil conditions for your region for the current month?

2. How do the current soil precipitation index (SPI) conditions compare to the three-month, six-month, and 12-month data? Is your region experiencing drier, wetter, or unchanged conditions?

3. What if any direct or indirect impacts of the SPI have you observed in your community -- for example, have there been any floods in your community over the past year or have drought conditions forced water usage restrictions?

Part D

Acid rain has many consequences not only for the points of origin, but also for those downwind who receive acidic rainfall. How many acid raindrops are falling on your head? To determine the pH of your local precipitation, go the ***United States Environmental Protection Agency Acid Rain Program*** page (WWW 10.3). First, click on What is Acidity and read what pH values represent. You should also read Acid Rain effects On Water before scrolling down to the bottom of the page and clicking on pH Map of the United States (1996). Find your location on the map and interpolate the pH value.

1. Is your community's built or natural environment at risk for acid rain -- why or why not?

Activity 10.2: Highly Hydrological: Drought and Out in Basins and Hills

INTRODUCTION: Droughts and floods are a natural part of the climate system but human responses to such disasters vary as do the consequences. How we choose to cope with these calamities is based on scientific knowledge and cultural beliefs. For example, if you live in a floodplain, chances are, at some point in time you and your property will be at risk. Yet, we continue to live in hazardous locations and rebuild after a disaster, often on the same spot. In this activity, we will examine the causes and consequences of variations in precipitation which result in droughts.

Activity 10.2 Field Work

Part A

We begin by visiting the ***National Drought Mitigation Center*** home page (WWW 10.4) and clicking on Why Plan?. Read through this section and as you progress, be sure to click on the following links within the article for more details: Impacts, List of Winners , Definition , Hydro-Illogical Cycle, Upper Missouri River Basin.

1. How do media-based meteorologists often mislead us into thinking there is such a thing as "normal weather?" Conversely, do you think weathercasters sensationalize "normal" weather extremes into news events? Can think of any examples from your local television stations?

2. How do National Drought Mitigation Center (NDMC) scientists view the relationship between drought and global warming? Do you agree or disagree with this assessment and why?

3. What are the four major defining categories for drought? Which economic activity is first affected by drought? Why is it so difficult for scientists to find a single definition for drought?

4. Who were the agricultural "winners" during the 1987-89 drought? How did energy and transportation sectors likewise benefit from the drought?

5. You know what the hydrologic cycle looks like from Figure 32.1 in your text, but what is the "hydro-illogical cycle?" Could this model also be applied to flooding -- why or why not?

6. How did drought effect the Upper Missouri River basin between 1987 and 1992? Which economic sectors were affected by the drought? How were irrigation and municipal water supplies compromised by the drought? What aspects of the natural environment suffered due to lower water levels? What role did the Army Corps of Engineers play in the decision making process? Why is this a good case study example of the hydro-illogical model?

Part B

Return to the ***NDMC*** home page (WWW 10.4) and click on Impacts then select Coping and Recovering from Drought. When you come to the part of this section on dust storms, follow this link to the ***Discovery Channel Online's*** "Day of the Black Blizzard" to travel back in time to the catastrophic drought of the 1920s and 1930s.

1. What are the "Dust Bowl Blues?" How did these "blues" weave their way into the "social fabric" of dust bowl communities? Why were sleeping pills in such great demand during this period?

2. Why were there so many jackrabbits during the dust bowl era?

3. How were the basic tasks of everyday life complicated by dust storms?

4. What brought about an end to the Dust Bowl era?

5. Is this region still prone to droughts and how did changes in precipitation amounts change peoples' perception of conservation programs?

6. What lessons have we learned from the Dust Bowl? Do you think the United States could experience a similar event today---why or why not?

Activity 10.3: Environmental Change As Viewed From Above

INTRODUCTION: Few images are more dramatic than those remotely sensed from satellites orbiting the earth. Even more important is to be able to compare land surface changes over time and interpret how human activities have altered the environment. The following activities are based on satellite images collected by the United States Geological Survey (USGS). Human-induced environmental change and its associated impacts are the foci. You will be asked to view satellite images and interpret the landscape change. Launch the USGS ***Earthshots*** Web site (WWW10.5), and be sure to view all the images for each year, zooming in and out when you can. Reference maps and photos are included with most images to assist in your orientation.

1. Garden City, Kansas

Garden City is used as an example to help orient you to the website. Please review all the links for Garden City so you can get the most out of each USGS image. If you are not familiar with remote sensing, this first site will be very helpful.

a. Think back to the Dust Bowl discussion in the previous section. What agricultural land use practice changes do you think have taken place in the Garden City area since the 1920s? What do the red circles represent on the image could they be alien landing pads?

b. What is the Ogallala Aquifer and how has exploitation of this resource resulted in large-scale land use change? The Ogallala Aquifer is currently being depleted at a faster rate than it can be recharged. What do you think will happen to this region if the aquifer runs dry---are there any other water source alternatives?

2. Buraydah, Saudi Arabia

a. What specific agricultural land use practice do farmers in Buraydah have in common with those in Garden City?

b. What has enabled Saudi farmers to employ this particular practice and how is this different from the decisions made by farmers in Kansas?

3. Southern Mauritania

a. Take a look at Figure 32.5 in your text, "Areas Threatened by Desertification," and determine the risk factor for Mauritania. What evidence of desertification can you detect on the image for southern Mauritania between 1972 and 1990?

b. How have infrastructure developments added to the desertification problems?

c. What accounts for the bright red signatures indicating healthy growing vegetation near the town of Richard Toll? Do you think these crops are consumed locally or produced for export markets and why?

4. Phnom Penh, Cambodia

a. How would you translate "Phnom Penh" into English?

b. How do monsoonal rains alter the physical landscape and why do you think the 1985 image shows more surface water than the image for 1973?

c. Who is the Khmer Rouge and how did they change the demographic and landscape characteristics of the region?

d. Why were skilled professionals targeted for extermination by the Khmer Rouge and how did this in turn result in problems with the irrigation system?

5. Imperial Valley, California

a. How would you describe the Salton Sea and how was it formed?

b. How has irrigation changed the landscape of the Imperial Valley, both urban and rural?

6. Chernobyl, Ukraine

a. Why have three-headed cattails and increasing numbers of wildlife flourished in the area of the damaged Chernobyl nuclear power plant?

b. Compare the 1986 and 1992 images of Chernobyl. How do the colors of agricultural lands differ between the two time periods and what accounts for the vegetation changes?

6. Great Salt Lake, Utah

a. What does the Great Salt Lake have in common with the Salton Sea and how are the challenges faced by the region different from those in the Imperial Valley?

b. How are changing precipitation patterns threatening to make this the "Great Not-So-Salty

Lake?"

7. Kara-Bogaz-Gol, Turkmenistan

a. From a geopolitical point of view, would the KGB be worried about the KBG? In other words, how has the changing level of the Kara-Bogaz-Gol affected the political geography of Turkmenistan?

b. What do the Caspian Sea and the Great Salt Lake have in common?

c. How have changing levels of the Caspian Sea changed the physical and cultural landscapes in the region?

d. How have the changing water levels in the KBG and Caspian Sea affected the region's salt industry? How have salt production methods and transportation technology evolved over the past century?

8. Aral Sea, Kazakstan

You can compare these images to those in your text in Figure 32.3 "The Dying Aral Sea."

a. What are the major factors that have contributed to this incredible shrinking lake?

b. Has the health of Aral Sea area residents been affected by changes to the lake's ecosystem?

c. It has been said that "it's not nice to fool Mother Nature." Does the destruction of the Aral Sea lend credence to that expression---why or why not?

9. Saloum River, Senegal

a. What is a mangrove and what types of flora and fauna would you expect to find if you toured the Saloum River region?

b. Why are the mangroves experiencing environmental stress and how can this be detected from Landsat images?

10. Rondônia, Brazil

a. Deforestation can be as devastating as desertification as evidenced in this series of satellite images. Compare the images from 1975, 1986, and 1992. How would you describe the vegetation changes and why do "feathering" patterns emerge on the landscape?

b. Based on this series of images from Brazil, what do you think the Rondônia region will look like in another six years? What will be the environmental and human costs for Brazil and the world?

NOTES

NOTES

NOTES

NOTES

NOTES

NOTES

NOTES

NOTES

NOTES

NOTES

NOTES

NOTES